OFFICIAL GUIDE to POPULAR

ANTIQUES

CURIOS

The Price to Buy & Sell...

by

HAL L. COHEN
NAWCC #0014993

OFFICIAL PUBLICATION OF:
HC Publishers Inc.
220 5th Avenue, NYC 10001

An Allograph Book

2

ACKNOWLEDGEMENTS

The Author, Editors, and Publishers wish to express our thanks and appreciation to al those individuals and organizations who contributed sections, photographs, illustrations pricing, and information. In a book as complex and comprehensive as this, the help o many people is required. If any names are omitted, it is through oversight, not intent.

VERY SPECIAL THANKS TO:

MR. LOU YOUNG and MISS SHANI KAPLAN—The Den of Antiquity, 106 MacDougal St., N.Y.C.— Ladies and Mens Antique Jewelry.

MR. SIDNEY STRANGE—Sidney Strange Antiques for Men, 855 Second Ave., N.Y.C. 10021— Instruments, Tools, Gadgets, Ironware, Medical Instruments, Toys, Banks, Locks & Keys.

MR. BARNY—1145 Second Ave., N.Y.C. 10021, Clocks and Watches.   MR. PHIL PADULA

MR. JOSEPH FINELLI—Clocks & Things, 209 Columbus Ave., N.Y.C.

MR. ABE KESSLER—Abe Kessler Antiques, 533 Third Ave., N.Y.C. All Types of Furniture.

MR. ERNEST L. PETTIT—P.O. Box 361, Wynantskill, N.Y. 12198. Collectible Tin Containers.

MR. HUBERT B. WHITING—40 Friend St., Wakefield, Mass. 01880. Old Iron Still Banks.

MR. VAN DEXTER—"Second Childhood", 283 Bleecker St., N.Y.C.—Toys of all types.

AGC—52 First St., Hackensack, N. J. 07601.

MR. LESLIE GOULD—391 Tremont Place, Orange, N. J. 07050.

MR. WALTER ENGEL—N.Y.C., Gramaphones, Phonographs, Music Boxes, etc.

MR. CHARLES McSORLEY—Political Americana, Box 21, Closter, N. J.—Political Buttons, Tokens

MR. DAVID LATNER—Currier & Ives Prints.

MERRITT'S ANTIQUES INC.—R.D. 2, Douglassville, Pa. 19518.

GUY & GLADYS SAULSBURY ANTIQIES—Spicer, Minnesota 56288.

MR. BOB LESSER—Character Clocks & Watches, Pen & Pencil Sets.

THE SHELBURNE MUSEUM — Woodworking Tools, pictures courtesy of the Shelburne Museum, Shelburne, Vermont. Mr. BRADLEY SMITH, Ass't. to the Director.

CHARLES E. TUTTLE CO., INC. Wooden Ware pictures from "EARLY AMERICAN WOODEN WARE" by Mary Earle Gould, published by Charles E. Tuttle Co. Inc. Available from book stores or the publisher.

CAN MANUFACTURERS INSTITUTE, INC. — Pictures of Antique Cans, courtesy Santo J. Barca, Assistant to the President.

JAMES B. BEAM DISTILLING CO. — Beam, Kentucky. Courtesy Mr. Martin Lewin, Vice. President. Pictures of Beam Bottles.

MUSEUMS AND ORGANIZATIONS: New York Historical Society (Miss Caroline Schoon). The Museum of the City of New York. Metropolitan Museum of Art. Cooper Union Musuem. The Henry Ford Museum. The Edison Institute. Bennington Museum. Museum of Fine Arts. Smithsonian Institute. Old Sturbridge Village. Henry Francis DuPont Winterthur Museum. Colonial Williamsburg. The Society for the Preservation of New England Antiques. Victoria & Albert Museum. The Brooklyn Museum. The Lightner Expositan. The Seamans Bank of New York.

N. Flayderman & Co. Inc. Gorham Silver Manufacturing Co. The Home Insurance Company. The Rookwood Pottery Company. The Royal Doulton Company. The Steuben Glass Company. Corning Glass Company. E. J. Towle Company.

BIBLIOGRAPHY: Handbook of Early Advertising Art-Hornung. Source book of Antiques & Jewelry Designs — Hornung. 1897 Sears Roebuck Catalog. From Tinfoil to Stereo — Read & Welch. Source Book of French Advertising Art — Braziller. Wishbook — 1865. American Copper & Brass — Kauffman. Treasure at Home — Mebane. Pioneer Post Cards & American Card Catalog — Burdick. Currier & Ives Checklist — Cunningham. Currier & Ives Printmakers to the American People — Peters. The Art of Coppersmithing — Fuller, 1893. A History of Toys — Fraser. American Glass — McKearin. The Book of Pottery & Porcelain — Cox. Weathervane Catalog — J. W. Fiske, 1875. Rogers Statuary Catalog — 1876. Thayer & Chandler Catalog — 1908. Otto Young Catalog — 1900. Belknap Hardware Catalog — 1910. Parke Benet Galleries Catalog. The Old Print Shop Catalogs — Beam Bottles, Cembura.

AND: Antique Trader. Spinning Wheel. Antiques Journal. Relics Magazine. Antiques Magazine. Arts & Antiques Magazine.

TABLE OF CONTENTS

3

This 3rd edition of the Official Guide to Popular Antiques & Curios presented with the hope that it will better acquaint the general public wit the fascinating world of antiques, curios, and collectables. It is also designe to assist the dealer and veteran collector as well. Although we are concerne primarily with American antiques, this edition also deals with items c European design and origin.

WHAT IS AN ANTIQUE?

According to the United States Tariff Act of 1930, an antique is: "A work c art, (except rugs and carpets made after the year 1700) collections in il lustration of the progress of the arts, works in bronze, marble, terra cotta parian, pottery or porcelain, artistic antiquities and objects of ornamenta character or educational value which shall have been produced prior t 1830". This date was not arbitrarily chosen, rather it marked the beginnin of the Era of Mass Production. For after 1830, increasingly larger number of items which had originally been hand-crafted were produced by machine However, through common usage by dealers, collectors, authors and th general public, the term "antique" has come to include any item of historica or cultural significance, regardless of date or method of manufacture.

WHAT IS A COLLECTABLE?

A collectable, on the other hand, is any object which because of its beauty rarity, significance in popular culture or oddity possesses intrinsic value to a collector. Jim Beam bottles are an excellent example of collectables. Pro duced originally during the early 1950's, they are today eagerly sought afte by dealers, and collectors. Collectables cover a wide variety of objects; from "classic" automobiles to military mementos from the Civil War to Worlc War II. Because of the interest in American tradition and history, or "Ameri cana", many of these items have been incorporated into the decorative schemes of modern homes.

Average Buying Price

The AVERAGE BUYING PRICE (A.B.P.) is the amount an authorized dealer *will pay you* for a particular antique or curio. Once an item is purchased from a dealer it disappears into a private home or collection and is permanently removed from the active market. Consequently, because of this scarcity, dealers welcome people with genuine and desirable antiques to sell. We have given A.B.P.s. for many categories. However, where it has not been included in a category, a good "rule of thumb" would be to calculate the Average Buying Price as 50-35% of the retail price. As with the retail price, the A.B.P. is contingent upon scarcity, source and desirability. Added to this is the condition of the object. For example, an antique clock retailing for $100.00. A dealer would pay you perhaps $50.00 if it were in perfect running order. In non-functioning condition however, this same clock would be worth far less due to the prohibitively high repair costs to the dealer. Therefore, more than any other single factor, condition determines the Average Buying Price.

How to judge the condition of antiques

As was mentioned previously, condition is one of the major determinants of the price of an antique. In this book, all prices quoted are for good condition unless otherwise noted. The following examples demonstrate what you should look for and expect of any item advertised to be in good condition.

GLASSWARE: Firm color, no cracks, chips or major flaws.

POTTERY: Solid Glaze, no chips or cracks.

MECHANICAL TOYS, BANKS: In Good mechanical working order. Original paint in good condition.

GUNS: Good mechanical order, legible engravings, reasonably good finish. No missing parts.

WOODENWARE: No major chips or cracks. No warped wood.

COPPER, BRASS & PEWTER: Untarnished, no dents or cracks.

CARDS AND PRINTED MATTER: Clean, legible, unstained. No rips or tears.

LAMPS: No cracks, chips or major flaws. Mechanically good.

AN INTRODUCTION TO ANTIQUES

HOW TO USE THIS BOOK

The contents of this book have been divided into general categories and arranged alphabetically. However, some of the larger categories such as clocks, glassware, china and pottery have been grouped under the main alphabetical listing and then sub-divided into unit categories for easy reference. For example, to find "Cameo" glass, look first under "GLASSWARE" and then to the letter "C". Where illustrations are shown, they are accompanied by corresponding numbers on the listing of the item. Where this is not possible, a caption is supplied for identification.

INVENTORY CHECK LIST

Appearing beside each listing is a check box. This will enable you to keep an accurate record of items which you own, or would like to own as well as their condition. You may show the condition of an object by placing one of the following symbols in the check box.

◨ "As found"   ◩ "Good"   ⊟ "Fine"   ⊠ "Excellent"

To the left of the check box, a simple cross will serve to remind you of an article that you would like to acquire, while a check mark will mean you already own it.

×☐ "Want"   ✓☐ "Have"

Pricing

We are not in the antiques business. As publishers of this book we have endeavored to make it as accurate and up-to-date as possible. We do not, however buy, sell or appraise antiques, and our only desire is to inform and educate on the fascinating subject of antiques and curios. All prices contained herein are intended to serve only as a guide, and are not warranted as to accuracy. As a general rule, rare pieces move upward faster than commonplace.

Retail Price

The RETAIL PRICE is the amount you would have to pay an authorized dealer for a particular antique or curio. The retail prices in this book have been compiled from dealers, auction lists, catalogs, antique magazines, and other authoritative publications. It is affected by a wide variety of factors including source, desirability and condition. Combined with this is the fact that genuine antiques are becoming increasingly more scarce due to the fantastic demand of collectors, dealers and the general public. Given the above variables in the market, these prices may jump abruptly at any time.

A WORD ON REPRODUCTIONS

Over the years, a great many antique objects have been reproduced. Mechanical Banks, Glassware, Pottery, Furniture, Political Campaign Items, Posters, Toys, Advertising Cards, Woodenware, Clocks and many others have been faithfully duplicated from the original mold, plate, or style. Many of these are excellent, and some are difficult to tell apart from the original. Reproductions are a form of collectable in themselves, however they are *not* the original. They should not be grouped, priced, or sold as the original object.

The best protection against acquiring a reproduction while paying for the original is to *buy only from a reputable dealer*. He will generally have had many years of experience in the field and will be able to differentiate between the two. This is not to say that he himself cannot make an error, however the chances that he will do so are greatly reduced. A reputable, ethical dealer will always stand behind what he sells.

To find your local dealer, check the phone book under "ANTIQUES" and "ANTIQUES DEALERS". If there are none near you, visit an antiques show, flea market, an antiques auction, or convention. There you will find many dealers at one time. The following publications have ads of many dealers who may be able to help you.

We recommend these publications as excellent sources of information and articles on antiques and collectables.

ANTIQUE TRADER Babka Publishing Co. Inc. **P. O. Box #1050** **Dubuque, Iowa 52001** **(single copy: 30c)**	ANTIQUE JOURNAL Babka Publishing Co. Inc. Box #467 Kewanee, Illinois 61443 (single copy: 50c)
ANTIQUES MAGAZINE Straight Enterprises Inc. 551 Fifth Avenue New York, N. Y. 10017 (single copy: $1.50)	SPINNING WHEEL Everybodys Press Inc. Exchange Place Hanover, Penna. 17331 (single copy: 75c)

RELICS MAGAZINE
Western Publications Inc.
P. O. Box #3338
1012 Edgecliff Terrace
Austin, Texas 78704
(single copy: 35c)

These plates were made particularly for children. The interior decorations were usually of Aesop's Fables, great men, life-like animals or famous maxims. The alphabet was generally inscribed upon the outer rim. ABC plates were made from pottery, porcelain, pewter, tin or glass.

All prices are for Good Condition

Item & Description:	*A.B.P.	Retail
CHINA:		
☐ 8½″ Dog wearing glasses	13.75	23.50
☐ 8½″ Red Riding Hood and the Wolf	13.25	23.00
☐ 8½″ Red Riding Hood. Delft	10.50	18.00
☐ 8″ Fishing Elephant	10.50	18.00
☐ 8″ Biblical scene. Samuel and Eli	9.00	16.00
☐ 8″ Elves. German 3-Crown	13.00	17.50
☐ 8″ Crested golden wrens	9.00	16.00
☐ 8″ Punctuality	10.00	17.00
☐ 8″ Rabbit. Hands in sign language exterior	11.50	20.50
☐ 8″ Whittington and cat	13.00	23.00
☐ 8″ Sergeant	9.00	15.50
☐ 7¾″ Washington Capitol	10.00	18.00
☐ 7½″ See-Saw, Marjorie Daw. Dark blue	8.75	15.50
☐ 7¼″ Robinson Crusoe saves Friday	11.00	19.00
☐ 7¼″ Hunter and his dogs	10.00	17.00
☐ 7¼″ Little Jack Horner	11.00	19.00
☐ 7¼″ Meakin China. Sport scene	11.75	21.00
☐ 7¼″ Red Riding Hood and the Wolf	12.25	21.50

All prices are for Good Condition

Item & Description	*A.B.P.	Retail
7¼" Dancing Master	8.75	15.50
7¼" The Pony	9.50	18.00
7" Allertons. Comic scene	8.50	16.00
7" Ben Franklin	9.50	17.00
7" Sailor capturing seal. England	10.50	18.00
7" December scene. Man, turkey, goat. Green	10.00	18.00
7" Rugby match	11.50	20.00
7" Girl bathing. Animal exterior	9.00	17.00
7" Puppy and kitten in pitchers	9.00	16.50
7" The Guardian. Staffordshire	10.50	18.00
7" Kittens wearing clothes	10.25	18.50
7" Tired of play	9.00	17.00
6¼" Lord's Prayer. Transfer	7.50	13.50
6¼" Owl. Hands in sign language exterior	12.00	21.50
6" Bullfinch, goldfinch and canary	10.50	19.50
6" Cane center	6.00	10.00
6" Boys playing at marbles	10.50	19.00
6" Donkey and foal. Boy and girl exterior	9.00	16.50
6" Biblical scene. Reuben saving Joseph	9.00	16.50
6" Those Children	10.25	18.00
5¼" Robinson Crusoe	10.50	19.00
5" General U. S. Grant	9.50	19.00
5" David and Goliath. Color	9.00	18.00
CLEAR GLASS:		
6½" Dog's Head	8.00	14.00
5" Elephant	8.00	16.00
5" Star	7.00	13.00
TIN:		
8¾" Hi Diddle Diddle Nursery Rhyme	8.50	15.00
8" I Killed Cock Robbin Nursery Rhyme	7.00	12.00
8" Sparrow & Robbin Verse	7.00	12.00
6¼" Jumbo	7.75	14.00
6" Old Into Young	7.00	12.50
5½" Victoria-Albert	9.00	14.50
5½" Washington Center	8.00	17.00

*A.B.P. — Average Buying Price — See Page 5

ALMANACS

Americans of the 18th and 19th centuries used almanacs as a guide f(
everyday life. Crops were planted and harvested according to the moon phas
Social activities were guided by these books. **A fair offer for purchase by**
dealer would be 50% of Stated Retail Value.

Almanacs printed 1880-1900's are not rare. The price range for most is $1-$5

All Prices shown are for Good Condition

Item & Description	*A.B.P.	Reto
☐ 1776-North American Almanac. S. Stearns	12.00	28.0
☐ 1783-New England Almanac. Bickerstaff	10.00	20.0
☐ 1791-Hartford Almanac. Strong	9.00	16.5
☐ 1794-New England Almanac. Daboll	7.00	15.0
☐ 1796-Hartford Almanac. Strong	7.00	15.0
☐ 1797-Hagerstown Almanac. First edition	30.00	50.0
☐ 1805-New England Almanac. Daboll	8.00	16.5
☐ 1808-New England Almanac. Daboll	6.00	13.0
☐ 1808-Farmer's Almanac. Virginia, B. Bates	10.00	20.0
☐ 1816-New England Almanac. Daboll	6.00	11.0
☐ 1818-New England Almanac. Daboll	8.00	14.0
☐ 1828-Ontario Almanac. Oliver Loud. Canandaigua	6.00	12.0
☐ 1829-Western Almanac. Rochester	5.00	9.5
☐ 1834-Poor Richard's Almanac. Rochester	6.00	12.0
☐ 1837-Anti-Slavery Almanac. New England	6.00	12.0
☐ 1843-Presbyterian Almanac	3.50	6.0
☐ 1855-True Americans Almanac. Rare	12.00	21.5
☐ 1867-Western Almanac. Perkins	4.00	7.5
☐ 1869-Hagerstown Town & Country Almanack	2.00	3.5
☐ 1871-Farmer & Mechanics Almanac. Scovill	3.00	5.0
☐ 1872-Tarrytown Almanac	3.50	5.7
☐ 1874-United States Almanac. Hostetter	2.00	3.5
☐ 1880-Hagerstown Almanac. Gruber	2.00	3.5
☐ 1885-Presto Fertilizer Co.	1.00	1.7
☐ 1895-"The Life Boat", Boston, D. Sarsaparilla	3.50	6.5

*A.B.P. — Average Buying Price

Poor Richard, 1736.

AN

Almanack

For the Year of Christ

1 7 3 6,

Being BISSEXTILE or LEAP YEA

And makes since the Creation

By the Account of the Eastern Greeks
By the Latin Church, when ☉ ent. ♈
By the Computation of W. W.
By the Roman Chronology
By the Jewish Rabbies

Wherein is contained,

The Lunations, Eclipses, Judgment
the Weather, Spring Tides, Planets Motic
mutual Aspects, Sun and Moon's Rising an
ting, Length of Days, Time of High V
Fairs, Courts, and observable Days.
Fitted to the Latitude of Forty Deg
and a Meridian of Five Hours West from
but may without sensible Error, serve all t
jacent Places, even from *Newfoundland* to
Carolina.

By RICHARD SAUNDERS, Ph

PHILADELPHIA:
Printed and sold by B. FRANKLIN, at t
Printing-Office near the Market.

THE

BALLOON

ALMANAC,

For the Year of our LORD, 1788.

BISSEXTILE, OR LEAP YEAR.

PENNSYLVANIA:

Printed by F. BAILEY, J. STEELE, and J. BAILEY; and
Sold by F. Bailey, *Philadelphia*, J. Ba
le, at the Printing Offic

TOWN & COUNTRY

ALMANACK,

OR

Complete Farmer's Calendar,

FOR THE YEAR OF OUR LORD

1821:

Being the First after Leap Year, and the
45th of Columbian Independence.
From Creation, according to the Scriptures, 5783.

Matters Curious, Useful and Entertaining.

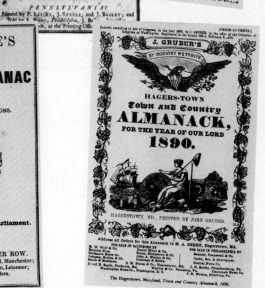

OLD MOORE'S

IMPROVED

WEATHER ALMANAC

For 1845,

WITH NUMEROUS ILLUSTRATIONS.

Registered according to Act of Parliament.

LONDON:
W. STRANGE, 21, PATERNOSTER ROW.

Machin, Dublin; Menzies, Edinbro'; Heywood, Manchester;
Webb & Co., Leeds; Allen, Nottingham; Allen, Leicester;
Hall, Birmingham; and all Booksellers.

[PRICE 10 CENTS.]

Entered, according to Act of Congress, in the year 1889, by J. GRUBER, in the office of the Librarian of
Congress, at Washington. Registered in the Patent Office, February 5, 1884.

J. GRUBER'S

BY INDUSTRY WE THRIVE

HAGERS-TOWN

Town and Country

ALMANACK,

FOR THE YEAR OF OUR LORD

1890.

HAGERSTOWN, MD., PRINTED BY JOHN GRUBER.

Address all Orders for this Almanack to M. A. BERRY, Hagerstown, Md.

FOR SALE IN BALTIMORE BY

M. W. Wolf & Co.
Moulton Bros.
Baltimore News Co.
Johnston, Sutton & Co.
Smith & Shaban.
David H. Smith, Frederick, Md.
Washington News Co., Washington, D. C.

Daniel Miller & Co.
Sultzer, Murphrine & Co.
John A. Horner & Co.
Cushings & Bailey.
S. M. Bloom & Co., Sharpstown, Md.
Warden & Co. Staunton, Va.

FOR SALE IN PHILADELPHIA BY

Bunnell, Fennerwald & Co.
Carey, Bro. & Greenwoor.
Central News Co.
J. N. Brailer, Chambersburg, Pa.
Cincinnati News Co.
F. B. Weidon, Pittsburg, Pa.

The Hagerstown, Maryland, Town and Country Almanack, 1890.

AMERICAN & ENGLISH TOBY JUGS

Prices quoted for ORIGINALS only. Reproductions are made.

All Prices are for Good Condition unless otherwise noted.
Item & Description   **Retail**

English Tobies:

1. ☐ Coachman. 9½" high. Full figure with drinking cup hat. Sharp color 160.00

2. ☐ Bearded Sailor. 9" high. Marked, complete with lid 280.00

3. ☐ English Couple. Man and Woman, both standing. Pr. 350.00

4. ☐ Man with pipe and drinking jug. Very colorful 162.00

5. ☐ Royal Bayreuth Coachman. Wearing frock coat and hat .. 60.00

6. ☐ Royal Doulton. Bearded Gladiator. Wearing armor 80.00

7. ☐ Royal Doulton. Dick Turpin the bandit. Head with mustache wearing mask and three-cornered hat 85.00

8. ☐ Royal Doulton. God Bacchus. Wearing crown of leaves. With vined handle 85.00

9. ☐ Royal Doulton. Merlin The Magician. With owl standing on shoulder of bearded sorcerer 85.00

10. ☐ Royal Doulton. Robinson Crusoe. Bearded figure wearing coconut helmet. Reinforced handle 100.00

11. ☐ Staffordshire. 8" high. Coachman with whip and boots .. 225.00

☐ Ralph Wood. With bucolic features, holding ale jug and small measure. Blue coat, yellow breeches. Unglazed face 330.00

13. ☐ Ralph Wood. With brown coat, green vest and chair, yellow breeches with black shoes. 10" high 240.00

American Tobies:

14. ☐ George Washington. Full bust of head. Late 19th century 160.00

15. ☐ Napoleon. 10½" high. Full dress uniform 225.00

16. ☐ Rockingham. Marked "Lyman, Fenton & Co., Bennington" 220.00

17 ☐ Rockingham. Marked "American Pottery Co." 220.00

18. ☐ Santa Claus. 7" high. Red with white blendings 70.00

19. ☐ Washington. Lenox Toby. Full dress uniform 240.00

8.

9.

12.

13.

17.

19.

AUTO ITEMS

In the first decade of the Twentieth Century, the "Horseless Carriage" became the automobile. Over three hundred separate types were developed, the majority of which have long since disappeared. Separate pieces, accessories, and sometimes even entire automobiles remain for the avid collector. A fair offer

All Prices shown are for Good Condition. Cars: Restored Condition

Item & Description	*A.B.P.	Retail
Audel's Guide to Automobiles (1916)	9.00	16.50
Auto Green Book. 1st volume (1922)	4.00	10.00
Auto Green Book. New England states. (1922)	3.50	8.50
Automobile Handbook. (1918), Putman	5.00	10.00
Brass Hood Ornament. Figure of Mercury. (1927)	15.00	15.00
Carbide Tank. Plated brass, made for running board....	35.00	70.00
Chrysler Touring Sedan. (1933)	1110.00	1800.00
Clock. Dashboard, key-wind type. New England manufactured, 8 day movement, working	15.00	30.00
Duster. Silk, excellent condition, man's model	11.00	25.00
Ford Roadster. (1926) Model "T"	1060.00	1500.00
Ford Touring Car. (1920) Model "T"	1060.00	1800.00
Headlamps. 1915 Cadillac, brass, pair	40.00	80.00
Horn. Brass Power. Klaxon (1908)	27.50	45.00
Horn. English Brass. "King of the Road"	30.00	60.00
Horn. Early bulb-type. Brass, single twist. ca. 1916	30.00	60.00
"How To Build Automobiles". Bubler (1904)	12.00	25.00
Lamp. Driving, solid brass	20.00	50.00
Lamps. Model T Ford. Black enamel, pair	15.00	35.00
Lamps. Ford-type, 10" high, 5" square. Brass & tin. Both electrified and refinished, pair	30.00	70.00
Maxwell. 1912 Roadster. Completely restored.	3000.00	4500.00
Motor Meter. Dodge (1915)	11.00	25.00
Motor Meter. Boyce (1916) Round meter with wings....	15.00	30.00
Pump. Tire. Ford markings, working condition	4.50	10.00
Radiator ornament. Buick markings, made of blue glass	10.00	15.00
Rover Car. English 1910, excellent condition	3000.00	4500.00
Steering Wheel. Wood & brass. Early Durant. ca. 1920's	12.50	30.00
Stock Certificates. Hudson & Nash		ea. 3.50

*A.B.P. — Average Buying Price

DRIVING LAMP

HOOD
ORNAMENT

DRIVE SAFELY

MOTOR
METER

SILK DUSTER

BULB-TYPE HORN

1926 MODEL "T" FORD ROADSTER

BANKS MECHANICAL

Mechanical banks stand as the most popular of all toys, sought after as memorabilia, collectors items, decor, and as advertising and promotion by Banks, Insurance Companies, Investment Firms, etc.

First produced by Hardware and Tool Plants, as new products, after the Civil War. Many companies produced or patented 243 designs. The better known companies being, Stevens of Cromwall, Connecticut, Ives Blaklee Co., Bridgeport, Connecticut, and Hubley of Lancaster, Pennsylvania. The main features of mechanical banks are:

   1. Generally made of iron   2. Painted bright and attractive colors
          3. Performing mechanical movement on deposit of coin

Dealers purchasing price for these banks can be figured on the basis of price plus desirability, plus condition. A dealers offer of approximately 50% of the stated retail value would be very fair for banks in "Good" condition. In some cases the rarity and fine condition of a bank may alter the dealers offer.

Several designs of these banks are being reproduced today. The prices stated do not apply to reproduced items.

"MODERN" Banks made in the 1920's & 30's, different versions of previously made banks.

	Item	Retail			Item	Retail
1.	☐ Acrobats	500.00		18.	☐ Bull and Bear	750.00
2.	☐ Always did 'spise a mule. Darky on Bench	75.00		19.	☐ Cabin*	50.00
3.	☐ Always did 'spise a mule. Darky riding Mule*	75.00		20.	☐ Called Out**	1000.00
				21.	☐ Camera, Kodak*	1000.00
4.	☐ Artillery, 4 Sided Block House*	100.00		22.	☐ Cannon, U. S. and Spain*	800.00
5.	☐ Artillery, 8 Sided Block House	800.00		23.	☐ Cat Jumping for Mouse	1500.00
				24.	☐ Cat and Mouse*	250.00
6.	☐ Bank Teller**	1600.00		25.	☐ Chief Big Moon	200.00
7.	☐ Bad Accident	200.00		26.	☐ Chinaman reclining	400.00
8.	☐ Bear, hugging Tree	125.00		27.	☐ Circus	1500.00
9.	☐ Bear, standing on Hind Legs	175.00		28.	☐ Circus Ticket Taker*	300.00
				29.	☐ Clown on Globe	175.00
10.	☐ Bowery Bank**	660.00		30.	☐ Cow, kicking*	500.00
11.	☐ Bowling Alley**	1500.00		31.	☐ Columbia Magic	50.00
12.	☐ Boy Scout	225.00		32.	☐ Confectionery	900.00
13.	☐ Boy on Trapeze*	200.00		33.	☐ Creedmore*	75.00
14.	☐ Boys stealing Watermelons	225.00		34.	☐ Dapper Dan	150.00
15.	☐ Buffalo*	100.00		35.	☐ Dentist*	750.00
16.	☐ Buffalo, bucking*	400.00		36.	☐ Dinah and the Fairy	315.00
17.	☐ Building, 8 sided	75.00		37.	☐ Dog, speaking	125.00
				38.	☐ Trick Dog on 6 piece base	175.00
				39.	☐ Trick Dog—Modern	100.00

*Reproduced Item   ***EXTREMELY RARE BANK—Price would depend on Purchaser's evaluation.*

4.

3.

35.

29.

30.

39.

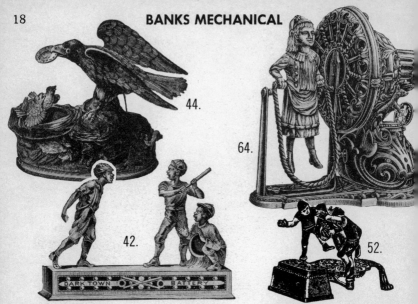

Average Buying Price: A dealer's offer of 50% of stated Retail value would be very fair for banks in "Good" condition.

Item	Retail	Item	Retail
40. ☐ Dog on Base*	125.00	57. ☐ Frog on Stump	60.00
41. ☐ Dog on Turntable	75.00	58. ☐ Giant	1500.00
42. ☐ Darktown Battery	200.00	59. ☐ Globe on Arc	30.00
43. ☐ Dinah	200.00	60. ☐ Goat, Billy	800.00
44. ☐ Eagle and Eaglets*	125.00	61. ☐ Goat, Butting	250.00
45. ☐ Elephant and Clowns	250.00	62. ☐ Guessing Bank	700.00
46. ☐ Elephant Modern	65.00	63. ☐ Gem	75.00
47. ☐ Elephant Howdah with Man	150.00	64. ☐ Girl Skipping Rope	1000.00
48. ☐ Elephant, moves trunk, small.	50.00	65. ☐ Goat, Frog and Old Man*	650.00
49. ☐ Elephant, moves trunk, large	50.00	66. ☐ Halls, Excelsior	50.00
50. ☐ Elephant, jumbo, on wheels	500.00	67. ☐ Hen, Setting	350.00
51. ☐ Elephant, 3 Stars*	500.00	68. ☐ Home, Bank	175.00
52. ☐ Football—Calamity	500.00	69. ☐ Home, Bank, tin	65.00
53. ☐ Fortune Teller, safe	300.00	70. ☐ Humpty Dumpty*	100.00
54. ☐ Frog on Lattice	65.00	71. ☐ Independence Hall	65.00
55. ☐ Frogs, two	150.00	72. ☐ Indian Shooting Bear	175.00
56. ☐ Frog on Rock	60.00	73. ☐ Jocko, Musical	500.00

*Reproduced Item

"MODERN" Banks made in the 1920's & 30's, different versions of previously made banks.

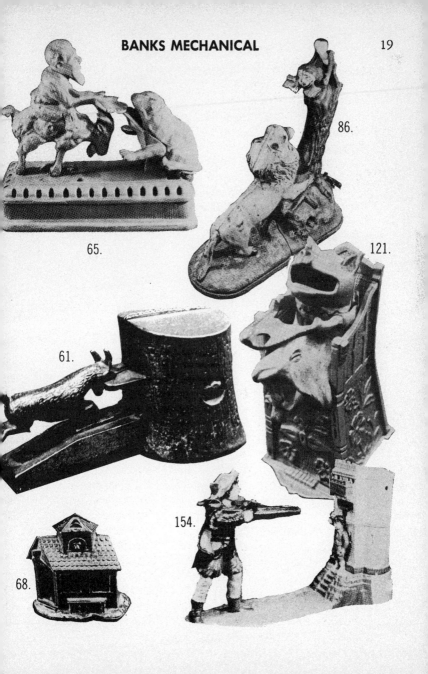

65.

86.

121.

61.

154.

68.

BANKS MECHANICAL

Average Buying Price: A dealer's offer of 50% of stated Retail value would be very fair for banks in "Good" condition.

Item	Retail
74. ☐ Jolly Nigger, bust●	40.00
75. ☐ Jolly Nigger, High Hat●	100.00
76. ☐ Jolly Nigger, moves Ears, old●.	350.00
77. ☐ Jonah and the Whale in Boat*..	350.00
78. ☐ Katzenjammer Kids	600.00
79. ☐ Keene Registering	170.00
80. ☐ Kick Inn	250.00
81. ☐ Kiltie	500.00
82. ☐ Leap Frog*	300.00
83. ☐ Liberty Bell	150.00
84. ☐ Lighthouse	250.00
85. ☐ Lilliput, Halls	100.00
86. ☐ Lion and Monkeys	150.00
87. ☐ Little Joe	150.00
88. ☐ Locomotive Bank	600.00
89. ☐ Magic	100.00
90. ☐ Magician*	300.00
91. ☐ Mammy and Child	300.00
92. ☐ Mason and Hod Carrier	300.00
93. ☐ Merry-go-Round, semi mechanical*	75.00

76.

Horse Race Bank...................500.00

Item	Ret
94. ☐ Minstrel, Tin	100
95. ☐ Minstrel, Cross Legged	300
96. ☐ Monkey & Organ Grinder, Mod.	75
97. ☐ Monkey and Parrot	350
98. ☐ Monkey and Cocoanut	275
99. ☐ Mosque	150
100. ☐ Mule and Barn	150
101. ☐ Mule, Bucking	350
102. ☐ Multiplying Bank	100
103. ☐ National Bank	350
104. ☐ North Pole**	1500
105. ☐ Novelty	75
106. ☐ Organ Bank, Medium*	125
107. ☐ Organ Bank, Cat and Dog	150
108. ☐ Organ, Bank, Monkey, Boy, Girl	175
109. ☐ Organ Bank, & Monkey, Tiny..	225
110. ☐ Organ Grinder and Bear	600

●NAME USED AS PER ORIGINAL MANUFACTURER. *Reproduced It

EXTREMELY RARE BANK — *Price would depend on Purchaser's evaluation.*

81.

116.

146.

THE BEA

	Item	Retail			Item	Retail
☐	Owl, Moves Head*	65.00	137.	☐	Santa Claus at Chimney	175.00
☐	Owl, slot in Book	90.00	138.	☐	Schley, Admiral, at Santiago**	290.00
☐	Owl, Slot in Head	125.00	139.	☐	Scotchman, Tin	125.00
☐	Panorama	600.00	140.	☐	Sewing Machine	1000.00
☐	Picture Gallery	650.00	141.	☐	Shoot and Chute**	2750.00
☐	Professor Pug Frog*	900.00	142.	☐	Squirrel and Tree Stump	400.00
☐	Paddy and Pig*	200.00	143.	☐	Stump Speaker	175.00
☐	Pegleg Beggar	400.00	144.	☐	Tabby Bank	150.00
☐	Pelican	200.00	145.	☐	Tammany*	65.00
☐	Pig, Bismark	1000.00	146.	☐	Teddy and the Bear*	175.00
☐	Pig in Highchair	175.00	147.	☐	Telephone	75.00
☐	Pony—Trick Pony*	150.00	148.	☐	Trolley Motor Bank**	1250.00
☐	Preacher in Pulpit**	685.00	149.	☐	Turtle**	1000.00
☐	Presto, Mouse on Roof**	835.00	150.	☐	Uncle Remus*	800.00
☐	Presto, Small Building	75.00	151.	☐	Uncle Sam*	175.00
☐	Pump and Bucket	400.00	152.	☐	Uncle Tom	150.00
☐	Punch and Judy*	150.00	153.	☐	U.S. Bank	600.00
☐	Rabbit, Small	125.00	154.	☐	William Tell*	150.00
☐	Rabbit, Tall	175.00	155.	☐	Wireless	150.00
☐	Rabbit and Cabbage	100.00	156.	☐	Woman in Shoe**	785.00
☐	Ram, Bucking	800.00	157.	☐	Woodpecker	800.00
☐	Red Riding Hood**	1425.00	158.	☐	Worlds Fair Bank*	200.00
☐	Roller Skating**	2000.00	159.	☐	Weeden's—tin	300.00
☐	Rooster	75.00	160.	☐	Windmill—tin	50.00
☐	Stollwerck, small—tin	125.00	161.	☐	Zoo	300.00
☐	Sweet Thrift—tin	125.00				

produced Item   **EXTREMELY RARE BANK—Price would depend on Purchaser's evaluation.**

Still Banks were made of iron, white metal, tin or pottery; comprising alm⟨
all figures, machines, buildings, animals, etc. A slot was provided to insert t⟨
coin. These banks, while not scarce, are hard to find in mint or fine conditi⟨
Good condition will mean no chips or breaks, paint bright, but not shiny.
dealer's offer of 50% of stated Retail value would be very fair f⟨
banks in "Good" condition.

Numbers used from: "Old Iron Still Banks"
H. B. Whiting, 40 Friend St., Wakefield, Mass. 01880.

	Item	Retail		Item	Reta
1. ☐	Arabian Sate #346	18.00	13. ☐	Cat, sitting, Bow Tie #244	32
2. ☐	Building Bank, large #411	24.00	14. ☐	Clock, Grandfather #222	4C
3. ☐	Building Bank, small #305	18.00	15. ☐	Clown, #28, #29*	32
4. ☐	Baseball Player #10	30.00	16. ☐	Coin "Deposit Back" #371	22
5. ☐	Bear, Sitting or Standing #330, #329	32.00	17. ☐	Columbia Worlds Fair Building #428-#431	28
6. ☐	Bear, Teddy #331	22.00	18. ☐	Cow #200	30
7. ☐	Billiken "Good Luck" #48	26.00	19. ☐	Deer, Antlers #195	28
8. ☐	Boy Scout, 6" high #14	38.00	20. ☐	Dog, Shepherd	28
9. ☐	Bull Dog, Sitting or Standing #105, #112*	30.00	21. ☐	Dog & Tub #392	32
10. ☐	Buster Brown & Dog #2	35.00	22. ☐	Dog, St. Bernard #104*	30
11. ☐	Camel, Standing, sm. #202•	30.00	23. ☐	Donkey & Saddle #197	38
12. ☐	Cash Register #241	26.00	24. ☐	Donkey, Standing #198	32
			25. ☐	Duck, Large #322	30

*Reproduced Item   **•Camel Standing, large—Very Rare.**

Prices on large categories such as "Horse," "Lion," "Pig," etc. Banks,
are approximate and can range up and down.

Average Buying Price: A dealer's offer of 50% of stated Retail value would be very fair for banks in "Good" condition.

	Item	Retail
26. ☐	Columbia Dome Building	36.00
27. ☐	Elephant w/Howdah #68	36.00
28. ☐	Elephant on Tub #55*•	28.00
29. ☐	Frog on Lattice #402	24.00
30. ☐	Gas Stove, York #139	36.00
31. ☐	General Pershing #312	38.00
32. ☐	Globe, Earth	32.00
33. ☐	Hansel & Gretel Cigar Box	38.00
34. ☐	"Home Savings Bank"	26.00
35. ☐	Horse, Black Beauty #82	28.00
36. ☐	Horse, Prancing, Rearing, Standing #70, #87	32.00
37. ☐	Independence Hall**	20.00
38. ☐	Indian Head, 2 Sides #291	28.00
39. ☐	Indian, Standing #39*	42.00
40. ☐	Junior Safe #350	22.00
41. ☐	Kitten w/Ball #247	34.00
42. ☐	Liberty Bell, Glass	20.00
43. ☐	Lion, Small #94	22.00
44. ☐	Lion, Standing, Lg. #89*	30.00
45. ☐	Lunch Pail	28.00
46. ☐	Mail Box #116-#128*	24.00
47. ☐	Mutt & Jeff, Gilt #13	42.00
48. ☐	Negro #42	24.00
49. ☐	Negro, 2 Faces #43-44	28.00
50. ☐	Old South Church	40.00
51. ☐	Owl #203, #204	28.00
52. ☐	"Pass Around The Hat"	28.00
53. ☐	Pig #173-#184*	28.00
54. ☐	Pig, "Thrifty" #175*	28.00
55. ☐	Polar Bear	32.00
56. ☐	Policeman, Irish #8*	38.00
57. ☐	Policeman, Standing*	34.00
58. ☐	Postal Savings Bank	28.00

44

27

	Item	Retail
59. ☐	Puppy, Sitting #114	22.00
60. ☐	Rabbit, Large #100*	32.00
61. ☐	Radio, Crosley #141	28.00
62. ☐	Refrigerator, General Electric #237	28.00
63. ☐	Rival Bank	27.00
64. ☐	Rooster, Standing #186	26.50
65. ☐	Safe, Royal Safe Deposit	28.00
66. ☐	"Security Safe Deposit", safe	35.00
67. ☐	Sheep #191-#192*	28.00
68. ☐	Soldier, W.W.I #15	38.00
69. ☐	State Bank #441	24.00
70. ☐	Statue of Liberty #269	28.00
71. ☐	Steamboat, Iron	42.00
72. ☐	Tank Bank, U.S.A. W.W. 1 #161	32.00
73. ☐	Teddy Roosevelt #309	48.00

*Being Reproduced   •3 Varieties Known   **4 Varieties Known

Jewel boxes were quite popular in the Victorian period. They were generally made of a heavy white metal and then plated with either silver or gold. The interiors were generally covered with a soft felt, satin, or cotton.

1.

5.

6.

7.

All prices are for Good Condition.

	Item & Description:	*A.B.P.	Retail
1. ☐	Kidney-Shaped. Rosy lining	3.50	8.00
2. ☐	Large Box. Lined, ornate exterior design	9.00	13.50
3. ☐	Medium Box. Gold color. Floral ornamentation	4.00	8.00
4. ☐	Small Box. Lined, silver plated	4.00	9.00
5. ☐	Dome Top, silver plated, filigree design	6.00	12.00
6. ☐	Silver plated, ornate with birds, swings & opens	11.00	22.00
7. ☐	Wavy Square, silver plated, engraved top w/lock	7.00	15.00

*A.B.P. — Average Buying Price — See Page 5

NOTE: Sterling or "Coin" Silver — double price.

The War Between The States produced many articles which are today treasured by collectors.

U.S. CAVALRY HAT

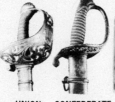

UNION SWORD   CONFEDERATE SWORD

MILITARY DRUM $250.00

Item & Description: Prices are for Good Condition	*A.B.P.	Retail
Ammunition Pouch. Grain leather. Issuance depot markings	8.00	18.00
BAYONETS:		
Sharpened steel with scabbard	5.50	11.50
For cal. 45-70	6.00	13.00
Belt. Navy sword. Embossed emblem on buckle	12.00	24.00
BELT BUCKLES:		
Brass. With U.S. eagles	10.00	21.00
Brass. With lead backing. Marked "U.S."	4.00	9.25
Navy Commissioned Officer. Brass with anchor and eagle insignia	11.50	23.50
Officer's. Wreath below eagle	8.25	16.50
Soldier's. Regiment's state on front	6.00	13.00
Soldier's. Marked "U.S."	6.00	13.00
Bullet Former. Wooden handles and iron body	8.00	16.50
Button. Confederate regiment	2.00	5.20
Canteen. Union army, with cover & strap	4.00	9.00
Carbine Holster. For Sharps repeating rifle	8.00	18.20
HELMETS:		
Shako. Buttons on sides	9.50	19.50
With band. First Rhode Island Volunteers	28.00	58.50
Pay Table. With pay information for officers	21.00	42.25
SWORDS:		
Union Cavalry	32.50	65.00
Confederate Infantry	55.00	110.50
EPAULETTES:		
Artillery. Officer's red. Pair	13.00	26.00
Cavalry. Braided. Pair	11.50	23.50

BELLS (Metal)

In warning him of danger, summoning him to prayer, calling him to r
and tolling the passing of great figures, the bell has been an important pa
man's life. Made in various sizes and of different materials, bells are
collector's items.

**Original
Pieces Only**

**All prices are
for Good Condition**

Item & Description:	*A.B.P.	R
1. ☐ Bell. Small. Straight handle	13.00	2
2. ☐ Calling Bell. Sculptured handle, silver plating	10.50	1
3. ☐ Chinese Brass Bell	8.50	1
4. ☐ Church Bell. Solid brass, triple tier	36.25	7
5. ☐ Church Bell. Solid brass, single tier	24.00	6
6. ☐ Clapper. Solid brass, 3"	8.00	1
7. ☐ "Cutter"-type bell. With iron strap. Set of 3	12.00	2
8. ☐ Dog Bells. 4" high, sculptured handles. Pair	15.00	2
9. ☐ Elephant Bell	8.00	1
10. ☐ Ships Bell, Brass Dolphin belfry	69.00	10
11. ☐ Hand Bell. 12½" high, solid brass	22.00	4
12. ☐ Lady. Sculptured figure 4" high	10.00	1
13. ☐ Mass Bell. Solid brass	21.50	3
14. ☐ School Bell. Wooden handle (Small)	12.00	8
15. ☐ School Bell. Large, wooden handle	16.00	24
16. ☐ Soldier. Roman Centurion, 3½" high	9.00	1
17. ☐ Town Crier Bell. Large, with wooden handle	30.00	
18. ☐ Trolley Car Bell. Heavy iron. 8" Diameter	22.00	48
19. ☐ Turtle Bell. Mechanical, made in German	16.50	30

*A.B.P.—Averag Buying Price.

NOTE: Reproductio re made.

BELLS

(Metal)

(Glass)

All prices are for Good Condition

Item & Description:	*A.B.P.	Retail
SLEIGH BELLS:		
0. ☐ Iron string of 30 bells	18.50	38.00
1. ☐ Iron string of 25 bells. Rich leather strap, graduated sizes	43.00	85.00
2. ☐ Brass string, 25 bells,	33.00	68.00
GLASS BELLS		
3. ☐ Amber Bell. Glass handle	26.50	49.50
4. ☐ Bristol Wedding Bell. Clear sculptured handle, Red barrel, swirl pattern. With clapper, 14" high	33.00	62.50
5. ☐ Cranberry Glass, Clear handle, swirl pattern	28.00	68.00
6. ☐ Cut-glass Bell (Brilliant)	13.50	32.00
7. ☐ Clear dark green bell	20.00	36.00
8. ☐ Nailsea Bell. Solid glass handle, loops & swirls in color	36.50	72.50
VENETIAN GLASS BELLS:		
9. ☐ Ruby red, enamel decoration	20.00	42.50
0. ☐ Latticino, crossed curved colored lines on clear glass, 5" high	28.00	52.50

BELLS

34.

51.

38.

Prices on Original Be

	Item & Description	*A.B.P.	Re
31. ☐	Brass Bell. Musical chimes. 7" H.	14.50	21
32. ☐	Brass Bell. Shaped as Stork. 5" H.	10.00	15
33. ☐	Chinese Gong. Heavy brass set on stand. 9" H.	14.00	24
34. ☐	Cow Bell. Has iron ring for strap attachment	10.00	15
35. ☐	Cow Bell. Iron with heavy clapper	8.50	14
36. ☐	Figure Bell. 19th cent. lady with hoop skirt	11.00	16
37. ☐	Dinner Bell. Enamel on metal. Made in China	25.00	32
38. ☐	Dinner Bell. Made of polished sterling silver	20.00	28
39. ☐	Doll Bell. Dressed in pink satin gown	10.00	15
40. ☐	Elephant Bell. Heavy cloisonne decorations	15.00	23
41. ☐	Hand Bell. Made of brass with decorations	20.00	28
42. ☐	Hand Bell. Heavy brass with wooden handle	14.00	21
43. ☐	Indian (from India) Bell. Red and black with elephant	26.00	35
44. ☐	Mission Bell. Miniature with stand, clapper	20.00	28
45. ☐	Mission Bell. Miniature from Spanish California	40.00	55
46. ☐	Peddler's Bell. 2½" H. No decorations	10.00	15
47. ☐	Porcelain Bell. Tall handle, floral decoration	15.00	23
48. ☐	Porcelain Dinner Bell. 8" H. Painted figure	50.00	65
49. ☐	School Bell. Brass with short handle	10.00	14
50. ☐	School Bell. Polished brass with wood handle	15.00	23
51. ☐	School Bell. Cast iron, 30" diameter. Very large	110.00	200
52. ☐	School Bell. Brass with no handle	14.00	21
53. ☐	Sheep Bell. Curved with long arched handle	20.00	28
54. ☐	Ship's Bell. Brass, 1845 with inscription	30.00	90
55. ☐	Ship's Bell. Polished brass with bracket	20.00	36

*A.B.P. Average Buying Price

Bottles were used in the trade for containing tonic and shampoo. They ere made from a variety of transparent, translucent and opaque glasses.

OTE: *Reproductions are made.*

GLASS SQUIRT TOPS
FOR BARBERS' BOTTLES.

MILK GLASS

BOHEMIAN   HOBNAIL

ROUND BASE

AMBER GLASS

All prices are for Good Condition

Item & Description:	*A.B.P.	Retail
Amberglass	16.00	38.00
Amethyst	17.50	42.00
Amethyst. Enamel, blown and shaped	19.00	45.00
Bohemian Glass. Hand-painted floral exterior	22.50	50.00
Clear. Blue base, ribbed sides	13.00	30.00
Cobalt. Dark blue, heavy enamel. Pair	31.00	75.00
Cranberry. Matched pair	39.00	78.00
Cranberry. Portrait of woman on exterior	29.50	58.50
Cut Glass. Cover of sterling	13.00	30.00
End-Of-Day (Spatter-ware)	21.00	52.00
HOBNAIL		
Amberglass	21.00	52.00
Dark Blue	24.00	55.00
Opalescent	21.50	60.00
Honey-colored amberglass	24.00	62.00
MILKGLASS		
Hexagonal base	10.00	22.00
Rounded base	10.00	24.00
Straight-formed neck	10.50	21.00
Sapphire blue, Thumbprint pattern	25.00	60.00
Striped. Opalescent color	22.50	45.50
Tiffany Glass Type	40.00	110.00

A.B.P. — Average Buying Price.

BOTTLES — AVON

Among the most recent collectables are the popular assortment of Avon
Bottles. Originally containing perfumes, powders and toiletries of Avon
Products, Inc., these bottles are produced in an assortment of unique shapes,
sizes and colors. The listing below contains some of the most sought-after
examples of this contemporary art form. Prices will vary according to the
rarity and condition of the item, while color variations are quite common
owing to manufacturing techniques.

In 1965, Avon introduced a men's after shave in an attractive Stein decanter
and a men's cologne in an amber Boot. It was at this point that collectors
began acquiring Avon bottles, realizing the intrinsic beauty and future
worth of these items. Today, Avon collecting is still gaining in popularity,
promising to be one of the most important collectables.

Pictures: Courtesy Avon Products, Inc., N. Y. C.

All prices are for mint condition

Item and description	Retail
1. ☐ Alpine Decanter. Sprayed glass bottle simulates texture and color of leather. Tapered screw-type cap attached by chain	42.
2. ☐ Bud Vase. Tapered glass decanter with gold pattern at top of neck. Stopper is glass knob	7.
3. ☐ Cologne Silk Bottle. Embossed frosted glass with colored band around neck. Embossed plastic cap	5.
4. ☐ Dollars and Scents. Milk glass replica of paper money roll. Realistic green lettering and design. Screw-type plastic cap. Red rubber band around roll	23.
5. ☐ Dueling Pistols. Richly embossed pair of gold guns with matching plastic screw-type caps. With box	17.5
6. ☐ First Edition. Glass decanter in shape of book. Name etched on cover surrounded by scrolls. With screw-type plastic cap in gold color	10.0
7. ☐ Gavel. Rich amber glass head with silver band on neck. Sculptured brown plastic screw-type handle	14.0
8. ☐ Golden Apple. Richly frosted metallic-tinted glass in shape of apple. Stem cover serves as handle	7.5
9. ☐ Lavender Sachet Bottle. Four-sided embossed apothecary-type bottle with sculptured glass cap	12.5
10. ☐ Miss Lollypop Spray Mist. Doll-faced plastic covered mist container in soft shade of pink. Has necklace and white plastic hat cover	7.5

1.

4.

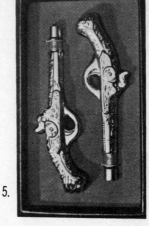

5.

6.

7.

10.

12.

13.

17.

1...

All prices are for mint condition

Item and description

Re...

11. ☐ Perfume Bottle. Clear glass container with overlay of antique-finish brass leaves and pedestal base. Brass-colored plastic screw-type cap .... 15...

12. ☐ Perfume Petit Snail. Transparent glass replica of snail has screw-type metallic gold head .... 10...

13. ☐ Pipe Dream. Amber glass pipe with silver ring, black bit and curved plastic holder. 7" high .... 20...

14. ☐ Pony Post. Carefully detailed green glass hitching post with gold colored ring on sculptured, fluted column. Screw-type plastic cap .... 9...

15. ☐ Pump. Embossed black opaque glass replica of 19th century town water pump. Metallic gold plastic handle and screw-type cap .... 7....

16. ☐ Renaissance Trio. Luxurious bottles in classic minaret design. Tear-drop metallic gold plastic cap .... 7....

17. ☐ Riviera Decanter. Clear glass decanter with embossed neck and silver florentine-type base. Silver-colored plastic screw-type cap .... 11...

18. ☐ Royal Orb. Clear glass circular bottle with red letters and red band at neck. Embossed gold plastic top .... 27...

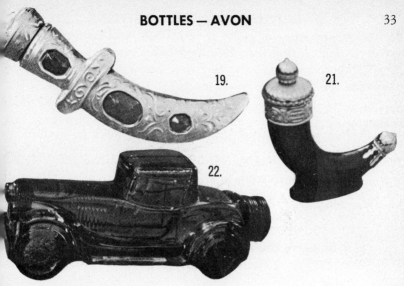

19.

21.

22.

Item and description	All prices are for mint condition	Retail

9. ☐ Scimitar. Embossed metallic gold sword with ruby red bejewelment. Matching gold-colored cap **12.50**

20. ☐ Sea Shell. Clear glass fluted, fan-shaped bottle with gold and white label. Fluted gold metallic plastic screw-type cap **8.00**

21. ☐ Spicy After Shave. Clear glass bottle with red and black label. Black bulbular plastic top **7.00**

22. ☐ Sterling Six Car. Glass-bodied roadster replica with black plastic spare tire which serves as cap. Several mold numbers and variations in top are available. One model has cloth-like roof **8.50**

23. ☐ Unforgettable. Clear glass bottle with gold letters and embossed gold cut-out covering at shoulder **7.50**

24. ☐ Topaze Cologne Mist Bottle. Slender yellow plastic-covered glass bottle with pearlized collar that serves as a spray button cover. Imitation topaze stone adorns cap **10.00**

25. ☐ Viking Horn. Amber glass decanter shaped like Viking's battle horn. Embossed screw-type cover **17.50**

26. ☐ Windjammer Bottle. Clear blue glass bottle with plastic cap with silver colored ring. Bottle has white sails with gold lettering. 5 oz. capacity **8.50**

BOTTLES — JIM BEAM BOTTLES

These bottles originally were started by the James B. Beam Distilling Company to package their excellent Beam Bourbon Whiskey in a special Christmas decanter for gift giving in 1953. The fabulous success of this first issue led to the many series and varieties of "Beam" bottles.

Most of the bottles are produced in finest regal china, however, some are of beautifully colored glass. Each Beam decanter has the year of issue stamped on the bottom. The interest in these popular "collectables" grows constantly.

*A.B.P. — Average Buying Price: This is the approximate price a dealer would pay for a wanted bottle in Mint condition.

Our thanks and appreciation to the James B. Beam Distilling Co., Beam, Kentucky, and Mr. Martin Lewin, Vice President, for color & black & white pix of Beam bottles.

JIM BEAMS (Centennial Series)

Item, Description & Date	*A.B.P.	Retail
1. ☐ Alaska Purchase — 1966: Blue and gold bottle with star-shaped stopper. Mt. McKinley pictured with State flag on top. Regal china. Height, 10"	13.00	25.00
2. ☐ Cheyenne Wyoming — 1967: Circular decanter in shape of a wheel. Spokes separate scenes of Cheyenne history. Regal china	4.00	12.50
3. ☐ Civil War North — 1961: Blue and grey bottle depicting Civil War battle scenes. Stopper has Lee's face on one side, Grant's on the other. Regal china. Height, 10¾"	23.50	42.00
4. ☐ Civil War South — 1961: One side portrays the meeting of Lee and Jackson at Chancellorville. On the other side a meeting of southern Generals. Regal china. Height, 10¾"	23.00	41.00
5. ☐ St. Louis — 1964: The silhouette of St. Louis is depicted facing on the Mississippi River. Regal china. Height, 11"	9.00	25.00
6. ☐ St. Louis — 1964: re-issue. As above	10.50	22.00
7. ☐ Laramie Wyoming — 1968: Centennial Jubilee	5.75	13.50

1.

2.

3.

7.

1.

3.

5.

All prices shown are for Mint Condition:

	*A.B.P.	Retail
First National Bank of Chicago — 1964: Sky blue circular bottle. "1st" is heavily embossed.	875.00	1650.0
1. Katz Cat — 1967 Yellow	15.00	35.00
2. Foremost (Black & Gold) — 1956: Regal black bottle with embossed gold in chunks or nuggets. Regal china. Height, 15¼"	60.00	125.00
The Broadmoor Hotel — 1968: Model of famous Atlantic City Hotel 1918-1968	4.00	12.00
4. Foremost (White & Gold) — 1956: Tapered decanter has square sides and curved bottom. Nuggets of gold are embossed on the white surface. Regal china. Height, 15¼"	60.00	125.00
5. Harolds Club (Man in a Barrel I) 1958: Created for Harolds Club, Reno, Nevada. Man standing in barrel has lost all but his hat, monocle, tie, collar, and black spats. Regal china. Height, 14¾"	260.00	450.00

*A.B.P. — **Average Buying Price** — See Page 5

Item, Description & Date	*A.B.P.	Retail
6. ☐ Harolds Club (Man in a Barrel II) 1958: Twin brother of Club man number I. Harolds Club inscribed on bottom of barrel. Regal china. Height, 14¼"	170.00	325.00
7. ☐ Harolds Club (Nevada State) 1963: "Harolds Club of Reno" inscribed on base. Otherwise, same as State bottle. Regal china. Height, 11½"	90.00	195.00
8. ☐ Harolds Club (Pinwheel) 1965: Fiery Pinwheel casting, spinning paths of gold on blue, with "Harolds Club, Reno" insignia in the center. Regal china. Height, 10¼"	70.00	125.00
9. ☐ Harold's Club: — 1967 Slot Machine Made in Blue tone	10.00	25.00
10. ☐ Marina City — 1962: Commemorating Modern Apt. complex in Chicago. Light blue with Marina City in gold on the sides. Regal china. Height, 10¾"	28.00	50.00
11. ☐ First National Bank of Chicago — 1964: Sky blue circular bottle, heavily embossed with ornate scroll work in center. Regal china. Height, 11½"	1,000.00	1,500.00

6.

9.

10.

All prices shown are for Mint Condition:

Item, Description & Date	*A.B.P.	Retail
1. ☐ Blue Cherub — 1960: Blue and white decanter with heavily embossed figures. Scrolls and chain around neck. Regal china. Height, 12½"	52.50	100.00
2. ☐ Flower Basket — 1962: Blue Basket filled with pastel flowers and green leaves resting on gold base. Regal china. Height, 12¼"	31.50	63.00
3. ☐ Golden Chalice — 1961: Chalice with grey-blue body, gold accents. Band of embossed pastel flowers on the neck. Regal china. Height, 12¼"	42.00	90.00
4. ☐ Grey Cherub — 1958: Checkered design, bordered with scroll work, accented with 22 karat gold. Regal china. Height, 12"	75.00	150.00
5. ☐ Majestic — 1966: Royal blue decanter on a base of golden leaves. Regal china. Height, 14½"	16.50	38.00
6. ☐ Marbled Fantasy — 1965: Decanter on a marbled base, set in a cup of gold with a heavy gold ring around the center. Regal china. Height, 15"	35.00	75.00

*A.B.P. — **Average Buying Price**

8.   9.   12.

All prices shown are for Mint Condition:

Item, Description & Date	*A.B.P.	Retail
7. ☐ Royal Dimonte — 1957: Black and white bottle. Hand painted with 22 karat gold and bordered in gold. Regal china. Height, 15½"	45.00	100.00
8. ☐ Royal Gold Diamond — 1964: Diamond-shaped decanter set on a flaring base, all in mottled gold. Regal china. Height, 12"	26.50	53.00
9. ☐ Royal Gold Round — 1956: Mottled with 22 karat gold, in classic shape with graceful pouring spout Regal china. Height, 12"	110.00	185.00
10. ☐ Royal Porcelain — 1955: Gleaming black decanter, tapered with a large flared pouring lip. Regal china. Height, 14½"	115.00	230.00
11. ☐ Royal Rose — 1963: Decanter embossed with hand painted roses on a background of soft blue. Regal china. Height, 17"	27.00	54.00
12. ☐ Tavern Scene — 1959: Two tavern scenes are embossed on sides, framed in a wide gold band. Regal china. Height, 11½"	40.00	85.00

BOTTLES — JIM BEAM (State Series)

5.

1.

9.

All prices shown are for Mint Condition:

Item, Description & Date	*A.B.P.	Retail
1. ☐ Alaska — 1958: Star-shaped bottle in turquoise blue. Symbols of Alaskan industry in corners of star. Regal china. Height, 9½"	45.00	90.00
2. ☐ Alaska — 1964-65, re-issued. As above	33.00	68.00
3. ☐ Colorado — 1959: Light turquoise showing pioneers crossing the rugged mountains with snow capped peaks in background. Regal china. Height, 10¾"	27.00	55.00
4. ☐ Hawaii — 1959-60: Tribute to 50th State. Panorama of Hawaiian scenes; palm trees, the blue pacific, outriggers, and surfboarders. Regal china. Height, 8½"	47.00	85.00
5. ☐ Idaho — 1963: Bottle in the shape of a State of Idaho. Skiier on slope on one side and farmer on other side. Regal china. Height, 12¼"	50.00	90.00
6. ☐ Kansas — 1960-61: Shows harvesting of wheat on one side, on the other, symbols of the modern age with aircraft, factories, oil wells, and dairies. Regal china. Height, 11¾"	36.50	78.00

*A.B.P. — Average Buying Price — See Page 5

All prices shown are for Mint Condition:

Item, Description & Date	*A.B.P.	Retail
7. ☐ Kentucky — 1967: State map on bottle shows products of Kentucky. Tobacco, distilling, farming, coal, oil, and industries. Regal china.	8.00	16.00
8. ☐ Montana — 1964: Tribute to gold miners. Names of Alder gulch, Last Chance gulch, and Bannack are embossed on bottle. Regal china. Height, 11½"	55.00	115.00
9. ☐ Nebraska — 1967: Bottle bears the words, "Where the West Begins" with a picture of a covered wagon drawn by oxen. Regal china	8.00	16.00
10. ☐ Nevada — 1964: Circular silver and grey bottle bearing outline of State with embossed mountain peaks, forests, and a factory. Regal china. Height, 11½"	51.00	92.00
11. ☐ New Jersey — 1963-64: Grey map of State filled with embossed colorful fruits, vegetables, and flowers, set on pyramid shaped bottle. Regal china. Height, 13½"	11.00	27.00
12. ☐ North Dakota — 1964: Embossed memorial picture of a pioneer family in yellows, greens and browns. Regal china. Height, 11¾"	42.00	90.00
13. ☐ Ohio — 1966: Bottle in shape of State. One side bears State seal, other side has pictures of State industries. Regal china. Height, 10"	8.00	17.00

7.   8.   10.   11.

All prices shown are for Mint Condition:

Item, Description & Date	*A.B.P.	Reta
1. ☐ Cats — 1967: Trio of three cats. Colors; black, white, and white with tan. Regal china	6.50	13.0
2. ☐ Doe — 1963: Pure white neck markings, natural brown body. Regal china. Height, 13½"	21.00	40.0
3. ☐ Dog — 1959: Long-eared setter dog, soft brown eyes, black and white coat. Regal china. Height, 15¼"	55.00	80.0
4. ☐ Duck — 1957: Green-headed Mallard, bright yellow bill, brown breast, black wings. Regal china. Height, 14¼"	29.00	55.C
5. ☐ Eagle — 1966: White head, golden beak, deep rich brown plumage, yellow claws. Regal china Height, 12½"	8.00	17.0
6. ☐ Fish — 1957: Sky blue Sailfish, pink underside, black dorsal fin and side markings. Regal china. Height, 14"	33.00	62.5
7. ☐ Fox — 1965: Bushy-tailed Fox with white pants, dark green coat, and scarlet cravat. Regal china. Height, 12¼"	20.50	39.0
8. ☐ Horse (Black) — 1962: Black Horse with white nose blaze, white hooves, and black tail. Regal china. Height, 13½"	10.00	32.0
9. ☐ Horse (Black) — 1962, reissued 1967: As above	12.50	27.0
10. ☐ Horse (Brown) — 1962: Brown Horse with white blaze on nose, black hooves and tail. Regal china. Height, 13½"	10.00	32.0
11. ☐ Horse (Brown) — 1962, reissued 1967: As above	12.50	27.0
12. ☐ Horse (Grey) — 1962: Grey Mustang with grey flowing mane and tail. Regal china. Height, 13½"	10.00	32.0
13. ☐ Horse (Grey) 1962, re-issued, 1967: As above	12.50	27.0
14. ☐ Oregon — 1959: On one side is a fisherman at a steam, and on the reverse are some of the high snow-capped peaks of Oregon. Regal china. Height, 8¾"	30.00	85.0

All prices shown are for Mint Condition:

Item, Description & Date	*A.B.P.	Retail
15. ☐ Pennsylvania — 1967: Bottle is in shape of a "keystone" of an arch with State seal in center. Regal china.	4.50	10.00
16. ☐ West Virginia — 1963: Blackwater Falls pictured on one side; on reverse, the brilliant Cardinal, the State bird. Regal china. Height, 10¼"	90.00	150.00
17. ☐ Wyoming — 1965: Rectangular blue and grey bottle. One side pictures bucking bronco and reverse pays tribute to Old Faithful. Regal China. Height, 12"	32.50	75.00
14. ☐ Pheasant — 1961: Ring-necked Pheasant with red-circled eyes, green and blue head, and soft brown plumage. Regal china. Height, 13"	10.50	21.00
15. ☐ Pheasant — 1961, re-issued, 1966: As above	8.00	16.00
16. ☐ Ram — 1958: Stylized Ram in soft tans and browns. Calendar mounted on green base. Regal china. Height, 12½"	67.00	125.00

*A.B.P. — Average Buying Price — See Page 5

6.   7.   8.   14.

1.   2.   3.

All prices shown are for Mint Condition:

Item, Description & Date	*A.B.P.	Retail
1. ☐ San Diego — 1968: Gold bottle celebrates the founding of San Diego in 1769. Embossed on front is a Father with cross and Soldier with halbert. Reverse scene in yellows, orange, and black depicts representive travelers of overland route. Regal china. Height 10"	5.00	15.00
2. ☐ Antioch — 1967: Decanter, resembles Indian Head nickel, honoring Diamond Jubilee of city of Antioch. Front of decanter, Indian "Sequoit". Reverse side pictures blue diamond rays and words "Antioch, Illinois 75th Year Diamond Jubilee 1892-1967". Regal china. Height 10"	7.50	15.00
3. ☐ Santa Fe — 1960: Celebrates 350th anniversary of city of Santa Fe and Governor's Palace. Blue colors of bottle framed by gray Indian border design. Gold lettering. Reverse side embossed figure of Indian woman with mountains in background. Plain cork stopper. Regal china. Height 10"	140.00	235.00

*A.B.P. — Average Buying Price.

All prices shown are for Mint Condition:

Item, Description & Date	*A.B.P.	Retail
1. ☐ Richard's New Mexico — 1967: Decanter in shape of the state. Created for Richard's Distributing Company of Albuquerque, New Mexico. Words "New Mexico" and "Richard says: Discover New Mexico" in blue. Embossed design of Taos Pueblo. Reverse side, scenes of famous areas of New Mexico. Regal China. Height, 11"	10.00	20.00
2. ☐ Zimmerman Two Handled Jug — 1965: Small dark green container. Covered with embossed leaves and grape pattern. Handles scrolled like shells. Regal China. Height, 10¼"	60.00	135.00

1.   2.   3.

BOTTLES — JIM BEAM (Additional Executive Series)

Item, Description & Date	*A.B.P.	Retail
3. ☐ Prestige — 1967: Avocado green and gold. Shape resembles earlier Flower Basket. Design of gold leaves around base. Gold curving handle extends to graceful pouring lip. Stopper, green and gold. Case of green leather, lined in green velvet, embossed in gold. Regal china. Height, 12½"	16.00	35.00

Item, Description & Date	*A.B.P.	Retail
1. ☐ Oregon — 1959: Honor Centennial of the state depicting famous scenery. Regal China. Height 8¾"	30.00	50.00
2. ☐ New Hampshire — 1967: Inscribed on decanter, state motto, "Live Free or Die" with nickname "The Granite State". Also, state seal. On reverse, scenes of sports and historical spots. Stopper, gray china profile of "The Old Man of the Mountain". Regal china. Height 13½"	5.00	13.00
3. ☐ Illinois — 1968: Decanter honors the Sesquicentennial of the state. Inscribed below embossed log cabin is slogan "The Land of Lincoln". Stopper of bottle has outline map of state on large capitol I. Regal china. Height 12¾"	5.00	12.50

All prices shown are for Mint Condition:

2.

3.

Luxardo or "Ardo" decanters are included in many of the finest bottle collections in the world. These distinctive, colorful glass and Majolica containers are exported to over 50 countries around the world including the United States.

1930 saw the first Majolica amphoras imported here. Between three and six new designs are selected every January for that year's production. The most popular, such as the *Cellini* bottle first created in the early 1950s still continues to be used — it is an outstanding example of the Luxardo line. Sometimes however, a design is dropped after only one year's use, one example is the *Chess Set* of 1959. Too difficult and too costly to produce, it was dropped from the line.

Collectors are unaware of the names given to most of the Luxardo decanters or when they were made or imported. Early collectors often removed the paper labels which prevents proper identification.

The Zara decanters created before World War II are extremely rare and are expected to receive both a larger premium and become a greater challenge to collectors. The "First Born" of the Murano Venetian glass, if ever located, will command a still higher price and the Naponelli "signed" decanters will increase in price as time passes considering the limited number that were imported.

Collectors will find many of these bottles for sale at flea markets giving the knowledgeable collector an unusual opportunity to find real buys at low low prices. An added value to all Luxardo decanters should be stressed: they are all hand made and hand decorated, no two are alike, and it is probable that bottles in mint condition bearing their labels will bring the highest prices.

All prices listed are for empty bottles.

Pictures courtesy: Girolamo Luxardo Co., & Lourie Liquor, N.Y.C.

1.    2.    3.

BOTTLES — LUXARDO

All prices shown are for Mint Condition:

Item, Description & Date	Retail

MAJOLICA FIGURALS:

1. ☐ Gondola—1959: Highly glazed in Black, Orange and Yellow with trim in Red & Blue. One stopper on upper prow of Gondola. Separate stopper bears the rostrum or could be laced on prow of boat. Also in miniature Majolica. Height 12¼" 15.00
   Majolica miniature. Height 4½" 6.00

2. ☐ Tower of Fruit—1968: Decanter composed of pastel flowers—with a pink rose bud stopper. Majolica. Height 22¼" 20.00

3. ☐ Calypso Girl—1962: Calypso girl balances basket of flowers on top of white striped cloth wrapped around her head and shoulders. Stamped on base "SAM Rep. S. Marino" Majolica. Height 11" 14.00

MAJOLICA SPECIALTIES

4. ☐ Egyptian—1959: Majolica amphora, created to serve as a lamp base made in brown earthen colors. Resembles fresco work of Middle Kingdom of Egypt. Imported again in 1968—inscription on base "Made Italy Exclusively for Luxardo." Majolica. Height 14¼" 16.00

5. ☐ Apothecary Jar—1960: Glazed in White with a band of ornate black letters around middle of jar, elaborate floral bands bordered with Green & Black. Black stopper. Imported again in 1968, with light Blue & Orange bands. "Gentian" on label. "Ceramica Titano Rep." San Marino on 1968 base 16.00

VENETIAN GLASS FIGURALS

6. ☐ Green & Gold Fish—1960: Designed and hand blown by the glass blowers of Murano. Sides highly luminous, glass filled with silver flecks. Back & Belly in dark green underlayed with silver. Fins infused with flecks of real gold, as is the tail. Base is detachable. Glass. Height 10" 30.00

7. ☐ Alabaster Goose—1960: Hand made of varying shades blue-green and white glass, with white wings. Poised on crystal base—imported again in 1967, 1968. Glass. Height 15½" 30.00

8. ☐ Squirrel—1968: Newest addition to the Luxardo glass figurals. Hand blown by glass blowers of Murano. Translucent amethyst glass. Detachable crystal base. Glass. Height 11½" 40.00

MAJOLICA DECANTERS

9. ☐ Blue & Gold Amphora—1968: Tall slender, Blue & Gold. One side decorated with detailed country scene painted on white background. Handles in form of folded leaves, blue with band of gold. Majolica Height 22" 15.00

1.

2.

3.

8.

5.

*See Page 201
for Color Picture*

BOTTLES-ANTIQUE WHISKEY BOTTLES

These bottles were used to hold the contents of early American Distillers. They can be found in all parts of the United States. The Western states are usually the best hunting areas. Value is set by rarity, condition, tops, construction, embossing and appearance.

CONDITION: As nearly mint as possible. Bad scratches, cracks, stains, reduce a bottles value. Bubbles are not considered detrimental.

EMBOSSING: An embossed, or raised design increases the bottles value. Pictures or unusual names, or many words, are most desired.

TOPS: A drippy or "glopped" top, a sheared top cut by hand, or a top with ice pick marks are the most valuable.

CONSTRUCTION: Look for unusual seams, bubbles, whittle marks, concave bottoms.

Item & Description	Rarity	*A.B.P.	Retail
1. ☐ CARTAN & McCARTHY, San Francisco. Whittled, yellowish-green amber, glopped top	Very Rare	35.00	70.00
2. ☐ COLUMBIAN, Kentucky Bourbon. Very dark amber with picture of explorer	Ext. Rare	95.00	150.00
3. ☐ CRESCENT BOTTLE, no embossing except crescent. Three-piece whittle-mold liquor bottle. Deep grn.	Rare	20.00	35.00
4. ☐ J. H. CUTTER, bottled by A. P. Hotaling & Co. Old looking, yellowish-green amber, whittled effect, glopped top, concave bottom	Very Rare	35.00	70.00
5. ☐ J. F. CUTTER, extra, trademark, shield, Old Bourbon. Very crude glopped top, yellowish-green tinted amber	Very Rare	35.00	70.00
6. ☐ J. H. CUTTER, Old Bourbon, A. P. Hotaling, sole agents. Crown on neck, gold amber, whittled, concave bottom, glopped top	Ext. Rare	80.00	150.00
7. ☐ J. F. CUTTER, trademark, E. Martin Co., San Fran., Calif. Light golden amber, very weak strike, deep whittle effect	Ext. Rare	95.00	150.00
8. ☐ GUNDLACH, Bundschu Wine Co. Bacchus Brand. Figure of Bacchus raising glass	Ext. Rare	95.00	150.00
9. ☐ PEPPER DISTILLERY, hand made sour mash. Pepper & Co.	Very Rare	35.00	70.00

*A.B.P. — Average Buying Price — See Page 5

Item & Description	Rarity	Retail
10. ☐ Circular-Sided Bottle. Heavy floral embossing around rim, sides and base. Contained Bullseye Whiskey. No other identification	Ext. Rare	22.50-28.00
11. ☐ Coblentz & Levy. Amethyst bottle with long neck. Inscribed with name and address of Oregon distillers	Rare	8.00-10.00
12. ☐ Commodores Royal O.K. Kentucky Bourbon. Narrow neck with crest and crown on front	Rare	10.00-12.00
13. ☐ Gambrinus Brewing Co. Amber color with tapering neck. Trademark in center of circle	Rare	5.50-7.00
14. ☐ King George IV. English Whiskey in olive color. Inscribed: "Proprietors. The Distillers Company Ltd."	Rare	10.00-20.00
15. ☐ Louis Taussic & Co. Amethyst whiskey bottle with screw threads inside neck. Anagram inside circle. San Francisco	Rare	20.00-30.00

16.

17.

18.

19.

Prices shown are for good condition

Item & Description	Rarity	Ret
16. ☐ Old Pioneer. Whiskey pinch bottle with heavy indentations on sides and square neck. Name inscribed across front	Very Rare	15.00-20.0
17. ☐ Gold Thimble. Very dark amber pinch bottle. Scotch whiskey distilled in Glasgow. Inscribed: "Scotch Whiskey, Bloch Bros. Glasgow". Pointed top	Very Rare	10.00-15.0
18. ☐ Old Times Whiskey. Squat bottle with thatched wicker case. Inscribed: "First Prize World's Fair 1893"	Ext. Rare	35.00-50.0
19. ☐ The F. Chevalier Co. Whiskey bottle with screw-threaded neck. Name and embossed castle along with name "Castle Whiskey" Dark amber	Ext. Rare	25.00-35.0
20. ☐ Ye Old Mossroof Bourbon. Triangular top of bottle embossed in shape of roof. Window below. Inscribed: "RS Roehling I Schutz Inc. Chicago". Very dark amber	Very Rare	35.00-50.0

One of the most versatile and long-lasting substances known to man, brass composed of zinc and copper. Throughout the years, brass has been used to fill literally thousands of man's needs.

ANDIRONS

BEDWARMER

COWBELL

BOOT JACK

Item & Description: Prices are for Good Condition	*A.B.P.	Retail
ANDIRONS:		
] Sculptured Griffins. Matched pair	24.50	48.00
] Queen Anne. 9" high, matched pair	35.00	70.00
] Climbing rope columns. 20" high	23.00	46.00
] Sculptured posts. Curved bases. 25" high, lacquered and polished pair	36.25	72.50
] Basket. With handle and basketweave	9.50	19.25
] Bed Warmer. Handle of pine	32.50	65.25
BELLS:		
] Cowbell	6.50	13.00
] Dinnerbell. Aquatic creatures	8.00	16.00
] School Bell. Wooden handle, 6" high	9.75	19.50
] Slave Bell. Polished with striker. 19" high	27.50	55.00
] Sleigh Bells. Graduated to 1¼", leather strap	39.00	78.00
] Bird Cage. Small	13.50	27.00
] Boot Jack	8.00	16.50

*A.B.P. — Average Buying Price

Item & Description Prices are for Good Condition	*A.B.P.	Re
BOXES:		
☐ Tobacco box. Portrait of Queen Victoria or other rulers.	47.00	9?
☐ Hammered box. Measures 7" x 7" x 2½"	5.00	1(
BOWLS:		
☐ 6" diameter	4.00	?
☐ 7" diameter	5.00	1C
☐ 8" diameter	6.00	1?
☐ Bucket. Deeply burnished and lacquered. 12" x 18"	27.00	55
☐ Medium size	22.00	45
☐ Card Holder	5.50	11
CANDELABRA:		
☐ Triple-branch. 11" high	27.00	55
☐ 7-branch. Arms turn separately. 18" high	38.00	76
☐ Candle-holder	8.00	16
☐ Candle-holder. With three accessories	20.00	40
CANDLESTICKS:		
☐ 9", burnished Beehive. Pair	26.00	52
☐ 9¾". Pair	30.00	60
☐ 11⅛". Pair	31.00	67
☐ Flying Dragon Type	15.00	30
☐ Cannon. Solid brass. Large	30.00	60
☐ Chafing tray and dish	36.00	72
☐ Cigar trimmer. Bureau size	7.00	14
☐ Coal Container. Brass scoop, handle and holder. Many sculptured parts	48.50	97
☐ Coal carrying hod	50.00	100
☐ Coffee maker. With burner	15.00	31.
☐ Cuspidor. Mechanical animal	18.50	37.
☐ Door knock. Head of Medusa (1865)	13.00	29.
☐ Door-stop. Fox	14.00	28.
FIREPLACE EQUIPMENT:		
☐ Brass fender. Post and rail, iron bottom.	34.00	68
☐ Foot Warmer	20.00	40
☐ Fire Fork. Bird handle	6.75	13.
☐ Fire Lighter. New England-type	10.50	21
☐ Trivet. Sculptured leaf	27.00	55.

TOBACCO BOX

CANDLESTICKS

CANDELABRA

COAL SCOOP

TRIVET

DOOR KNOCK

Item & Description Prices are for Good Condition	*A.B.P.	Reta
FRAMES (PICTURES)		
Oval-shaped, 6″	8.00	16.0
Florentine, with easel	18.00	36.5
Mirror Oval. Flying cherub	11.25	22.5
Mirror Oval. Flying cherub, large	16.50	34.2
Ginger Container. Engraved Chinese motif	13.00	36.5
Canal Horn. Excellent lacquering. 24″ high	20.00	39.5
Inkstand. Highly decorated, English	18.00	36.0
Inkwell. With tray, English-type	21.00	42.
Jardiniere. Hammered and embossed	8.50	19.0
Jardiniere. Stag handles	28.00	55.5
KETTLES:		
6-quart capacity	13.00	26.0
8-quart capacity	16.25	32.5
10-quart capacity	17.50	35.0
11-quart capacity	19.00	38.0
Ladle. 15″ handle	8.50	17.0
Ladle. 14″ iron handle, dated 19th century	11.00	22.0
Lamp. Store-front, brass shade, hanging-type	38.50	77.0
Lock and Key. Solid brass	13.00	26.0
Milk Pan	14.00	30.0
Mortar & Pestle	11.00	24.5
Mortar & Pestle. Large mortar	13.00	29.5
Pail. 15″	16.00	32.0
Pan, Warming. Perforated top	35.00	68.5
Pot Hanger. Adjustable elevation ratchet	31.00	62.0
POWDER HORNS:		
Eagle	21.00	44.2
French Fleur De Lis	14.00	29.5
Flower design	18.00	32.5
Roasting Jack	23.00	49.0
SAMOVARS:		
With burner	47.00	94.5
With large burner. Russian-type	60.00	120.5

*A.B.P. — Average Buying Price — See Page 5

BRASS

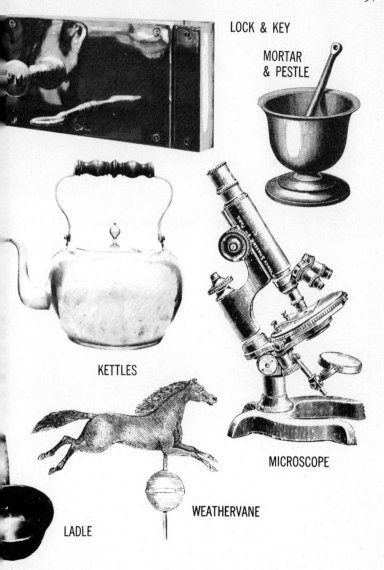

LOCK & KEY

MORTAR
& PESTLE

KETTLES

MICROSCOPE

WEATHERVANE

LADLE

BRASS

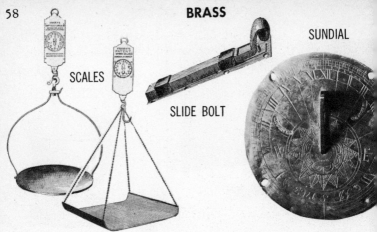

SCALES

SLIDE BOLT

SUNDIAL

Item & Description	Prices are for Good Condition	*A.B.P.
SCOOPS:		
Candy		4.25
Scale, small		5.50
Scale, large		11.00
Sugar		10.00
Scuttle. Ornate handle, hammered brass		45.00
Sew Bird		6.50
Skimmer		12.50
Slide Bolt		5.00
Steamship Whistle. Small		16.00
Stove. Portable, charcoal		16.00
Sundial. 8-sided, excellent condition		37.50
Tea Kettle. Glass handle, curved feet		30.00
TRAYS:		
For Decanter		7.00
Rounded. Heavy brass		16.00
Trivet. Fox and Tree		16.00
Umbrella Stand		9.00
Umbrella Rack. Lion holders		12.00
Urns. High sculpture. Pair		44.00
Weather Vane Arrow. Filigree glass and brass		40.00

COOKING MOLDS

COOKING MOLDS 59

Originally quite functional, today old food molds are used to decorate modern kitchens. They were made of various materials, pewter. copper, iron, wood, crockery, etc.

NOTE: Reproductions are made.

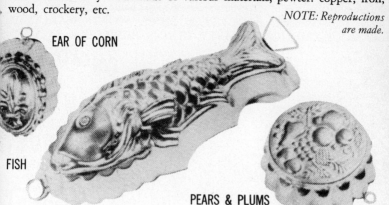

EAR OF CORN

FISH

PEARS & PLUMS

All prices are for Good Condition — **Original Pieces Only**

Item & Description:	*A.B.P.	Retail
Cigar. 9 sections	6.00	12.75
Ear-Of-Corn. Crockery	5.00	12.00
Ear-Of-Corn. Pewter	6.25	13.50
Fire Truck. Pewter	9.50	20.00
Fish. 4" long	5.50	13.00
Frog. Copper	5.00	10.50
Heart	5.00	10.50
Lamb. Cast iron. 9" high, 14" long	17.00	35.00
Lion. Copper top	6.50	13.50
Pears, plums	14.00	31.00
Pudding. Copper cast	11.25	23.50
Rose. Tin with copper lid	8.50	18.00
Saint Nicholas. Pewter	9.00	19.00
Turkey. Pewter	7.25	15.00
Woodchuck. Crockery	7.75	16.00

.B.P. — **Average Buying Price**

CARDS — ADVERTISING

In the late 19th century, business firms began advertising their prod
through the use of trade cards. Both printed and lithographed, these pict
were of places, scenes and events and carried the name of the company's proc
The most valuable are: CLIPPER SHIPS, SPORTS, EARLY AUT
FAMOUS AMERICANS, EARLY TRAINS, BICYCLES & BALLOONS

KERR & CO.   COLGATE & CO.

Item & Description:	Prices are for Good Condition	*A.B.P.	R
☐ Ayer Co. Sarsaparilla		.75	
☐ Arbuckles Coffee		.95	
☐ Ayers Cards		.75	
☐ Babbits Co. Soap. Little girl and cat		.75	
☐ Bixby Boot Black. Shoeshine boy		.75	
☐ Colgate & Co., Cashmere Bouquet Toilet Soap		.75	
☐ Kerr & Co., Aesops Fables		.75	
BROWN'S CARDS			
☐ Toothpaste		.50	
☐ Tramp and Iron Stove		.50	
☐ Young girl holding sign		.50	
☐ C. Ware Co.		1.00	
CLARK'S			
☐ Negro with snare drum		.75	
☐ "Advice to Wives"		.75	
☐ Decker Bros. Musical instruments		.50	
☐ Diamond Co. Dyes		.75	

e Stereoscope came into being around 1850 in the United States. It was an tremely popular family pastime, taking viewers to wherever their cards came m. Their journeys were only limited by the amount of cards that they had. e effect, when seen through a viewer, created an optical 3 dimensional scene.

Hand-Held Stereoscope Viewer,
slides to focus....$9.50

Prices Shown are for Good Condition:

Item & Description	*A.B.P.	Retail
CARDS — 100 Per Set:		
Denmark	5.50	11.75
Egypt. Sphinx, Pyramids, The Nile, etc., with map and book	6.50	13.00
Germany. Berlin. The Rhine, Nuremberg	5.50	11.75
Holland. Windmills, Amsterdam, Tulip Fields, etc.	5.50	11.75
Italy. Rome, Venice, Capri, etc., with book and map	5.50	11.75
Norway. Complete with book and map	6.50	13.00
World War I. Battle Scenes and Soldiers. Two boxes of complete prints	14.00	27.50
SINGLE CARDS — Listings state maximum prices:		
Advertising Cards of all types	.60	1.20
Automobiles. Various makes (pre-1905)	1.00	3.00
Civil War Photographs (Anthony-Brady)	4.50	9.50
Indians. American Plains, Cowboys, Forts, (post-1885)	1.10	2.50
Panama Canal. Ships and Locks	.50	1.00
Presidents of the United States (pre-1885)	1.75	3.50
Ships. Sail, Steam, etc. (pre-1885)	1.75	3.50
Spanish American War. Famous Battles	.50	1.00
Tissues. French and American	1.10	2.25
Trains. Steam Engines, Union Pacific (pre-1885)	1.50	3.75
Western Scenery. Deserts, Mountains, Plains	1.60	3.25
Whaling	.75	1.50
World War I. Battles, Soldiers	.75	1.25

A.B.P. — Average Buying Price — See Page 5

Photography became a popular pastime in the 1870's. Many types of camera were produced between 1870-1941 that today are valuable and collectab Pre-1870 cameras are the most valuable. Prices quoted are for pieces in go working order.

Ret

1. ☐ Detective Camera—a Tom Thumb pat. 1889, 2-5/8" square, one double plate holder. ca. 1890......................... 140.(

2. ☐ Detective Novelty Camera—Expo Camera Co., N.Y. Miniature watch shape 2-1/4" Diameter............................ 200.(

3. ☐ School Identification Camera—U.S. Camo-Corp., Kansas City, Mo... 80.(

4. ☐ A wooden-bodied camera—Wolensak "Alphax" shutter, Bausch & Lomb Zeiss "Protar" f/4.5 8-3/4" lens—hand crafted... 80.(

5. ☐ Early Roll Film—Eastman Kodak #4 Jr. 4 x 5 in., 48 exp., Bausch & Lomb Universal Lens, 1892-1897..................... 65.0

6. ☐ Folding Roll Film Camera—Flush back Kodak—"Model A." 3-1/4 x 4-1/4" pictures on 118 film, Bausch & Lomb "Rapid Rectilinear" lens. circa 1903...................... 70.0

7. ☐ Folding Plate Camera—Conley Camera Co. (Sears Roebuck & Co., Dist.) 4 x 5" Glass Plates, "Rapid Rectilinear" lens. ca. 1907.. 65.0

8. ☐ Folding Film Camera—Eastman Kodak "No. 3A Folding Brownie" for pictures 3-1/4" x 5-1/2" on 122 film. ca. 1914 50.0

9. ☐ Folding Plate—Seneca Mfg. Co. Folding Plate 3-1/4" x 4-1/4" glass plate, "Rapid Rectilinear" Lens, Seneca "Uno" shutter, ca. 1910... 70.0

10. ☐ Half Plate Daguerrotype Camera, mahogany portable Tripod, ground glass viewer. For taking half plate (4-1/4" x 5-1/2" photographs). Lens marked, "Voigtlander & Sohn in Wien und Branshweig," ca. 1852.................................... 2600.0

11. ☐ Plate Camera—Scovill Mfg. Co. view camera—takes 6" x glass plates—lens barrel of Brass is marked "R. Morrison N.Y." Circa 1888.. 110.0

12. ☐ Panoramic Camera—Eastman Kodak "No. 4 Panorami Kodak," Model B—Lens swings 140 degree arc, pictures are 3-1/2" x 12" on 103 film................................... 75.0

13. ☐ "Vest Pocket Autographic Kodak" 127 roll film. "Kodak Ball Bearing Shutter". "Kodak Anastigmat" F.7.7 84mm lens. Ca. 1915.. 40.0

Courtesy: Parke Bernet

Daguerreotypes were the first photos made. The process was discovered i
1839 by Daguerre, a Frenchman. The most valuable and collectable are: Civ
War, Western, City Views, Famous People. They are usually mounted and framed

4.

1.

5.

Item & Description	Retail
1. ☐ Accordionist—a young man in profile, ca. 1850	60.00
2. ☐ P. T. Barnum—Seated with Standing Woman	110.00
3. ☐ Brighton—Fountain in the Old Steyne Gardens. ca. 1850	130.00
4. ☐ Child with Bird—Boy with large bird in cage	50.00
5. ☐ Class picture H. C. Young's school, Town of Greenwich	60.00
6. ☐ Cooper Union—Copy of architects drawing, 1854	90.00
7. ☐ Farm—2-1/2 Story Farmhouse—Barn—Carriage house and outbuildings	50.00
8. ☐ Man with Gun—Sighting down single barrel shotgun	60.00
9. ☐ Mother & Child—Child seated on Mother's lap	40.00
10. ☐ Negro—Woman wears plaid dress, bandana and holds white child	60.00
11. ☐ S. P. Peck Apothecary—2 views inside & out Bennington, Vt., 1850	220.00
12. ☐ Survey Party—10 men well dressed—2 tents, covered wagon	100.00
13. ☐ Rutgers Female Institute—class picture	300.00
14. ☐ Zachary Taylor—In General uniform—Gold tinted buttons	35.00
15. ☐ Officer in full dress uniform standing with sword at side	35.00
16. ☐ Solomon and his wives—copy of a "risque" painting	35.00
17. ☐ Winter Street Scene—A frame house, snow on ground	60.00
18. ☐ Gamblers—2 men posed for a card game—"Brady"	50.00
19. ☐ Farm Wagon pulled by pair of matched black horses	25.00
20. ☐ Union Soldiers—Standing bayoneted rifles in hand, 1864	30.00

Courtesy: Parke Bernet

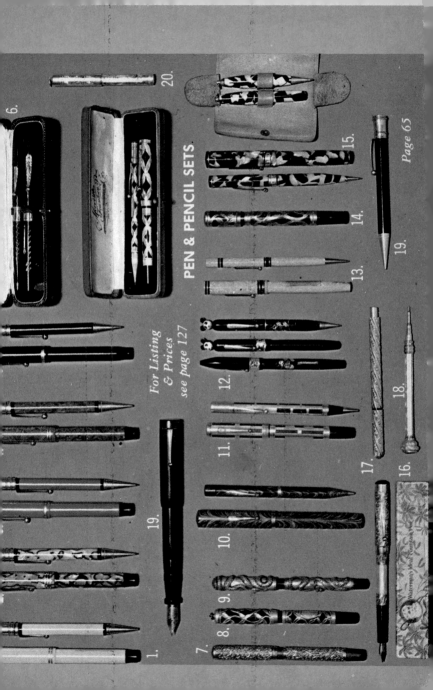

PEN & PENCIL SETS.

For Listing & Prices see page 127

Page 65

1.

2.

3.

4.

5.

INGERSOLL
MICKEY MOUSE
CLOCK

ELECTRIC

CHARACTER CLOCKS & BOXES

For Listing & Prices see page 120

For Listing & Prices see pages 120-121

CHARACTER & COMMEMORATIVE
POCKET WATCHES

Page 67

CHARACTER WRIST WATCHES AND BOXES

For Listing & Prices see page 121

27.

28.

29.

26.

23.

22.

25.

30.

Page 68

CHARACTER WRIST WATCHES AND BOXES

31.

32.

33.

34.

35.

36.

37.

38.

39.

40.

41.

ROW 1. — POLITICAL & STATE. ROW 2 & 3 — STATE, CENTENNIAL & REGAL CHINA

For Complete Listing & Prices see pages 34-46

ROW 1. — TROPHY SERIES. **ROW 2.** CHINA SPECIALTIES. **ROW 3.** EXECUTIVE SERIES.
For Complete Listing & Prices see pages 34-46

1.

2.

3.

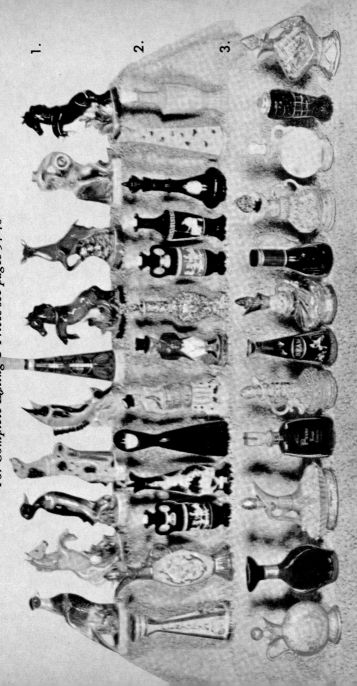

Page 71

For Listing & Prices on Antique Clocks see pages 84-115

THE COLORFUL WORLD OF ANTIQUE CLOCKS

Photo: Mr. Barnard

COCA-COLA COLLECTIBLES

he Coca-Cola Company has through the years produced countless items to
romote the sale of Coca-Cola. The list of collectibles includes bottles, glasses,
ays, knives, toys, bottle openers, cigarette lighters, thermometers, playing
ards, fountain servers, and various items of printed ephemera. The older
ems in particular (pre-World War II) are the most valuable.

ALL PRICES FOR ORIGINAL ITEMS ONLY

	Item & Description	Retail
1. ☐	Ball Point pen 4" with telephone dialer..................	each 1.75
2. ☐	Coca-Cola playing cards 2 scenes "Lady in Red" & "Couple with Puppy"......................	set 6.75
3. ☐	Cards with World War II Fighting Planes.................	11.00
4. ☐	Coca-Cola playing cards — King size bottle of Coke depicting picnic setting...	4.50
5. ☐	Cigarette lighter — musical — one plays "Dixie", one plays "Things go better with Coke"..................	ea. 15.00
6. ☐	Cigarette lighter — Disposable...............................	5.50
7. ☐	Crock fountain dispenser 1890's, hand painted	600.00
8. ☐	Clock — Electric 18" Dia. Dated 1952, running........	15.00
9. ☐	Clock — Wall electric. Enameled sheet 18" dia.........	35.00
10. ☐	Case of 28 bottles, miniature, gold finish................	22.50
11. ☐	Coca-Cola bottle circa 1915 applied paper label	22.50
12. ☐	Coca-Cola rare presentation bottle. Gold 6-1/2 oz. size reads, "Oklahoma 1903—1967", 1000 made..	28.00
13. ☐	Knife — Floating fishing knife, wood handle w/case	6.50
14. ☐	Knife — Pocket knife, with bottle opener, nail file	6.50
15. ☐	Measuring tape — retractable 6 ft., Gold bottle in relief	7.50
16. ☐	Truck, metal, 11" long, "Coca-Cola" on sides........	32.50
17. ☐	Truck, iron, 11" long, "Coca-Cola" on sides...........	67.50
18. ☐	Toy truck, 8 bottles coke..................................	42.50
	TRAYS:	
19. ☐	Tray — girl in fur stole, 1925 (full color).................	20.00

Illustrations Courtesy: Coca-Cola Company.

COFFEE MILLS

ONE WHEEL

WOOD MILL

TWO WHEEL

WALL TYPE

WALL TYPE With clear jar

Prices are for Original Pieces

Item & Description prices are for Good Condition	*A.B.P.	Retail
IRON:		
Stubby, with cap dome and urn-cup	17.50	25.50
Two-wheel. Large, repainted	75.50	115.00
Two-wheel. With handle. Ornate finial on dome	82.00	145.00
One-wheel. With crank	26.50	42.00
Small Mill. 9" high. Dated early 1870's	40.50	66.50
Wall-type. With clear jar	7.50	12.00
Wall-type. With metal container	11.00	16.50
White Iron, china jar. Delft scene. German	35.75	59.50
WOOD:		
Dovetailed. Iron lid and cup. Door at base	18.00	26.25
Dovetailed. Pewter cup, iron crank and drawer	20.50	32.50
Urn-shaped iron cup, sliding drawers.	17.50	25.00
Iron cup, with crank	16.25	22.50

*A.B.P. — Average Buying Price

BISQUE CHINA

Unglazed light colored porous china which appears to be unfinished is known as Biscuit or Bisque. Sometimes decorated, but more often not, plates, cups, saucers and pitchers gained popularity in this country during the late 1800's. Today, because of the numerous reproductions and imitations on the market, the interest in, and prices of Bisque have dropped sharply.

CANTON CHINA

An inexpensive light-colored porcelain, Canton has been popular in Europe and the United States for well over two centuries. Generally decorated with blue enamelled floral or landscape patterns, this unmarked porcelain was known as Bistre when finished in brown.

CALENDAR PLATES

CHELSEA CHINA & CHINA MUGS

Produced from the early 1700's to the mid-1820's, during a period spanning almost one hundred and fifty years, Chelsea china was of the same type and quality as Dresden ware. Intricate designs, colorations and floral patterns underglazed on a smoothly-baked finish, mark this superb and much sought-after china. The four "Chelsea Periods" may be determined by the following insignias marked at the base of each piece.

1. Raised anchor and inscribed triangle—1740-1756
2. Ruby anchor — 1756-1761
3. Gold anchor — 1761-1770
4. CHELSEA-DERBY inscription — 1770-1823

HAVILAND & LIMOGES CHINA

During the early 1840's, an American importer named David Haviland established a china factory at Limoges in southern France. From there, a large quantity of china was exported exclusively to the United States. This china was of particularly fine quality, consisting of several different patterns of which the most popular was the bird and floral design. From popular usage, the names Haviland and Limoges were both used. However, the china is identical. Decoration marks varied from 1842 to the mid-1950's. All true Limoges are marked.

MULBERRY & MOSS ROSE

CHINA (BISQUE)

All Prices are for Good Condition Unless Otherwise Noted.

Item & Description	*A.B.P.	Retail
Bisque:		
Animal Dish. Hen with cover...	8.00	16.50
Baby Piano. Delicate coloring. Mint condition.................	12.00	24.00
Box. Small child sitting on stool. With cover....................	16.00	32.00
Busts. 5-1/2" H. Sevres sculptures Louis 13th, Henri III. Excellent condition. The pair	125.00	250.00
Figurine. 6" H. Nude figure reclining...............................	21.00	42.50
Figurine. 5" H. Boy in clown costume.............................	15.00	30.00
Figurine. 6" H. Prussian soldier with rifle.......................	17.50	35.00
Figurines. 11" H. Boy and girl with dog...........................	50.00	100.00
Figurine. Bright Irish setter on cushion...........................	10.00	20.00
Girl. In fancy dress with musical instrument....................	16.00	32.00
Inkwell. Woman seated on sofa. Two ink holders and sander. Late Victorian period. Rare.	35.00	70.00
Match Holder. Young girl with doll...................................	15.00	30.00
Snow Babies. With sled..	27.50	55.00
Tea Pot. Bird shape. Lid finial is a fly.............................	15.00	30.00
Toothpick Holder. Girl with basket and rabbit.................	12.50	25.00
Vase. 6" H. Youth sitting under wide tree.........................	10.00	20.00
Vase. Young girls sitting among flowers..........................	13.00	26.00
Vase. Boy leaning against tree stump..............................	12.00	24.00

CHINA (CANTON)

	*A.B.P.	Retail
Canton:		
Basket and Tray. With openwork handles........................	45.00	90.00
Bowl. Deep with sharply-cut corners...............................	62.00	124.00
Bowl. 7" diameter. Rich blue finish.................................	12.50	25.00
Creamer. Chip on handle...	10.00	20.00
Cream Pot. Covered with double lid. Twisted handle........	20.00	40.00
Cream Pot. Blue design on off-white field........................	22.50	45.00
Cup. Demitasse. Climbing floral decor............................	6.00	12.00
Hot Water Plate. Blue and white......................................	20.00	40.00
Pitcher. Low, squat, rounded shape................................	24.00	48.00
Pitcher. 10" H...	90.00	180.00
Sugar Bowl. With two handles and cover.........................	30.00	60.00
Tile. Hand-painted tea-house scene. Blue and white........	20.00	40.00

*A.B.P. — Average Buying Price see pg. 5

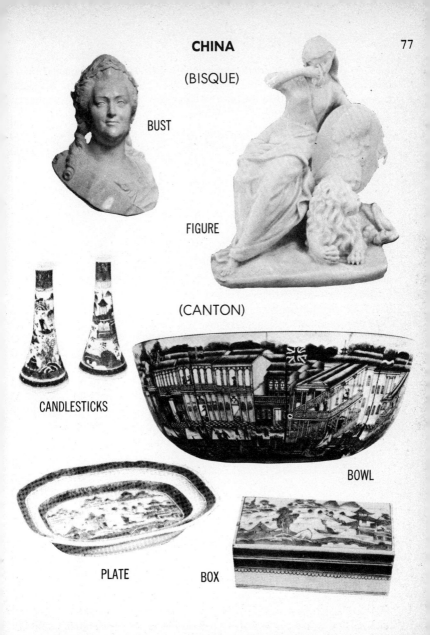

(BISQUE)

BUST

FIGURE

(CANTON)

CANDLESTICKS

BOWL

PLATE

BOX

CHINA (CALENDAR PLATES)

In the early part of the twentieth century, (1907-1926) china Calendar Plates attained great popularity in the United States. It is believed that Calendar Plates originated in England during the latter part of the nineteenth century. The plates varied in size from 7½″ diameter to 9¾″ diameter.

Item, Description & Date	*A.B.P.	Retail
1889—Massachusetts Bi-Centennial. Green ceramic....	15.00	30.00
1906—Floral. With twisting vines....................	13.00	26.00
1907—Santa Claus. With calendar in center...............	10.00	20.00
1908—Harvard Medical School..................................	16.00	32.00
1909—Calendar on border. With American Eagle..........	12.50	25.00
1909—Three women with seasonal flowers................	9.00	18.00
1910—Flowers and Berries..................................	10.00	20.00
1911—Lincoln Portrait......................................	13.50	27.00
1912—Indian Maiden...	7.50	15.00
1912—Girl picking holly in snow.............................	9.00	18.00
1912—Aircraft. Bi-plane in flight............................	7.50	15.00
1912—President Plate. McKinley, Garfield and Lincoln. Inscribed: "Our Martyrs"................................	10.00	20.00
1913—White Rock Girl.......................................	11.00	22.50
1913—Roses with advertisement for Canada..............	13.50	27.00
1914—Hunting scene. Man with dog.........................	8.00	16.00
1914—Star Spangled Banner Centennial. Washington to Wilson border, Panama Canal center...........	9.50	19.00
1916—Calendar in circle of birds and flowers..............	6.00	12.00
1922—Dog watching rabbit. Souvenir plate................	8.00	16.00
1923—Calendar decorated with flowers in border. Rustic scene in center..................................	6.00	12.00
1924—Peace plate. Doves circling calendar in center..	9.00	18.00

*A.B.P. — Average Buying Price — See Page 5

CHINA
(CHINA MUGS)

SUGAR CONTAINER

(CHELSEA)

CREAMER

PLATE

Item & Description All prices are for Good Condition	*A.B.P.	Retail
CHINA MUGS:		
"All The King's Horses, etc.". Humpty Dumpty. Blue....	55.00	110.00
"A Good Boy's Present". Bright yellow........................	52.00	104.00
Bryant & McKinley portraits. Sepia & white background	11.50	23.00
"Changing the Seasons". Four separate scenes............	15.00	30.00
Mother Goose Nursery Rhymes. Set of 3. Excellent con.	37.50	75.00
Zoo Animals. Lion, elephant and monkey....................	16.00	32.00
CHELSEA:		
Apple Basket. 7" H. Decorated miniature....................	25.00	50.00
Butter Dish. With insert. Covered.............................	10.00	20.00
Creamer. Floral pattern covers exterior......................	15.00	30.00
Cup and Saucer. Green leaves on white background......	8.00	16.00
Coffee Pot. Swirled grape design in blue.....................	45.00	90.00
Figure Group. 5-1/4" H. Boy & girl holding lamp.	100.00	198.50
Plate. 10" diameter. Rich lavender.............................	17.50	35.00
Sugar Container. Floral enamelling............................	40.00	81.00
Tea Pot. Lavender decor...	42.50	85.00

CHINA

Item & Description All Prices are for Good Condition	*A.B.P.	Retail
HAVILAND:		
☐ Bowl. 9" diameter. Marimar pattern..........................	7.00	14.00
☐ Bowl. 9-1/2" dia. Pink, green floral. Scalloped rim........	11.50	23.00
☐ Butter Dish. Covered with glass insert.......................	15.50	31.00
☐ Cake Plate. Chenonceaux pattern. Scalloped edge........	11.50	23.00
☐ Candlesticks. 4" H. Tapering stems. Pair....................	12.50	25.00
☐ Celery Dish. Floral and leaf decor.............................	13.50	27.00
☐ Creamer. Flying cherubs. Handles and edges finished in simulated gold. Signed.....................................	15.50	31.00
☐ Cup and Saucer. Lisbon pattern................................	12.00	25.00
☐ Dish. With cover. Signed..	17.50	35.00
☐ Dessert Set. Serving tray and five plates. Scrolled floral design. Gold trimmed rims. The set....................	30.00	60.00
☐ Gravy Container with attached tray. Gold bordered bowl with cover and ornate handles...........................	55.00	110.00
☐ Pitcher. 8" H. Scrolled vine & floral decor. Gold border	17.50	35.00
☐ Tea Tray. Scalloped edges. Montmery pattern. Signed..	15.00	30.00
☐ Vegetable Bowl. With cover. American Embassy pattern	30.00	60.00
LIMOGES:		
☐ Butter Dish. Green band with pink tea roses. Gold trim	7.00	14.00
☐ Bowl. Punch. Roses and green leaves decor. With 8 cups. Hand-painted and in excellent condition............	125.50	250.00
☐ Candlesticks. 8" H. Blue with floral decorations. Pair....	27.50	55.00
☐ Bowl. 9-1/2" dia. Floral decorations. Marked 'Delinieres'	10.00	20.00
☐ Cup and Saucer. Pastel and pink with gold trim............	7.50	15.00
☐ Dish. 5" diameter. Floral design with gold bands. Marked "T & V". Excellent condition..........................	15.00	30.00
☐ Hat Pin Holder. 4" H. Floral design...........................	7.00	14.00
☐ Pitcher. 7-1/2" H. Hand-painted cherries & leaves. Signed	25.00	50.00
☐ Plates. For dessert. Flying cherub in center with gold border. Set of five...	30.00	60.00
☐ Plate. 8-1/2" diameter. White flowers on green background. Gold scalloped edge...............................	7.50	15.00
☐ Plate. 9" diameter. In shape of fish. Signed................	15.00	30.00
☐ Platter. Forest green and brown border......................	11.00	22.00
☐ Sugar & Creamer. Violets & leaves on pink background	9.50	19.00
☐ Tray. With ruffled edges. Floral decorations...............	28.50	57.00
☐ Vase. 7" H. Footed. Roses & gold design. Marked "P.L."	15.00	30.00

*Average Buying Price

CHINA
(HAVILAND)

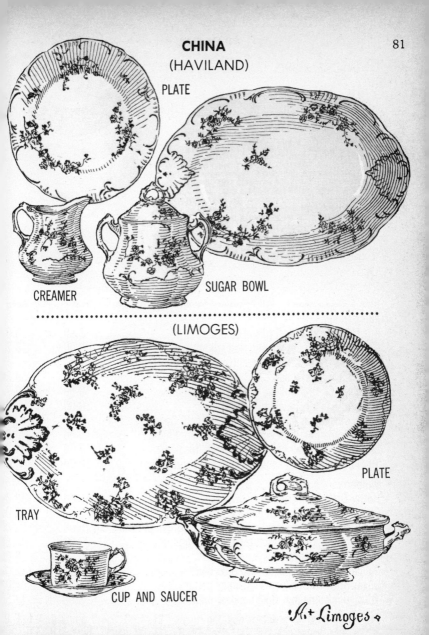

PLATE

CREAMER

SUGAR BOWL

(LIMOGES)

PLATE

TRAY

CUP AND SAUCER

A. Limoges

CHINA

(MOSS ROSE)   (MULBERRY)

SUGAR CONTAINER

PITCHER

GRAVY CONTAINER

PLATE

Item & Description All Prices are for Good Condition	*A.B.P.	Retail
Moss Rose:		
☐ Bowl. With cover. Soft pastel colors............................	7.50	15.0
☐ Compote. Floral center with rich gold banding..............	8.00	16.75
☐ Coffee Pot. Gold trim and curved handles. Porcelain with rich enamel finish.......................................	18.00	36.5
☐ Creamer. 6" H. Scrolling, stripes & bands in design......	9.50	19.7.
☐ Cup and Saucer. Haviland pattern............................	10.00	20.0
☐ Plate. Closed ear handles. White with gold banding......	8.00	16.0
☐ Sugar Container. With cover. Excellent condition..........	15.00	30.0
☐ Sugar Jar. Scrolled handles. Marked "Meakin"............	12.00	24.0
☐ Tea Pot. 9" H. Long spout. Pink scrolls and stripes......	16.00	32.0
Mulberry:		
☐ Butter Dish. With cover..	18.00	36.0
☐ Cup and Saucer. Corean pattern. Missing handle..........	15.00	30.0
☐ Gravy Dish. With cover. Ladle and tray. Corean pattern	25.00	50.0
☐ Pitcher. Large with sculptured classical figures............	22.00	44.5
☐ Plate. 10" diameter..	9.00	18.0
☐ Sauce Dish. 5-1/2" diameter. Gold banding.................	7.50	15.0
☐ Sugar Bowl. With cover. Vincennes pattern..................	24.00	48.0
☐ Toothpick container. Gold banding on rim....................	8.50	17.5

*Average Buying Price

On The following pages you will find a comprehensive section on clocks and watches. Most of the items listed are American. They are arranged by type, alphabetically. Therefore, "CLOCKS-ACORN" would be followed by "CLOCKS-BLACK". All prices listed are for retail values for clocks or watches in fine working condition. We have endeavored to make these prices as accurate as possible, however, they are intended to serve as a guide only.

ALL ABOUT BUYING & SELLING

It is to be noted that all given prices are for timepieces in **GUARANTEED WORKING CONDITION,** assuming that cases, hands, labels, dials, decorated glass and hardware are original. Most clock or watch collectors can evaluate the extent of repair necessary to put a timepiece in proper working condition. If you *ARE NOT* in this category, you must be cautious when making your purchase.

Repairs can be expensive. A reliable clock or watchmaker may spend many hours repairing a timepiece. In addition, missing and broken parts have to be replaced and when not available, must be made to order.

If a timepiece is not working at the time of purchase and the seller tells you it needs just a *slight adjustment* or *just a little oil,* consider it **NOT WORKING . DO NOT BE LURED BY A SEEMINGLY LOW PRICE WITHOUT ANTICIPATING A POSSIBLE COSTLY REPAIR.**

If you are **SELLING** a clock or watch these same rules apply. A non-working timepiece cannot be sold for the same price as one in good working condition. Dealers are well aware of the high cost of repairing timepieces and will consider this when making a purchase from an individual.

—◦✦◦—

OUR THANKS TO

The following people for their help and cooperation in compiling this section.

Mr. JOSEPH FANELLI—"**CLOCKS & THINGS**", 209 Columbus Avenue, N.Y.C. For research, pricing, consultation and help in every way.

Mr. BARNY—1145 2nd Avenue, N.Y.C. For consultation, advice, and pictures of some of his fabulous timepieces.

Mr. WILLIAM DISTIN—Curator, Henry Ford Museum Clock Collection, Dearborn, Michigan. For pictures from their great clock collection.

Mr. ROBERT G. WHEELER, Vice President, The Henry Ford Museum.

Mr. PHIL PaDULA—NAWCC #0015368 for pricing on Alarm Clocks.

All prices shown are for Fine-Working Condition.

Item, Description & Date	Retail
1. ☐ Ansonia—Bee, several models, Top winds like a Craousel. Top has bell.	60.00
2. ☐ Ansonia Clock Co. — "Victory" dog and trumpeter 10¾" high	180.00
3. ☐ Ansonia Locomotive — Iron cased, pat. April 23, 1878	145.00
4. ☐ Ansonia Striking Doll — Alarm clock	165.00
5. ☐ Ansonia Swinging Doll—pat. April 29, 1889. The tree limb suspends doll swinging to and fro	205.00
6. ☐ Darche Flashlight Electric Alarm — Combination time piece, alarm, and deposit box. Pat. March 19, 1889	110.00
7. ☐ Darche Searchlight Electric Alarm — pat. Jan. 29, 1901. On battery box, July 12, 1916. 8¾" high	95.00
8. ☐ Electric Alarms	14.00-27.00
9. ☐ Kroeber Clock Co. — New York City. Bell on top, calendar on face. 3¾" dial	85.00
10. ☐ New Haven Clock Co.—Policeman standing on clock. "One of the Finest" engraved on front. Mfg. Muller & Sons. ca. 1890	125.00
11. ☐ Parker Clock Co. — Meriden, Conn. Two alarm bells under clocks. Height 7"	55.00
12. ☐ Seth Thomas — Heavy Bronze cased. One day long alarm. 9¼" high 4½" dial	35.00
13. ☐ Western Clock Co. — Baby Ben. Pat. Oct. 28, 1902	13.00
14. ☐ Western Clock Co. — Big Bens. 1910 plain or radium dial	35.00
15. ☐ Wm. L. Gilbert Clock Co. — Double top bell, alarm 7" high. Pat. July 7, 1885	75.00
16. ☐ Wm. L. Gilbert Rocking back and Forth—Alarm bell on top. Cord inside rocks bell. Columns are hollow	125.00
17. ☐ Wm. L. Gilbert Clock Co. — Two top bell carriage alarm. Glass on three side	90.00

1.

11.

12.

14.

White dial

Luminous dial

7.

Courtesy of The Henry Ford Museum, Dearborn, Michigan

Manufactured, probably exclusively, by the designer J. C. Brown of Forestville Manufacturing Co., Bristol, Connecticut, in the years 1847-1850.

Courtesy of The Henry Ford Museum, Dearborn, Michigan

All prices shown are for Fine-Working Condition.

Item, Description & Date	Retail
1. ☐ Original model Acorn—The house of J. C. Brown, in Bristol, which is still standing, painted on glass tablet.	4,200.00
2. ☐ Standard Acorn—picture of "State House Hartford" painted on glass tablet	1,800.00
3. ☐ Forestville Mfg. Co. clock. Tablet shows Merchants Exchange, Philadelphia	3,000.00
4. ☐ Type of Acorn Clock with side arms replaced by acorns on the baseboard	1,400:00
5. ☐ Acorn type—No side arms. Three feet high	900.00
6. ☐ Final Acorn type — No legs or side arms	700.00

A Connecticut shelf clock, cased in the shape of a rounded gothic arch. Average dimensions, 18½″ high, 11″ wide, 4″ deep. Made in the late 1840's. Many manufactured into the early 20th century.

New Haven Beehive.................110.00   Welch Beehive w/alarm.............95.00

All prices shown are for Fine-Working Condition with original glass and decal.

		Retail
1. ☐ Ansonia Clock Co.—Ansonia, Conn. Set alarm on face of clock. Country scene on gold leafed decal tablet...		100.00-135.00
2. ☐ Brewster & Ingrahams—Bristol, Conn. One of the earliest known. Etched glass front tablet, ca. 1847		115.00-150.00
3. ☐ Chauncey Jerome—New Haven, Conn. Hour strike. Winds at 4 and 8. Mirror tablet on front..................		115.00-150.00
4. ☐ E. & A. Ingraham—Bristol, Conn. Set alarm on face. ca. 1852-1855...		100.00-135.00
5. ☐ E. C. Brewster & Son (Noah)—Bristol, Conn.		100.00-135.00
6. ☐ Terry & Andrews—Lyre Movement.......................		115.00-150.00

CLOCKS — BANJO (1802-1968)

Patented in 1802 by Simon Willard. This beautiful and unique design is still being produced today. The name is derived from the case which is shaped like a banjo. The most valuable are those made from 1810-1830 and signed.

All prices shown are for Fine-Working Condition.

Item, Description & Date	Retail
1. ☐ Aaron Willard—Boston, Mass. Original painting on glass. Acorn finial, Roman numerals. ca. 1808. 33" x 10"......	2,200.00
2. ☐ Simon Willard, "S. Willard's Patent". Eagle finial on ball. 40-3/4" high. Wooden bracket. ca. 1805..	4,000.00
3. ☐ Curtis & Dunning—Concord, Mass. Original painting on glass. Hour strike. Winds at 3 & 9. 51" x 11-1/2". ca. 1815......	1,450.00
4. ☐ Edward Howard—Weight driven banjo, eight day. Figure 8 clock. Size can vary from 29" to 56"........	* 500.00-1,200.00
5. ☐ The E. Ingraham Co.—"Treasure" mahogany case, eagle finial. Two rod, strikes the hour. Arabic numerals. 39" high, 8" dial. Brass side arms. Hand painted front......	125.00
6. ☐ The New Haven Clock Co.—"Willard" weight driven banjo. Eight day movement. Wooden bracket	350.00
7. ☐ Sawin & Dyar—Boston, Mass. Brass side arms, eagle finial. Roman numerals. Painted glass front panels. ca. 1822......	1,100.00
8. ☐ Sessions Clock Co.—Mahogany case with bracket, eagle finial. Arabic numerals on large dial. 27" x 9-1/2" x 5"......	115.00
9. ☐ J. F. Tappan—Manchester, Mass. Combination banjo and alarm clock. Alarm bell on top. Wooden case, acorn finial......	960.00
10. ☐ John Sawin—Alarm Banjo, wood panels—wooden side arms. 2 hole winds at 4 and 2 o'clock. ca. 1810	900.00
11. ☐ Wm. L. Gilbert Clock Co.—Mahogany case and side arms. Pendulum, eight day spring wound movement. 27" x 9-1/2" x 5"......	115.00
12. ☐ William King Lemist—Boston, Mass. Mahogany case with acorn finial. Roman numerals, barbed arrow hands. 33" x 10"......	1,800.00

*Depending on size.

1.

2.

4.

3.

5.

Courtesy of The Henry Ford Museum, Dearborn, Michigan

All prices shown are for Fine-Working Condition.

Item, Description & Date	Retail

1. ☐ Ansonia "patent applied for" on case. Iron cased mantel clock. Size: 10-1/2" x 9-1/2". Dial: 5" dia. — 67.00

2. ☐ Ansonia—New York, dial face has escapement. No feet on marble case. Top is flat, patent date expires 1882.. 80.00

3. ☐ Ansonia—New York. Black wooden case with engraved flowers on front. Top is flat with scrolled feet. 6-1/2" dial. 10-1/2" x 18"............................ 65.00

4. ☐ Ingraham—"Albany" Three reeded columns on each side. Black wood case has flat top. Decorative metal feet. 5" dial, 11" x 17"...................... 75.00

5. ☐ Ingraham—"Count" Cathedral gong strike. Half-hour bell. Black iron case. Winds at 4 & 8. 5" dial, 12-1/4" x 10".. 50.00

6. ☐ E. Ingraham Co.—"Luzon" Scrolled wooden flat top case. Lion handles with rings on sides. Marbleized columns on front, decorative feet. 10-3/4" x 14-3/4", 7" high. ca. 1888............................... 60.00

7. ☐ F. Kroeber—New York. "Cairo" flat top cast iron case. Escapement on face of porcelain dial. Decorative metal feet. ca. 1875............................. 85.00

8. ☐ New Haven "Monarch". Flat top wooden case. Side has marbleized columns. 6-1/2" dial, 12" x 17-1/2"... 70.00

9. ☐ Sessions Clock Co.—Side arched columns contain statues. Arabic numerals on dial, winds at 4 & 8. Black engraved wooden case with feet and side lions. 5-1/2" dial, 12" x 16-1/4".................. 95.00

10. ☐ Waterbury—"Mosaic". Four reeded columns on each side. Scallop top black wooden case. Arabic numerals on 6" dial. Size: 11" x 17".................. 50.00

11. ☐ Waterbury Clock Co.—Escapement on dial. Flat top wooden case. 5-1/2" dial, 10" x 11-1/2". ca. 1881.. 70.00

12. ☐ French, black marble mantel clock. 8 day movement, time and strike, porcelain dial...................... 80.00-100.00

3.

4.

8.

9.

Courtesy of The Henry Ford Museum, Dearborn, Michigan

All prices shown are for Fine-Working Condition.

Item, Description & Date	Retail

1. ☐ E. Ingraham Co. — Bristol, Conn. Visible pendulum, round drop wall clock. Hours and days on same dial. Patent, Oct. 8, 1872 and Nov. 4, 1873.......... 165.00

2. ☐ E. Ingraham & Co. — Bristol, Conn. Figure 8 wall calendar clock. Round head and bottom. B. B. Lewis day and month calendar mechanism. 29-1/2" x 16-1/4" x 4-1/2". Ca. 1879.................. 375.00

3. ☐ E. Ingraham Co. — Bristol, Conn. Wall regulator w/calendar. Weight driven wall calendar clock. Eight day movement. 38" x 17" x 4-1/4".............. 145.00

4. ☐ Ithaca — Parlor calendar with black dials and ornate black walnut case. Clear glass pendulum bob. 19" high.. 1,200.00

5. ☐ Ithaca — Calendar shelf clock eight day movement. Single finial. Clock is 25" high.............................. 270.00

6. ☐ Ithaca — Oak case 8-day wall calendar clock.......... 300.00

7. ☐ B. B. Lewis Wall & Shelf Calendars — Spring or weight driven. Clock mechanism made by various companies. Day of week shown by hand at dial center. Month and day indicated by 2 hands on calendar (lower) dial. from 1862...................... 250.00-450.00

8. ☐ New Haven Clock Co. — Short drop octagon calendar. 12" face wall clock. 22" high, ca. 1875........ 150.00

9. ☐ Seth Thomas — Plymouth Hollow, Conn. Rosewood case, calendar clock. Double dial separated by glass tablet with painting of eagle in gold, holding an American flag with 33 stars, ca. 1860-61.......... 675.00

10. ☐ Seth Thomas — Plymouth Hollow, Conn. Nine sided head. Eight day "Regulator" weight driven clock. Patent dates on lower dial from Sept. 14, 1854 to March 4, 1862. 40-1/2" x 19" x 6-1/2".... 375.00

11. ☐ Welch Spring & Co. — Bristol, Conn. Double decker case, eight day weight driven movement, Lewis shelf calendar. 36-1/2" x 20-1/4" x 7".................. 400.00

12. ☐ Welch, Spring & Co. — Bristol, Conn. Spring driven round wall clock. 4 dials on face. Gale patent, ca. 1870... 700.00

3.

2.

5.

7.

8.

Ingraham Calendar—8 day time, half hour strike, gong. Height 21-1/2".........375.00

Courtesy of The Henry Ford Museum, Dearborn, Michigan

All prices shown are for Fine-Working Condition.

Item, Description & Date	Ret.
1. ☐ American Clock Co.—Acorn iron front eight day spring clock. Front hand-painted scene. Mahogany colored case. ca. 1855....................................	165.
2. ☐ Ansonia Clock Co.—Crystal Palace Clock. Made in many different models. ca. 1880........................	195.
3. ☐ Ansonia Clock Co. — New York. Cabinet antique, solid walnut case with brass trim. Corner brass finials. 2½″ x 3¾″. Center finial, eight day spring movement. 16″ x 9″ x 7½″. ca. 1880	85.
4. ☐ Wm. A. Bradshaw — 76 Pearl St., N. Y. C. Flat top shelf clock with tablet in door detached round side columns. Hand-painted tablet...............................	100.
5. ☐ Briggs — Rotary Pendulum Timepiece. Patented in 1855 by John C. Briggs. Made by E. N. Welch Manufacturing Co. Bristol, Conn. 7½″ high. ca. 1875	195.
6. ☐ J. C. Brown — Forestville Manufacturing Co., Bristol, Conn. Miniature 30 hour spring brass movement label. "Improved brass clocks, spring warranted not to fail . . ." 14¾″ high	135.0
7. ☐ J. C. Brown — Standard type steeple •*................	135.0
8. ☐ J. C. Brown — Twin Steepled Round Gothic•**........	270.0
9. ☐ Chauncey Jerome — New Haven, Conn. Flat top gold leaf side columned eight day clock. Tablet painted with city scene, including a horse car. 18″ high..........	150.0
10. ☐ Clarke, Gilbert & Co. — Winchester, Conn. OG entablature on hollow column which guide the weights. Movement is 30 hour brass. ca. 1840's....	335.0
11. ☐ D. S. Crosby — 1 Courtland St., N. Y. C. Eight day spring brass movement. 14¼″ high. ca. 1850	125.0
12. ☐ Waterbury porcelain (China) cased clock. Color decorations, half-hour strike, gong, porcelain dial. ca. 1890's..	85.00-125.0

•These clocks may also be listed as Steeple clocks.
*Ripple Front Steeple—300.00 (Illustrated)**Ripple Front Steeple—400.00

20.

26.

16.

E. Ingraham, Bristol, Conn.—
Mother of Pearl on Iron Front. ca.
1850, 16-3/4" H...................180.00

14.

Courtesy of The Henry Ford Museum,
Dearborn, Michigan

All prices shown are for Fine-Working Condition.

Item, Description & Date	Reta
13. ☐ Gilbert Manufacturing Co. — 1866-1871. One day alarm, case patent by George B. Owen, Independent Manufacturer. Gilbert and Owen merged...............	70.0
14. ☐ Wm. L. Gilbert Co. — Winsted, Conn. Round top alarm. TP. 11" x 8¼", 4" dial	80.0
15. ☐ E. O. Goodwin — 1852-1855. Bristol, Conn. Eight day spring brass clock movement. Empire case Crystal Palace decal on front of glass tablet......................	170.C
16. ☐ E. Ingraham & Co.—Bristol, Conn. "Doric" eight day strike. 16-1/2" x 10-1/2" x 4-3/4"...................	100.0
17. ☐ E. Ingraham & Co. — Bristol, Conn. "Venetian" type round top shelf clock. 18" high	80.0
18. ☐ E. Ingraham & Co. Four sided top, eight day dial. Time and strike...	85.0
19. ☐ Elias Ingraham — "Grecian" Zebra case, burl base, eight day movement with alarm	165.0
20. ☐ E. Ingraham & Co. — Small venetian, round top, one day alarm TP. 11½" high	135.0
21. ☐ Seth Thomas — Iron front decorated with painting and stenciling. 30 hour movement	95.0
22. ☐ Seth Thomas — Plymouth Hollow, flat top with heavier side columns. 19" high	110.0
23. ☐ Seth Thomas — Thomaston, Conn. Small round gothic, eight day clock. Dial marked "Made in U.S.A.". 11½" x 7¼", 4¾" dial. ca. 1890	67.0
24. ☐ Seth Thomas—Thomaston, Conn. Eight day. 15" cherry case. ST hands with alarm...........................	125.00
25. ☐ Smith & Goodrich—Bristol, Conn. 1847-1852. 30 hr. spring shelf clock with fusee brass. T & S movement, half-round molding outside door. 15-1/2" H...........	225.00
26. ☐ Waterbury Clock Co.—Porcelain front with floral, patriotic or other motifs. 30 hour movement.........	95.00
27. ☐ E. N. Welch Manufacturing Co. — Forestville, Conn. H. J. Davies 1879 patent	135.00

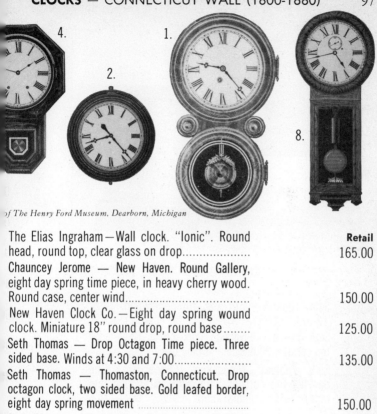

of The Henry Ford Museum, Dearborn, Michigan

	Retail
The Elias Ingraham—Wall clock. "Ionic". Round head, round top, clear glass on drop......................	165.00
Chauncey Jerome — New Haven. Round Gallery, eight day spring time piece, in heavy cherry wood. Round case, center wind...	150.00
New Haven Clock Co.—Eight day spring wound clock. Miniature 18" round drop, round base........	125.00
Seth Thomas — Drop Octagon Time piece. Three sided base. Winds at 4:30 and 7:00........................	135.00
Seth Thomas — Thomaston, Connecticut. Drop octagon clock, two sided base. Gold leafed border, eight day spring movement	150.00
Seth Thomas—Thomaston, Connecticut. Painted moon dial. Hooded wall clock. 36" x 17" x 6-3/4" dial..	250.00
Seth Thomas—Thomaston, Connecticut. Regulator type. Top has 12 sides, eight day weight movement. With bottom glass door. Winds at 2:30, 4-1/2" x 19-1/2", 6" dial..	235.00
Seth Thomas—8 day weight driven "Post Office Clock", oak, walnut or cherry. 12" dial w/second hand, 34" high...	215.00
Waterbury Clock Co.—12" drop octagon clock with two sided base. Winds at 6:00........................	135.00

2.

4.

Courtesy of The Henry Ford Museum, Dearborn, Michigan

CLOCKS — COTTAGE (1836-1916)

Item, Description & Date

1. ☐ Seth Thomas—With flat top rosewood case. 12-3/4" x 17-1/2" x 4". Eight day cottage clock....   85.00-

2. ☐ Seth Thomas — Plymouth, Connecticut. Three sided top cottage. 30 hour alarm time piece   85.00-

3. ☐ Seth Thomas—Thomaston, Connecticut. One day flat top cottage clock with alarm built into movements. Painted tablet. 9-1/2" x 7-1/4", 3-5/8" dial.......   60.00-

4. ☐ Waterbury Clock Co. — Flat top cottage. 30 hour alarm time piece. Decal tablet in door. 11" x 8", 4" dial   60.00-

CLOCKS — GIRANDOLE (1815-1818)

1. ☐ J. L. Dunning — Concord, Mass. Dark wood panels, and side arms. Spread winged, gold leafed eagle finial. ca. 1818   1,

2. ☐ Lemuel Curtis*—Concord, Mass. Originated this clock, perhaps 25 in all were made from 1815-1818.   12,000.00-14

*One of the rarest American clocks known.

1.   3.   6.

Courtesy of The Henry Ford Museum, Dearborn, Michigan

All prices shown are for Fine-Working Condition.

Item, Description & Date	Retail
☐ Nathaniel Hamlin—Augusta, Maine. ca. 1815. Case has flat top. 43" x 11", 7" dial.......................	4,800.00
☐ Samuel Milliken — Newbury Port, Mass. Engraved brass dial. ca. 1780	7,200.00
☐ Noah Ranlet — Gilmanton, New Hampshire. ca. 1810	3,600.00
☐ David Studley — Hanover, Mass. 45" x 14", 6½" dial. ca. 1815	3,600.00-5,400.00
☐ Joshua Wilder — Hingham, Mass. 43" x 11¼", 6" dial.	7,200.00
☐ B. Youngs — Schenectady, New York. 36" x 11", 7" dial. pre-revolution	2,400.00
☐ B. S. Youngs — Watervleit, New York. 36¼" x 10", 4½" dial. ca. 1770	2,400.00

NOTE: *Prices quoted for Tall Case Clocks are regional.*
In areas other than where these clocks were made prices can be considerably lower.

100 **CLOCKS** — GRANDFATHER (1738-1870)

All prices shown are for Fine-Working Condition.

Item, Description & Date   R

1. ☐ Isaac Blaisdell — 1738-1791 — Chester, New Hampshire. Flat top hood; engraved brass dial with
   spandrels and calendar endless rope drive one day
   metal movement, using a single weight. ca. 1762   2,40

2. ☐ Gawin Brown—Boston, Mass. Japanned and
   grained pine case. 89" x 21", 11" dial. ca. 1766......   6,00

3. ☐ Timothy Chandler—1764-1846—Concord, New
   Hampshire. ca. early 1800's. David Young signed
   maple case. "Joiner". 90" x 19", 10" dial..............   3,00

4. ☐ Isaac Doolittle — New Haven, Connecticut. Engraved brass. 10¾" dial with spandrels and brass,
   date "1745". 90½" x 20¼"   2,20

5. ☐ Jacob Eby — Manheim, Pennsylvania. Eight day
   clock with center mounted sweep second and calendar hands. 100" x 19". ca. 1835   2,40

6. ☐ Christian Forrer — Lampeter, Pennsylvania. Flat top
   hood. 1 day brass movement with one weight, endless chain drive. 84" x 20", 10¾" dial. ca. 1748   3,60

7. ☐ Thomas Harland — Norwich, Connecticut. Whales-
   tails on hood and silvered dial with moon phase.
   89½" x 20½", 10¼" dial. ca. 1780   6,00

8. ☐ Silas Hoadley—1786-1870—Eight day clock, 7
   lbs. of pull up weights. Escape wheel and pendulum can be seen in back of case.......................... 60

9. ☐ Thomas Jackson—Preston, Connecticut. Whales-
   tails and 3 pineapple finials on hood similar to
   a Thomas Harland case. 89-1/4" x 18-1/4"..........   4,80

10. ☐ Nathaniel Millikan — Lexington, Mass. Flat top
    hood, maple case. 88" high. ca. 1745   6,60

11. ☐ Samuel Milliken — 1720-1756 — Bradford, Mass.
    86" high. ca. 1745   6,60

12. ☐ Samuel Milliken — Newbury Port, Mass. Engraved
    brass dial and spandrels. 84" high. ca. 1752   6,00

NOTE: *Prices quoted for Tall Case Clocks are regional.*
In areas other than where these clocks were made prices can be considerably lo

7.   6.   4.   2.

Courtesy of The Henry Ford Museum, Dearborn, Michigan

Item, Description & Date	Retail
☐ Benjamin Willard — 1743-1808 — Grafton, Mass. With "105" on dial. 88" high with "209"	4200.00
☐ Simon Willard — White Iron dial with moon and calendar	7000.00
☐ Paine Wingate — Haverhill, Mass. White dial. ca. 1817	2200.00

NOTE: *Prices quoted for Tall Case Clocks are regional.*
In areas other than where these clocks were made prices can be considerably lower.

All prices shown are for Fine-Working Condition.

Item, Description & Date	Re
1. ☐ Barnes, Bartholemew Co.—Bristol, Connecticut. ca. 1835. Triple decker transition clock, painted glass tablet titled "View Near Natchez". 36" high....	200
2. ☐ E. G. Bartholemew—Bristol, Connecticut. ca. 1828. Transition Clock. Pineapple finials, paw feet. Single door with tablet, stenciled splat and half side columns. 30 hour standard weight, wood movement..	185
3. ☐ Basset & Gibbs — Litchfield, Connecticut. Miniature 23" looking glass clock; mirror in single door. Split half columns on case sides. Stenciled splat. ca. 1830	335
4. ☐ Rodney Brace — Northridgewater, Mass. Miniature 23" shelf clock. Mirror in single door. 30 hr. wood movement. ca. late 1820's	350
5. ☐ Birge, Mallory & Co.—Bristol, Connecticut. ca. 1840. Rare three decker miniature, gold leaf painted splat. 30 hour weight brass movement with rolling pinions. 25" high..................	425
6. ☐ Ephraim Downs—Bristol, Connecticut. ca. 1825. Transition shelf clock with claw feet and pineapple finials. Half column stenciled sides and splat. Standard 30 hour movement...................	300
7. ☐ C. & L. C. Ives — Bristol, Connecticut. Triple decker. Split deal with Roman chapters. Flower decoration, carved splat. Side columns in three parts with gold captals; unusual finials. ca. late 1830's	275
8. ☐ Dyer, Wadsworth & Co.—Augusta, Georgia. ca. 1838. Transition clock, triple decker and gold carved eagle splat; dial has black chapter ring, white Roman chapters. "Patent Brass Eight Day Clocks" label probably made by Birge, Mallory & Co.	300

All prices shown are for Fine-Working Condition.

Item, Description & Date	Retail

☐ E. K. Jones — Bristol, Connecticut. For O. Hart, Waterloo, N. Y. Half columned case with tablet of "Emily" in single door. 34" x 16½", 5" dial. ca. 1834 .... **165.00**

☐ Munger & Benedict—Auburn, N. Y. Ca. 1820. Eight day clock. Mirrored Empire type with flat top and spiral side columns. Dial winds at 2:00. 31-1/4" x 14" x 5-1/4"..................................... **400.00**

☐ Munger & Pratt — Ithaca, New York. Mirror on single door, carved splat. 30 hour wood movement. Eagle hands. 35½" x 16¼", 6" dial. ca. 1830 .... **165.00**

☐ Spencer Hotchkiss & Co.—ca. 1830's. Triple decker clock with three section side column, gold leaf center. Carved splat gold leafed. Eight day brass weight movement. 31" x 17" x 5-1/2".......... **335.00**

☐ Eli Terry — Transition clock, single door stenciled with tablet, side columns heavily stenciled. Broken arch splat with eagle insert. Flower decorated dial. 30 hour standard wood movement. 25" high. ca. late 1820's **335.00**

☐ Eli Terry, Jr. & Co.—Terrysville, Conn. ca. 1833. Two decker transition clock. Eight day wood weight movement. Lower door has glass tablet, carved side panel and splat with eagle. Claw feet. 38-1/2" x 18-1/2", 4-1/2" dial............................ **400.00**

☐ Henry Terry & Co. — Plymouth, Connecticut. Looking glass shelf clock. Single door with mirror, flat top splat with two small tablets stenciled columns. 30 hour wood, three weight movement; alarm at 5:30. ca. 1828 .... **250.00**

☐ R. & J. B. Terry — Bristol, Connecticut. Triple decker transition. Gold leaved crested capitols on three sectioned side columns. Plain splat gold leafed ball feet. Duplicated tablets. Arabic dial with adjustment opening, unusual finials. ca. 1835 .... **235.00**

More ornate form of banjo. The fronts of the cases have some type of a car
leaf motif.

All prices shown are for Fine-Working Condition.

Item, Description & Date	R
1. ☐ Albert Phipps, white with gilt front, 1829	110C
2. ☐ Lemual Curtis — Concord, Massachusetts. Shelf Lyre timepiece. 6" dial, 30" high	140C
3. ☐ William Grant — Boston, Mass. 38" high, carved front. ca. 1825	1100
4. ☐ Sawin & Dyar — Boston, Mass. Spread eagle finial. ca. 1822	1,10(

CLOCKS — MASSACHUSETTS SHELF (1800-1830)

1. ☐ Nathan Hale, Chelsea, Vermont. Hood with splat and three finials. Purple tablets in exquisite color. 34" x 13", 5½" dial. ca. 1815	3,60(
2. ☐ Levi Hutchins — Concord, New Hampshire. Tablet over tablet. Case mahogany veneer over pine eight day weight movement. Winds at 2:20. 45" x 12", 6" dial. ca. 1800	3,60C
3. ☐ Silas Parsons — Swansey, New Hampshire. Eight day weight with fret work on flat top. Kidney dial opening. Winds at 2:00. 36½" x 13½", 6½" dial. ca. 1815	3,600
4. ☐ John Sawin — Boston, Mass. Tablet over mirror, flat top hood. 30" x 13½", 6" dial. circa 1830	3,600
5. ☐ Aaron Willard — Boston, Mass. Alarm timepiece with quarter hour repeater. Broken arch top with single finial; mirror in lower panel. 30¾" x 13¼". 6" dial. ca. 1800	6,600
6. ☐ David Wood — Newbury Port, Mass. Hood surmounted with fret work and three pillars with finials. Mahogany paneled door in base. Winds at 2:00 39" x 13½", 6" dial. ca. 1815	9,000.

4.

2.

1.

CLOCKS — MASSACHUSETTS SHELF

1.

2.

6.

Courtesy of The Henry Ford Museum, Dearborn, Michigan

Manufactured from 1825 to 1918. Name derived from S-like curved mold
on door. Three sizes of OG alarm clocks

A. Seth Thomas — 16″ 30 hour spring movement.

B. Waterbury Clock Company — 19″ spring movement.

C. Terry & Andrews (1842-1850) Bristol, Conn. One day weight movement

All prices shown are for Fine-Working Condition.

Item, Description & Date	Re
1. ☐ Ansonia Clock Company — Ansonia, Connecticut. 30 hour brass weight movement. 26″ x 15½″ x 4″. ca. 1855	85.00-115
2. ☐ Boardman & Wells—Bristol, Connecticut. Flat OG. Movement—30 hour weight. "Boardman & Wells" painted on glass tablet. 26″ x 15-1/2″ x 4-1/2″....	85.00-115
3. ☐ Brewster & Ingraham — Bristol, Conn. Etched glass tablet	85.00-115
4. ☐ J. C. Brown — Forestville Mfg. Co. 30 hour brass weight movement. Alarm winds at 6:00. 26″ x 15½″ x 4½″. ca. 1850	85.00-115.
5. ☐ Chauncey Jerome — Bristol, Conn. Made before 1845. 30 hour brass weight movement. 28″ x 13″	
6. ☐ Jerome & Company — New Haven, Conn.	85.00-115.
7. ☐ Mauross Pritchard & Co. — Bristol, Conn. Tablet reads "View in Boston". 26″ x 15½″ x 4¼″. ca. 1841-42	85.00-115.
8. ☐ New Haven Clock Co. — Eight day with brass weight movement. 33″ x 14″, 4¼″ dial	
9. ☐ Jason R. Rawson—Saxton's River, Vermont. ca. 1839. Flat OG. Movement—30 hour wood	100.00-150.
10. ☐ Riley Whiting — Winchester, Conn. 30 hour wood weight movement. 25½″ x 18″. ca. early 1800's	100.00-150.
11. ☐ Seth Thomas — 30 hour brass movement	85.00-115.
12. ☐ Seth Thomas—Plymouth Hollow, Conn. ca. 1860's Alarm clock with 30 hour spring brass movement. 16-1/2″ high	85.00-115.

All prices shown are for Fine-Working Condition.

Item, Description & Date	Retail

3. ☐ Seth Thomas — Thomaston, Conn. OG Alarm. Green glass door tablet has painted dog's head. 16-1/2".. 85.00-115.00

4. ☐ Smith & Brothers — New York, N.Y. Flat OG with alarm winds at 5:30. 30 hour wood weight movement. Tablet may or not be original 26" x 15-1/2" x 4-1/2". " mith & Brothers" painted on bottom of tablet.. 85.00-115.00

5. ☐ Smith & Goodrich — Bristol, Conn. OG has 30 hour fuzee spring movement. 16"................................ 250.00

7. ☐ Waterbury Clock Co. — Waterbury, Conn. Movement — 30 hour spring alarm. 18-1/2" x 12", 3-3/4" dial... 85.00-115.00

8. ☐ E. N. Welch Manufacturing Co. — Forestville, Conn. Eight day spring movement. 4-3/4" dial. Glass tablet has painting of building. 18-3/4" x 12"........ 85.00-115.00

1.

17.

Courtesy of The Henry Ford Museum, Dearborn, Michigan

CLOCKS — PILLAR AND SCROLL (1818-1895)

America's first mass produced shelf clock. The original design was by Eli Terry

All prices shown are for Fine-Working Condition.

Item, Description & Date	Reta
1. ☐ Lucius B. Bradley — Watertown, Conn. Eight day weight brass movement, second hands on dial. 33" high. Made prior to 1830	1,200.0
2. ☐ Jacob D. Custer — (1805-1872) Norristown, Pa. Eight day brass movement, time & strike. 38" high. ca. 1840. Dial reads "Norristown Patent"	3,600.0
3. ☐ Ephraim Downs — Bristol, Conn. 31½" high. ca. 1820	650.00
4. ☐ Eratus Hodges — Torrington, Conn. Horizontal wood movement, one day. Winds at 3:00 & 9:00. 28" high. ca. 1820	720.0
5. ☐ Ansel Merrel — Vienna, Ohio. ca. 1828	465.0
6. ☐ Ethes North — Torrington, Conn. One day wood movement, weights. 35" high. Decending down, not over pulleys at case top	720.00
7. ☐ Seth Thomas — Eight day brass movement ca. 1895	185.00
8. ☐ Seth Thomas — Plymouth, Conn. Off center Pillar & Scroll. The pendulum does not hang in the exact center. 30" high. ca. 1818	900.00
9. ☐ E. Terry & Sons — Plymouth, Conn. Thirty hour.	650.00
10. ☐ Eli Terry — Plymouth, Conn. (1817-1818) 29¼" high	720.00
11. ☐ Samuel Terry — Bristol, Conn. ca. 1829	600.00
12. ☐ Riley Whiting — Winchester, Conn. Thirty hour	600.00

CLOCKS — SHIP CLOCKS

1. ☐ Seth Thomas — Round Metal cased eight day double spring drive with a lever balance wheel movement. 6¼" diameter	135.00
2. ☐ Seth Thomas — 30 hour Ships Bell Clock with metal case, bell below, strikes ships bell, not the hour	165.00
3. ☐ Chelsea—Boston, Mass. Ship Strike, round bronze case. ca. 1900 (Still made today)	195.00
4. ☐ Boston Clock Co.—Strike bell on top. One winding hole winds left to right, and right to left. ca. 1880..	225.00

3.

9.

10.

Courtesy of The Henry Ford Museum, Dearborn, Michigan

CLOCKS — SHIP CLOCKS

1.

2.

Clocks topped with spires. Elias Ingraham, of Bristol is credited with the desig There are four sizes of Steeple Clocks: (1) Sub-Miniature, Ansonia 10½ high. (2) Miniature, Waterbury Clock Co. 14¾" high. (3) Standard Set Thomas 20" high. (4) Steeple on Steeple Elisha Manross, 24" high.

	Item, Description & Date	Reta
1. ☐	Ansonia Clock Co.—Ansonia, Conn. Steeple 30 hour movement alarm timepiece...........................	115.0
2. ☐	Brewster & Ingraham — Sharp gothic twin steeple eight day. ca. 1845	275.C
3. ☐	Forestville Hardware & Clock Co. — Bristol, Conn. Sub-miniature 30 hour timepiece. Winds at 3:00. 12½" high. ca. 1853-1855	200.C
4. ☐	Forestville Manufacturing Co. — Round gothic twin steeple with ripple finish. Eight day spring movement. Tablet shows early view of the Whitehouse and Potomac river. ca. late 1840's	300.0
5. ☐	Wm. L. Gilbert Co. — Winsted, Conn. Miniature steeple. 30 hour ladder movement alarm timepiece, winds at 6:00. Curley maple sides; top and front, mahogany. 14½" high. ca. 1850-1860	125.0C
6. ☐	Chauncey Jerome—New Haven, Conn. Movement fuzee of standard steeple....................................	250.0C
7. ☐	Elisha Manross — Bristol, Conn. Movement of eight day steeple on steeple. Fuzee with cones of wood. ca. 1848	525.0C
8. ☐	Pond & Barnes—Boston, Mass. Steeple with alarm. Fuzee movement. ca. 1848.......................	325.0C
9. ☐	Elmer Stennes — Mass. Modern Steeple shelf clock	165.0C
10. ☐	Seth Thomas—"Sharon" steeple. After 1938 this clock made as an a/c TP, or an 8 day wind up..	100.0C
11. ☐	Waterbury Clock Co. — Waterbury, Conn. Miniature with 30 hour spring movement. 15" high. ca. 1875	115.00

4.

7.

11.

Waterbury Clock Co. — w/alarm
19-1/2" mahogany 95.00

CLOCKS — TERRY S.B. (1848-1868)

All prices shown are for Fine-Working Condition.

Item, Description & Date	Retail
1. ☐ S. B. Terry & Co. — Terryville, Conn. Plain wood cottage type case. Brass ladder movement one day timepiece. Winds at 6:00. 10-1/4" high..................	85.00
2. ☐ S. B. Terry — Timepiece, metal case with mother of pearl and stenciling inlay. Brass spring 30 hour movement with torsion bar control. ca. 1852........	**465.00**
3. ☐ Silas B. Terry — Wall regulator Rosewood case, eight day timepieces. winds at 2:00. 33" x 9½" x 3¾"	275.00
4. ☐ Silas B. Terry — Shelf clock with small solid case, not veneered, dial opening. Spring pendulum 30 hour movement. 12-1/2" high............................	**200.00**
5. ☐ Silas B. Terry — Terryville, Conn. Miniature reverse OG cased clock 13" high	**200.00**
6. ☐ Silas B. Terry — Shelf steeple clock, eight day spring, balance wheel control. 24½" high. ca. 1848	**3,600.00**
7. ☐ The Terry Clock Co. — Waterbury, Conn. Patent December 1, 1855. Eight day movement. Wall timepiece. Winds at 5:00......................................	250.00
8. ☐ The Terry Clock Co. — Waterbury, Conn. Round top Black iron cased one-day spring clock. 8" high. ca. 1868	70.00
9. ☐ Eight day timepiece pendulum controlled, black iron case. One day timepiece, pendulum controlled, black iron case	70.00
10. ☐ Terryville Mfg. Co. — Candle stand timepiece with metal dial, white milk glass base and glass dome. 30 hour torsion base control. 8¼" high. ca. 1852	**720.00**
11. ☐ Terryville Mfg. Co. — Small square based shelf timepiece, torsion base controlled. 10" high. ca. 1852	**400.00**
12. ☐ Terryville Mfg. Co. — Terryville, Conn. Small shelf steeple, 30 hour timepiece with horizontally mounted large balance wheel. 13" high. ca. 1852	**600.00**

1.

9.

6.

5.

Courtesy of The Henry Ford Museum, Dearborn, Michigan

CLOCKS — WALNUTS

All prices shown are for Fine-Working Condition.

Item, Description & Date	Retail
1. ☐ W. L. Gilbert Co.—Walnut eight day shelf clock, down swept finials on side. 24"x14-1/2". 5-1/2" dial	125.00
2. ☐ Wm. Gilbert Co.—Winsted, Conn. Eight day shelf clock. Black walnut. 19" x 10-1/2". 4-3/4" dial........	135.00
3. ☐ Ingraham & Walnut eight day alarm clock, Heavy upper section. 24" x 16", 5" dial	125.00
4. ☐ Ingraham — "Liberty" Walnut eight day. 20½" x 13¼", 5" dial	125.00
5. ☐ C. Jerome — Walnut case with religious motif. eight day clock. 21" x 11", 3½"	135.00
6. ☐ F. Kroeber—New York City. Black Walnut eight day shelf clock. Pendulum ball is cut crystal. 21" x 14-1/2". 5" dial..............	300.00
7. ☐ New Haven Clock Co. — Walnut eight day alarm clock. 20" x 13", 5" dial	125.00
8. ☐ New Haven Clock Co. — Walnut eight day. 20½" x 14¼", 5" dial	125.00
9. ☐ George Owen — Winsted, Conn. Walnut "Kidney". dial opening. Three finial top. 23" x 14" x 5". ca. 1880	125.00-185.00
10. ☐ Seth Thomas & Walnut case. Center of headpiece has Thermometer. Eight day alarm clock level mounted in base..............	125.00-185.00
11. ☐ Seth Thomas — Walnut case. Eight day clock. 22" x 13", 5½" dial	125.00-185.00
12. ☐ Waterbury Clock Co. — Walnut eight day. 20" x 13½", 4¾" dial	125.00-185.00
13. ☐ E. N. Welch Mfg. Co. — Black Walnut Miniture. 30 hr. alarm clock. 21" x 13", 5" dial	125.00-185.00
14. ☐ E. N. Welch Mfg. Co. — Victorian motif. Two knights in armor on horseback. Eight day alarm clock. 23" x 14½" x 5½"	125.00-185.00

WALNUT

OAK

Courtesy of The Henry Ford Museum, Dearborn, Michigan

CLOCKS — OAKS

All have glass fronts, most with floral, geometric or patriotic motifs stenciled or painted on the fronts.

All prices shown are for Fine-Working Condition.

Item, Description & Date	Retail
1. ☐ Oak clock with time and strike	85.00-125.00
2. ☐ Oak clock with time and strike and calendar	100.00-135.00
3. ☐ Political and Military carved oak clocks. Admiral Dewey, Admiral Schley, Admiral Sampson, President McKinley, President Roosevelt	115.00-165.00

All prices shown are for Fine-Working Condition.

Item & Description	Retail
Gold Filled — 10 & 14kt:	
1. ☐ Flower pattern. Fancy engraved. Escalloped edging on Hunting case	45.00-60.00
2. ☐ Ornate engraving on lower half of Hunting case. Two Birds in nest engraved on upper half of smooth finished gold	50.00-75.00
Gold and Silver	
3. ☐ American Chatelaine. Silver. Ligne, stem wind and set. Open face	45.00
4. ☐ Assorted engraved. Gold. Open face. Roman Numerals	75.00
5. ☐ Full engraved. Hunting case. Vermicelli border. American Chatelaine	55.00
6. ☐ Gold. Plain polished, corrugated. Open face	75.00
7. ☐ Ligne, stem wind and set. Silver. Open face. American Chatelaine	45.00
8. ☐ Silver. Ligne, Hunting case. Stem wind and set. Assorted fancy engraved. American Chatelaine	60.00
9. ☐ Vermicelli center. Raised colored gold ornaments on Hunting case. American Chatelaine	60.00
Rolled Gold Plate:	
10. ☐ Engine turned case. Medallion in center	50.00
11. ☐ Raised colored gold ornaments. Fancy engraved escalloped center	85.00
Solid Gold:	
12. ☐ Assorted full engraved. Bird in Flight	125.00
13. ☐ Fancy engraved. Raised colored gold ornamented. 1 diamond in center of engraved star	200.00

Courtesy: S. Rosenberg, Fresh Meadows, N.Y.

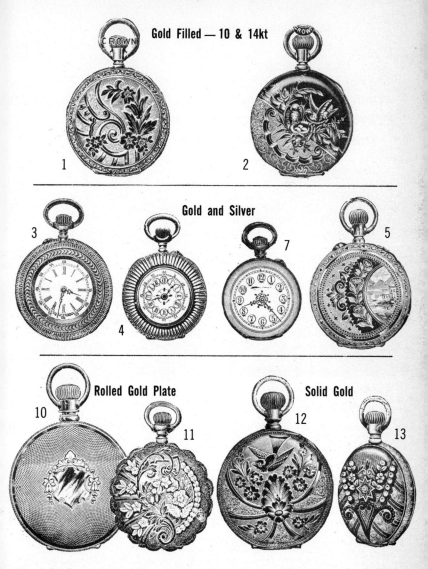

Gold Filled — 10 & 14kt

1

2

Gold and Silver

3

4

7

5

Rolled Gold Plate

10

11

Solid Gold

12

13

All prices shown are for Fine-Working Condition.

Item & Description	Retail

Gold Filled — 10 & 14kt.

14. ☐ Mesh textured. Gold filled. Hunting case.
Medallion engraved in center 60.00

15. ☐ Ornately engraved hunting case. Center engraving of Country Estate 75.00

Silver Cases with Gold Inlaid Decorations

16. ☐ Dog 60.00

17. ☐ Fire Engine 90.00

18. ☐ Locomotive 80.00

19. ☐ Steamboat 100.00

Solid Gold:

20. ☐ Engraved escalloped center. 8 diamonds in raised colored gold.
Ornament of Horses' head in Horse Shoe 270.00

21. ☐ Fancy engraved. Bird and Flowers in raised colored gold.
Hunting case 225.00

22. ☐ Head of Horse in Horseshoe. 7 graduated diamonds. Ornate
engraving on outer edge of Hunting case 300.00

23. ☐ Horse and Birds. 7 diamonds. Fancy engraving on Hunting case 315.00

24. ☐ Mesh design. Gold center with engraving of medallion in center.
Hunting case 150.00

25. ☐ Ornately engraved Hunting case. Diamond in center 260.00

26. ☐ Ornately engraved Hunting case. Locomotive in center 225.00

27. ☐ Two Horses. 5 diamonds. Fancy engraved outer edge
on Hunting case 270.00

Stop Watches Chronograph — Gold:

28. ☐ Engine turned minute repeater. Split 1-5 chronograph. Hunting case.. 700.00

29. ☐ Open Face. Vermicelli borders. Engraved 200.00

Courtesy: S. Rosenberg, Fresh Meadows, N.Y.

Gold Filled

Silver Cases Gold Inlaid Decorations

15

17

16

Solid Gold

22

21

24

Chronograph Gold

28

26

See Pages 66-69 for Color Photos

The following group of character and commemorative timepieces are extremely rare and difficult to find. They were manufactured by Ingersoll, Ingraham and the New Haven Watch Company from the end of the nineteen twenties until the beginning of World War II.

The character pieces are mostly of popular cartoon personalities. The Commemoratives were issued to honor a famous individual or deed, such as Lindbergh or Admiral Byrd, or the around-the-world flight of the Graf Zeppelin.

Reproductions are made. To check the authenticity of pocket watches check the metal back. It should be die stamped "MICKEY MOUSE INGERSOLL" or "ALWAYS FIND TIME FOR A GOOD DEED . . . Tom Mix". The original Buck Rogers pocket watch has an engraving of a one-eyed Martian monster on the back. In buying any of these pieces, caution is the byword.

Character watches are again being made, mostly political figures such as Spiro Agnew, Richard Nixon, George Wallace. A new Mickey Mouse and Minnie (for girls) is also on the market. In time these pieces too may become collectables.

The prices quoted herein are for **ORIGINAL PIECES IN MINT CONDITION.** Any imperfections on the face of the watch (scratch, dent, faded color, etc.) greatly reduce the value of the timepiece. Watches and clocks in the original boxes add considerable value to the quoted prices.

Prices may vary greatly depending on location.

A fair offer for purchase by a dealer would be 35% to 50% of stated Retail value.

	Item, Description and Date	Maker	Retail
1 ☐	Mickey Mouse Electric Clock............1933....Ingersoll..........		$560.00
	(In the original box)..		800.00
2 ☐	Big Bad Wolf Clock............................1934.... Ingersoll..........		450.00
3 ☐	Charlie McCarthy Clock......................1938.... Gilbert............		500.00
4 ☐	Bugs Bunny Clock...............................1951....Ingraham.........		225.00
5 ☐	Popeye Clock.....................................1929....New Haven......		560.00
6 ☐	Mickey Mouse Lapel Watch..................1935....Ingersoll..........		375.00
7 ☐	Mickey Mouse Pocket Watch................1933....Ingersoll..........		350.00
8 ☐	Big Bad Wolf Pocket Watch..................1934....Ingersoll..........		380.00
9 ☐	Donald Duck Pocket Watch..................1935....Ingersoll..........		300.00
10 ☐	Buster Brown Pocket Watch.................1927....Ansonia..........		350.00
11 ☐	Lone Ranger Lapel Watch.....................1939....Everbrite..........		350.00

Courtesy: Mr. Robert Lesser, 533 Third Avenue, New York, N.Y. 10016

See Pages 66-69 for Color Photos

All Prices For ORIGINAL PIECES—MINT CONDITION

Item, Description and Date		Maker	Retail
☐ Buck Rogers Pocket Watch	1935	Ingraham	400.00
(In the original box)			525.00
☐ Superman Pocket Watch	1959	Bradley	325.00
☐ Popeye Pocket Watch	1934	New Haven	500.00
☐ Tom Mix Pocket Watch	1933	Ingersoll	600.00
☐ New York To Paris (Lindbergh)	1928	Ingraham	225.00
☐ The Explorer (Admiral Byrd)	1928	Ingraham	275.00
☐ Zep Pocket Watch			
(Graf Zeppelin flight around world)	1929	Ingraham	275.00
☐ Boy Scout Pocket Watch	1933	Ingersoll	150.00
☐ New York Worlds Fair (1939)	1939	Ingersoll	200.00
☐ New York Worlds Fair (Table & Pocket)	1939	Ingersoll	200.00
☐ Mickey Mouse Wristwatch	1933	Ingersoll	300.00
☐ Big Bad Wolf Wristwatch	1934	Ingersoll	300.00
☐ Donald Duck Wristwatch	1935	Ingersoll	300.00
☐ Donald Duck Wristwatch	1948	Ingersoll	175.00
☐ Little Orphan Annie Wristwatch	1938	New Haven	175.00
☐ Superman Wristwatch	1939	Everbrite	180.00
☐ Smitty Wristwatch	1934	New Haven	195.00
☐ Popeye Wristwatch	1935	New Haven	195.00
☐ Dick Tracy Wristwatch (with animated gun)	1950	New Haven	150.00
☐ Howdy Doody Wristwatch	1949	Everbrite	150.00
☐ Dizzy Dean Wristwatch	1934	Ingersoll	150.00
☐ Babe Ruth Wristwatch	1947	Babe Ruth Co.	170.00
☐ Lone Ranger Wristwatch	1939	Everbrite	180.00
☐ Gene Autry Wristwatch (with animated gun)	1950	New Haven	150.00
☐ Annie Oakley Wristwatch			
(With animated gun)	1950	New Haven	135.00
☐ Rocky Jones Space Ranger	1951	Ingraham	150.00
☐ Lil Abner Wristwatch			
(With animated mule)	1950	New Haven	150.00
☐ Captain Marvel Wristwatch	1948	Fawcett	175.00
☐ New York Worlds Fair Wristwatch	1939	Ingersoll	200.00
☐ George Wallace Wristwatch	1971	Dirty Time Co.	16.00

Courtesy: Mr. Robert Lesser, 533 Third Avenue, New York, N.Y. 10016

COPPER

COAL HOD

COFFEE POT

SKILLE

BED HEATER

Original Pieces Only

Item & Description Prices are for Good Condition	*A.B.P.	Ret
☐ Bed Heater. Wooden handle, perforated design............	40.00	80.
☐ Boiler. Wash. Brass and copper	20.00	42.
☐ Burnished Copper Pan, 2 iron handles, 23" dia, 8" deep	20.00	42.
☐ Chafing Dish. Wooden handle and burner	28.00	57.
☐ Candy Kettle, 12" dia, 5½" deep, round shape, one handle	10.00	20.
☐ Coal Hod. Helmet type. Lacquered and polished	53.50	107.
☐ Coffee Pot. Pewter trim, copper body......................	12.00	25.
☐ Coffee Pot. Lacquered	17.00	35.
☐ Compote	17.00	35.
☐ Cooking Pan (cast) 12½" dia. 6" deep, heavy iron handle	15.00	30.
☐ Dow Pot. Dutch-type	85.00	140.
☐ Eagle. With heavy ball, from top of weathervane............	125.00	245.
☐ Funnel with handle	4.00	8.
☐ Jug. Water	15.00	31.
☐ Kettle, made for fitting into stove, 2 iron handles	28.00	56.0
☐ Milk Tank. 10-gallon capacity	17.00	34.0
☐ Megaphone. From sailing ship	28.50	57.0
☐ Pan. 10" diameter. Iron handle	28.50	57.0
☐ Saucepan. Covered and lacquered	20.00	40.0
☐ Skillet. With iron handle	19.00	38.0

*A.B.P. — Average Buying Price — See Page 5

NOTE: Reproductions are made.

WASH
BOILER

SAUCEPAN

Prices for
Original Pieces Only

TEAKETTLE

Item & Description Prices are for Good Condition	*A.B.P.	Retail
Teakettle. Early American	30.00	60.00
Teapot. Lacquered	17.50	35.00
Tray	14.50	29.50
Umbrella Stand. With lion grips	16.25	32.50
Vase. Sterling silver inlay	20.00	40.00
Wash basin, burnished, 14" dia, 6" deep	12.50	25.00
Wash Boiler with copper cover	19.00	37.50

.B.P. — Average Buying Price

DOLLS

Doll collecting has become one of the largest and most popular hobbies the United States. Ranging from simple rag figures to extremely orn parian, bisque and china dolls, these former playthings now comma increasingly higher prices.

Since fine examples are becoming exceedingly rare as time goes on, pri may jump considerably in these categories. Prices on all dolls will va according to condition, size, clothing and originality.

	Item and Description Prices are for Good Condition	*A.B.P.	Ret
1. ☐	Armand Marseilles Baby Doll. Blue eyes. Open mouth. Dressed	80.00	125.
2. ☐	Biedermeier China Doll. 12-1/2" H. Original body. Dressed	175.00	210.
3. ☐	Bisque Doll. 22" H. Closed mouth, kid body. Eyebrows	190.00	275.
4. ☐	Bisque Doll. 23" H. Jointed body. Human hair wig	15.00	24.
5. ☐	French Fashion Doll. Blue eyes, blonde wig	120.00	210.
6. ☐	French Character Doll. 20" H. in period costume	30.00	50.
7. ☐	Frozen Charlotte Doll. Alice in Wonderland	138.00	250.
8. ☐	German Fashion Doll. 24" H. Blue eyes with short blonde wig	80.00	128.
9. ☐	Gibson Girl. Blonde hair. Unclothed. Marked "Brack"	90.00	140.
10. ☐	Gibson Girl. Brown eyes. Original wig. Unclothed	86.00	131.
11. ☐	Handwerk & Henrich. Jointed body. Blue, movable eyes	60.00	85.
12. ☐	Happy Fats Girl. Bisque Girl. 4" high	14.00	26.
13. ☐	Jennie Lind. Black hair, silk dress w/jacket	190.00	280.
14. ☐	Jumeau Doll. Brown eyes. Original clothing	355.00	490.
15. ☐	Jumeau Doll. Composition body. Brown paperweight eyes	150.00	275.
16. ☐	Jumeau Doll. 17" high. Brown eyes and blonde mohair wig	150.00	275
17. ☐	Jumeau Doll. Portrait type. Bisque head	450.00	600.
18. ☐	J. D. Kestner. 13-1/2" high. Brown eyes. Open-close mouth	80.00	115.
19. ☐	Kathy Kruse Doll. Painted eyes. Cloth body	110.00	160.
20. ☐	Kewpie Doll. 3-1/2" high. Traveller with suitcase	70.00	100.
21. ☐	Kewpie Doll. 4-1/2" high. Made in Japan. Unclothed	6.00	10.
22. ☐	Kewpie Doll. Open mouth. Hand-painted features	25.00	45.

*A.B.P. — Average Buying Price see pg. 5

16.
JUMEAU
DOLL

17.
JUMEAU
DOLL

6.
French Fashion
Doll

JENNY
LIND

13.

126

MICKEY & MINNIE MOUSE

DOLLS

MISS KNOT

24.

23.

33.

SHIRLEY TEMPLE

	Item & Description	*A.B.P.	Ret
23. ☐	Miss Knot. Jointed Peg Wooden. 10" high.................	110.00	175.
24. ☐	Mickey and Minnie Mouse Dolls. Wooden bodies........	18.50	39.
25. ☐	Moon Mullins Doll. Comic Strip Character..................	19.00	43.
26. ☐	Martha Washington Doll. 18" high. Parian and bisque parts. Signed and dated...	90.00	150.
27. ☐	Paper Mache Doll. Blond sausage curls. Dressed......	60.00	87.
28. ☐	Parian Doll. 23" high. Boy wearing pants and shirt....	50.00	75.
29. ☐	Parian Doll. 24" high. Girl wearing long gown............	60.00	150.
30. ☐	Parian Girl Doll. Blond, painted eyes. Period clothing	47.50	60.
31. ☐	Schoenhut Doll. Walking type. Waxed covered wood..	110.00	175.
32. ☐	Schoenhut. Sailor. With original military costume......	100.00	135.
33. ☐	Shirley Temple Doll. 27" H. Blue eyes, open mouth....	90.00	120.
34. ☐	Tall Gladdie Boy. Composition body...........................	175.00	230.
35. ☐	Tall Character Doll. Dressed in soldier costume........	100.00	145.
36. ☐	Tall Character Doll. Blue eyes, jointed limbs..............	115.00	165.
37. ☐	Tall Character Baby. Glass eyes, jointed....................	70.00	100.
38. ☐	Tall Character Doll. Campbell Kid. Compo.................	34.50	68.
39. ☐	Wax Baby Jesus. Life size. Embedded hair strands.	160.00	300.
40. ☐	Wax Doll. Black wig. Compo arms and legs................	80.00	135.
41. ☐	Wooden Doll. Oriental child in kimono with hat..........	20.00	38.
42. ☐	Wooden Doll. Broken hands. Jointed head and neck..	10.00	18.
43. ☐	Wonder Boy. 16" H. Jointed body w/swivel head......	24.50	50.
44. ☐	Zulu Warrior. 24" high. Rare black warrior doll	600.00	875.

See Page 65 for Color Picture

rker and Waterman and Swann were the main contributors to excellence
design and high quality workmanship. The points were 14K gold and Parker
ve you six choices: Extra Fine, Fine, Medium, Broad, Stub and Oblique in
rmanite barrels guaranteed to be non-breakable. Waterman carved snakes
m solid silver and designed Art Nouveau filigree barrels in gold elegance.

The prices reflect the latest sales and information from other collectors;
r set and price divides 50-50 for pen or pencil.

**A fair offer for purchase by a dealer would be 30 to 50% of stated
etail Value.**

PRICES ARE FOR MINT CONDITION ONLY
Considerably Less Value—Other Than Mint Condition

	ITEM	Retail
	Parker Duofold Mandarin Yellow (set) Very Rare	$125.00
2	Parker Duofold Moderne Black and Pearl (set)	100.00
3	Parker Duofold Lacquer Red (Big Red) (set)	110.00
4	Parker Duofold Jade Green (set)	100.00
5	Parker Lapis Lazuli Blue (set)	100.00
6	Waterman chased with gold filled bands (set)	100.00
7	Waterman hand engraved gold pen	75.00
8	Waterman silver filigree pen	65.00
9	Waterman hand carved "Snake" pen—streling silver	95.00
	Waterman mottled brown. Pen is Number 8 point large size (set) Very Rare	125.00
1	Waterman (Bauhaus) silver set	100.00
2	Inkograph Mickey Mouse set made 1934 with head of Mickey at top, face on point and on barrel. (set of 2)	90.00
3	Swann bright orange (set)	95.00
4	Waterman Safety type Dropper filling pen, gold	75.00
5	Eversharp four piece set Black and Pearl	110.00
6	Waterman Gold and Mother of Pearl hand carved pen	125.00
7	Waterman deeply chased and carved gold pen	100.00
8	Victorian retractable dip pen and pencil with jewelled head	45.00
9	Parker Black Number 10 Point (Giant) pen and pencil	125.00
0	Swann Pen Co. silver chased, retractable for purse. Also worn on chain as a necklace	35.00

COURTESY OF: MR. ROBERT LESSER, 533 Third Avenue, New York, N.Y. 10016

FIREPLACE EQUIPMENT

Equipment for tending fires includes andirons, bellow, tools, scree
lighters and trammel hooks. They have been built of a variety of material a
can be as finely sculptured as the craftsman wished.

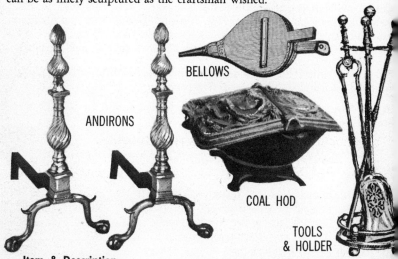

BELLOWS

ANDIRONS

COAL HOD

TOOLS
& HOLDER

Item & Description:

ANDIRONS:	Prices are for Good Condition	*A.B.P.	Ret
☐ Iron. Carved ball on top		12.00	32.0
☐ Solid brass. Good condition, 30" high. ca. 1850, pr.....		60.00	140.0
BELLOWS:			
☐ Leather. Flowered panel, 16" long		13.00	32.5
☐ Leather. Good condition. Small size		10.00	24.0
☐ Coal Hod. Frog style porcelain covered lift top		16.00	38.0
☐ Coal Hod. Burnished brass. Helmet-type w/scoop		42.00	90.0
☐ Coal Hod. Porcelain covered lift top		16.00	40.0
☐ Fender. Solid brass with clawed feet, 50" long		19.00	50.0
☐ Fender. Iron 12" high with brass trim		11.00	30.0
☐ Grate. Iron with legs, 9" high		12.00	24.0
☐ Lighter. New England-type. Brass		7.50	20.0
☐ Poker. Iron, 59" long		4.00	10.0
☐ Screen. Classical roman design		39.00	78.0
☐ Tools. Shovel, poker, tongs and holder. Brass		43.00	87.7
☐ Trammel Hook. 39" long. Forged iron, holds cook pots		25.00	68.0

*A.B.P. — Average Buying Price — See Page 5

Volunteer Fire units and the so-called "Bucket Brigades" played an
important part in the prevention of catastrophes in the early days of the nation.
Later, they served both realistic and ceremonial purposes.

Parade Trumpet

HELMETS

PARADE HELMET

Parade Trumpet

FIRE MARKS

FIRE BUCKETS

prices are for Good Condition

Item & Description:	*A.B.P.	Retail
Bucket. Early 19th century. Owner's name inscribed....	30.00	75.00
Brass Fireman's Belt Buckle. Fire engine engraved......	12.00	30.00
†FIRE MARKS:		
Hydrant. 1817	23.00	47.75
Tree. Late 18th century	24.00	48.00
United Firemans Insurance Company	16.00	32.00
HELMETS:		
Eagle. Mid-19th century, white eather. Cairns Bros.......	30.00	75.00
Embossed black leather w/brass eagle, ca. 1889..........	15.00	40.00
Firefighter Parade Helmet, spike top, Army type..........	16.00	32.50
FIRE TRUMPETS		
Silver plated with red tassel, engraved (Illus.).............	60.00	125.00
Nickel plated "working horn", tall...............................	25.00	65.00
Cairns Octagon sided, nickel plated, large, gold trumpet cord, ca. 1877..	50.00	110.00

Reproduced Items   *A.B.P. — Average Buying Price

In recent years, the trend has been for cobalt blue, black glass, amber, and glass fruit jars to command the highest prices. Jars with ground glass or ap lips and jars of limited production have also increased in value.

Amber jars are highly prized by collectors. Amber jars did not sell well w first manufactured, apparently because the amber color made the jar's contents difficult to see, and they were soon discontinued.

Amethyst-colored jars, another collectors favorite, are often quite old valuable. Glassmakers at one time attempted to make clear glass by adding mar ese, which caused a reaction in the iron present in the sand, creating a bluish-g tint. When exposed to the sun, this glass turns amethyst.

Other valued jars are jars with ground glass lips, which resulted from an method of commercial jar manufacture in which the lip was ground smooth, jars with whittle marks, which gave a diamond sparkle to the glass and resi from using cold molds.

When looking for fruit jars, it is important to remember that price and v also depend on geographical location. Particular jars were more popular and t fore, are now more plentiful, in various parts of the country.

An interesting side line to jar collecting is to collect "go withs", or i related to jars. These include old cook books, cookers, jar openers, lifters, sealing wax.

The following values are suggested for complete jars (with lid and clos in perfect condition (no cracks).

The lip of the jar has been identified by the following letters: A (applied G (ground glass lip), and M (machine made).

A fruit jar's value depends on age, colo and materials used i manufacture.

Pictures courtesy: "An Illustrated Guide for Collecting Fruit Jars."
R. B. Burris, 2941 Campus Drive, Visalia, California 93277

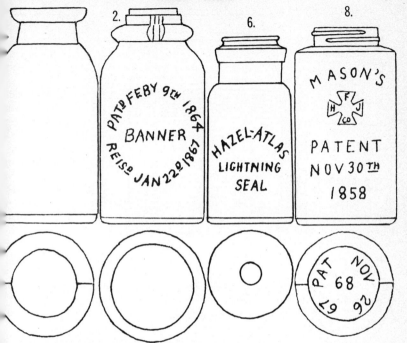

All Prices are for Perfect Jars with lid and closure

LIP: A (applied lip), G (ground glass lip), and M (machine made)

	Embossing	Lip	Height	Color	Retail
1. ☐	None	A	7½"	Amber	17.00
2. ☐	Banner Patd. Feb. 9th, '64 Reisd. Jan. 22d, 1867	G	7⅛"	Aqua	16.00
3. ☐	Trade Mark Banner Warranted	G	7½"	Aqua	7.00
4. ☐	Trade Mark Banner WM Warranted	M	7"	Aqua	4.00
5. ☐	Trade Mk. Banner Reg. U.S. Pat. Off. Wide Mouth	M	6⅞"	Aqua	4.00
6. ☐	Hazel-Atlas Lightning Seal	M	6"	Aqua	5.00
7. ☐	Mason's (CFJ Co. emblem) Improved Clyde, N. Y.	G	5¾"	Aqua	7.00
8. ☐	Mason's (Maltese Cross) Patent Nov. 30th, 1858	G	8⅝"	Amber	22.00
9. ☐	Mason's Patent Nov. 30th, 1858 (Maltese Cross)	G	5¼"	Aqua	8.00
10. ☐	Mason's Improved (Maltese Cross)	G	5¼"	Aqua	7.00
11. ☐	Mason's (Maltese Cross) Patent Nov. 30th, 1858	G	5⅜"	Aqua	5.00

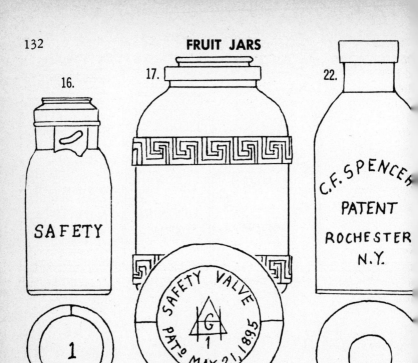

All Prices are for Perfect Jars with lid and closure

LIP: A (applied lip), G (ground glass lip), and M (machine made)

	Embossing	Lip	Height	Color	Re
12. ☐	Premium Coffeyville, Kas.	M	3⅛"	Ameth.	6
13. ☐	Reliance Brand Wide Mouth Mason	M	7"	Clear	4
14. ☐	C. Riessner & Co. N. Y. Pat. Feb. 12, '78	G	7⅛"	Aqua	9
15. ☐	Root Mason	M	8¾"	Aqua	3
16. ☐	Safety	G	6"	Amber	35
17. ☐	Safety Valve Patd. May 21, 1895	G	7¾"	Aqua	17
18. ☐	Smalley's Nu-Seal Trade Mark	M	7¼"	Ameth.	3
19. ☐	The Smalley Self Sealer Wide Mouth	M	5¼"	Ameth.	3
20. ☐	Trade Mark The Smalley Self Sealer	G	5⅞"	Ameth.	6
21. ☐	C. F. Spencer's Patent Rochester, N. Y.	A	7½"	Aqua	10
22. ☐	C. F. Spencer's Patent Rochester, N. Y.	A	10⅜"	Aqua	12

On the following pages you will find a comprehensive section on all types of furniture. Most of the items listed are American. They are arranged by type, alphabetically. Therefore "FURNITURE—BEDS" would be followed by "FURNITURE—CHAIRS". All prices listed are for retail values for furniture in good to excellent condition. We have intended to make these prices as accurate as possible, however they are intended to serve as a guide only.

A WORD ABOUT BUYING

A tapemeasure in your hand will prevent you from a 'headache' in your home. Measure before you buy, the naked eye is not a good judge of size. Buy what you see, not what you think you see. . . ." *Quote Abe Kessler.*

PERIOD FURNITURE

Keep in mind that long after the period, many items of a period were being made in various parts of the country . . . so that a Queen Anne table does not necessarily mean that it was made during 1702-1720 . . . but could have been made 50-75 years later, as it was still stylish to have that in one's home.

 ## ABOUT ABE KESSLER ("The Dealer's Dealer")

A word of introduction about the man who did the editing and pricing. Abe Kessler is the owner of "Abe Kessler Antiques", at 533 Third Avenue, at 37th Street, in New York City, in the heart of "Antique Row". He specializes in Furniture, Paintings, Art Objects, and Autographs.

He is a member of the Appraisers Association of America,

• •

BEDS

Sculptured wooden bed columns were not uncommon in Europe and the United States in the 18th and 19th centuries. Ornate turnings and carvings were particularly prevalent during the Queen Anne and Chippendale periods. Later, during the early Victorian period, brass bedsteads with sculptured sides were in vogue.

CHAIRS AND ROCKERS

During the latter part of the 1700's, the chair-makers art reached perfection. Arm and side chairs of the Queen Anne period were matched only by the new types of chairs created at the time such as splat, ladder, shield and fiddle-back chairs.

ALL ABOUT FURNITURE

In this section are listed many distinct styles and types of furniture. The differences between them are sometimes subtle and sometimes quite striking. While all dates given are approximate, we have attempted to make them as accurate as possible.

PERIOD	CHARACTERISTICS
JACOBEAN 1603-1665	Heavy, straight lines.
RESTORATION 1665-1688	Stubby, squat proportions. Heavy panelling and carving.
WILLIAM & MARY 1688-1702	Wood is generally scrolled and turned.
QUEEN ANNE 1702-1720	Graceful shell and fan carvings. Introduction of cabriole legs.
CHIPPENDALE 1745-1772	Solid construction with varied carvings, guilding and fretwork.
LOUIS XV 1720-1765	Turned carbriole legs, often claw and ball feet.
LOUIS XVI 1765-1789	
HEPPLEWHITE 1780-1790	Oval designs. Serpentine faces and tapering legs.
SHERATON 1790-1810	Graceful with emphasis on carving over inlay.
AMERICAN FEDERAL 1800-1815	Classic designs and lines. Emphasis on brass ornamentation.
LATE FEDERAL 1835-1880	Reliance on heavy inlay and carving.
REGENCY 1810-1830	Heavy emphasis on feathers, stars, and flying eagles.
DIRECTOIRE 1795-1808	Special attention to graceful lines and scrolled carvings.
AMERICAN EMPIRE 1815-1845	Use of brass for ornamentations.
FRENCH 1810-1875	Claw and ball feet, sometimes in shape of animal paws.
DUNCAN PHYFE 1800-1857	Graceful elongated lines.
EARLY VICTORIAN 1835-1870	Ornate scrollwork and carvings.
LATE VICTORIAN 1870-1900	Heavy leg work with emphasis on carving and inlay.

CHESTS

articularly popular during the Chippendale and Hepplewhite periods, chests om six to eight drawers high were popular from the time of the mid-1700's. onstructed primarily of mahogany, walnut or pine, many of these chests had rass and silver ornamentation with unique inlays or carvings. The highboys f the late Chippendale period were from six to ten feet high and have aintained great popularity up to the present time.

DESKS

Walnut and mahogany desks of all sizes and shapes have become extremely opular among collectors. During the Queen Anne and Hepplewhite periods, ssorted desks and writing stands took on a new and distinctive look, with rawer handles of brass, silver, and fine parquet etchings along the sometimes uted sides.

LOVESEATS

Gaining great popularity during the early Victorian period, loveseats differed rom sofas in width, height and style. Generally hand-turned and sculptured, he greatest amount of ornamentation went into the arms, back and frame vhich were generally of fine mahogany, walnut or rosewood. Among Victorian raftsmen, the floral and leaf design was by far the most popular.

MIRRORS

A constant article of furniture since ancient times, the mirror has adapted itself o every period of design. Hand-carved, richly-inlaid and sculptured, mirrors ave retained great popularity among collectors and dealers. Most desirable at he present time are those from the two Victorian periods.

SOFAS

First appearing in the latter part of the 18th century, the sofa has always been a opular article of furniture. For seven design periods, the sofa in its many forms vas made in a variety of shapes and sizes. Among the more popular pieces were he high-backed, scrolled frame Empire sofa and the ornately carved, polished nahogany Victorian couch.

TABLES

More clearly than any other piece of furniture, the table illustrates the lifferences between the design periods. The squat heavy legs of the Jacobean nd Restoration periods contrast sharply with the smooth cabriole turned legs f Queen Anne and Chippendale. Some of the best examples of the art of urniture making are seen in the fine Hepplewhite and Duncan Phyfe dinner nd tea tables.

Every distinct period of furniture design produced a number of odd objects which have survived mainly because of their curious appearance or purpose. The Early Victorian era produced the "Whatnot"; a series of stacked shelves for holding bric-a-brac. The Sheraton Period created the Ladder-chair or library steps; an object which begins as a chair and folds into a portable stairway for climbing tall shelves. Below are described a few of the many furniture oddities.

BENCHES

Generally used by workmen and craftsmen, these benches had a wide expanse of flat area with several drawers for storing equipment concealed below. Old cobbler's benches seem to be the most popular, and range in price from $75.00 to $150.00.

CUPBOARDS

A common sight in every 19th century kitchen, cupboards were used to store everything from cups, saucers and food preserves to medicines and shotgun shells. Made in a variety of wood including cherry, walnut and pine, corner and side cupboards are today priced from $150.00 upwards, depending upon the size and condition.

CRADLES

Infants cradles were widely used during the 18th and 19th centuries both in Europe and the United States. Made of pine or walnut, it was not unusual for these cradles to have ornate scrollwork or inlay. Hoods, arms and rockers were also not uncommon. The average retail price for a cradle of this type would be approximately $75.00.

DRY SINKS

Dry sinks were used to contain water for washing the hands and face. Widely used in the 19th century, these sinks are now quite rare, with prices for the poplar and pine sinks starting at $75.00.

SPINNING WHEELS

Spinning wheels have become synonimous with Colonial America. Much of the same ornamentation which decorated 19th century furniture was used on the spinning wheels of the era. Sheraton and Duncan Phyfe wheels were the most common. Today, the price of a good spinning wheel ranges anywhere between $75.00 and $150.00.

NOTE:
*Depending on woods
or decoration, values
quoted are general.*

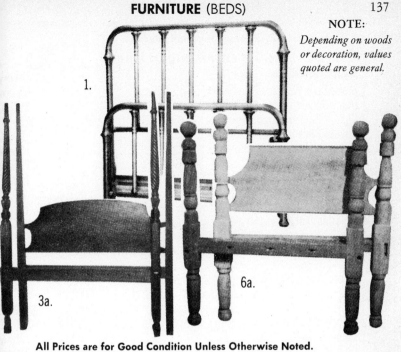

1.

3a.

6a.

All Prices are for Good Condition Unless Otherwise Noted.

BEDS	Item & Description	Retail
1a. ☐	Brass. Late Victorian period, English design (Illus.)....	150.00
b. ☐	Brass Beds (Depending on scroll work).....................	100.00 to 500.00
2. ☐	Carved Walnut. Head and footboards ornately decorated. Over 44" high. Excellent condition............	100.00
3a. ☐	Four Poster. Curving posts of walnut. Bamboo-like head and foot pieces (Illus.).....................................	182.50
b. ☐	Four Poster Beds with or without canopys................	175.00 to 750.00
4. ☐	Jenny Lind. Rough Walnut finish with one piece headboard and straight legs....................................	152.00
5. ☐	Spool Beds (Victorian) (Jenny Lind).........................	35.00 to 100.00
6a. ☐	Maple. Field Bed of heavy wood, low (Illus.)..............	75.00
b. ☐	Field Beds (Low) (Cannonball)................................	75.00 to 250.00
7. ☐	Sleigh Beds. Front end and back resembles old horse drawn sled..	75.00 to 200.00
8. ☐	Iron Beds. (Depending on scroll work)......................	50.00 to 250.00
9. ☐	Victorian Beds. (Eastlake).....................................	35.00 to 100.00

American beds are usually more costly.

FURNITURE (CHAIRS)

NOTE: *Different woods alter the values, example: Oak is not as valuable as mahogany.*

All prices are for Good Condition

CHAIRS OF AMERICAN MAKE

Item & Description	Retail
1. ☐ Brace Back Windsor Side Chairs	250.00
2. ☐ Brace Back Windsor Arm Chairs	350.00
3. ☐ Boston Rockers (Decorated)	125.00
4. ☐ Boston Rockers (Natural Woods)	100.00
5. ☐ Ladderback Arm Chairs	135.00
6. ☐ Ladderback Side Chairs	85.00
7. ☐ Victorian Arm Chair (Early)	150.00
8. ☐ Victorian Side Chair (Early)	65.00
9. ☐ Victorian Arm Chair (Eastlake)	60.00
10. ☐ Victorian Side Chair (Eastlake)	30.00

CHAIRS OF AMERICAN & ENGLISH MAKE

	American	English
11. ☐ Queen Anne Side Chair	500.00	200.00
12. ☐ Queen Anne Arm Chair	750.00	350.00
13. ☐ Queen Anne Wing Chair	3500.00	1500.00
14. ☐ Chippendale Arm Chair	750.00	300.00
15. ☐ Chippendale Side Chair	350.00	175.00
16. ☐ Chippendale Wing Chair	2000.00	1250.00
17. ☐ Hepplewhite Arm Chair	450.00	250.00
18. ☐ Hepplewhite Side Chair	250.00	125.00
19. ☐ Sheraton Arm Chair	300.00	150.00
20. ☐ Sheraton Side Chair	125.00	85.00

CHAIRS OF FRENCH MAKE *

	Retail
21. ☐ French Louis XV Arm Chair	500.00
22. ☐ French Louis XV Side Chair	250.00
23. ☐ French Louis XVI Arm Chair	500.00
24. ☐ French Louis XVI Side Chair	250.00
25. ☐ French Louis XV Bergere	750.00
26. ☐ French Louis XVI Bergere	750.00
27. ☐ French Louis XV & XVI Wing Chairs	850.00

*NOTE: Italian Chairs of the same periods usually retail for 25% less.

BRACE BACK WINDSOR
1.

BOSTON ROCKER
3.

LADDERBACK
6.

LOUIS XVI BERGERE
21.

LOUIS XV ARM CHAIR
26.

CHESTS

Chests come in various sizes, shapes and woods. Whether they be of multiple drawers, or blanket type, size plays a most important role in determining value of chests. The workmanship of the chest, and woods used in construction is also an important factor in value. Prices quoted here may vary depending on area.

> These are the 4 Prime Woods used in making all furniture
> LISTED BY VALUE
> **1. Mahogany**   **2. Maple**   **3. Cherry**   **4. Walnut**

BLANKET CHESTS OF AMERICAN MAKE

		Retail
1. ☐	Blanket Chest, Low	75.00
2. ☐	Blanket Chest, Tall with drawers below	100.00
3. ☐	Blanket Chest, Decorated	100.00

CHESTS OF AMERICAN & ENGLISH MAKE

CHIPPENDALE	American	English
4. ☐ Mahogany Chest	1250.00	750.00
5. ☐ Cherry Chest	950.00	
6. ☐ Maple Chest	1000.00	
7. ☐ Walnut Chest	650.00	500.00
HEPPLEWHITE		
8. ☐ Mahogany Chest	475.00	250.00
9. ☐ Cherry Chest	350.00	
10. ☐ Maple Chest	350.00	
11. ☐ Walnut Chest	225.00	150.00
SHERATON *		
12. ☐ Mahogany Chest	250.00	125.00
13. ☐ Cherry Chest	175.00	
14. ☐ Maple Chest	175.00	
15. ☐ Walnut Chest	125.00	85.00

*Note: Chests of the later period of Sheraton have panel ends at times, they are not as valuable as those with solid sides.

VICTORIAN CHESTS

		Retail
16. ☐	Early Victorian Marble Top Chests	100.00
17. ☐	Late Victorian Marble Top Chests (Sometimes called "Eastlake")	65.00

Basic Price

**CHIPPENDALE
CHEST OF DRAWERS**   4.

29.

**QUEEN ANNE
LOWBOY**

25.   **CHIPPENDALE
HIGHBOY**

35.

**HEPPLEWHITE
SIDEBOARD**

19.   **QUEEN ANNE
HIGHDADDY
(TALLBOY)**

These are the 4 Prime Woods used in making all furniture
LISTED BY VALUE
1. Mahogany   2. Maple   3. Cherry   4. Walnut

HIGHBOYS OF AMERICAN MAKE*

QUEEN ANNE
		Reta
18. ☐	Mahogany Highboy	3750.0
19. ☐	Cherry Highboy	3500.0
20. ☐	Maple Highboy	3250.0
21. ☐	Walnut Highboy	2000.0

CHIPPENDALE
22. ☐	Mahogany Highboy	3500.00
23. ☐	Cherry Highboy	3500.00
24. ☐	Maple Highboy	3250.00
25. ☐	Walnut Highboy	2000.00

Note: English pieces are usually 1/2 the value of listed American make items.

LOWBOYS OF AMERICAN MAKE*

QUEEN ANNE
26. ☐	Mahogany Lowboy	3500.00
27. ☐	Cherry Lowboy	3000.00
28. ☐	Maple Lowboy	3000.00
29. ☐	Walnut Lowboy	2500.00

CHIPPENDALE
30. ☐	Mahogany Lowboy	3750.00
31. ☐	Cherry Lowboy	3500.00
32. ☐	Maple Lowboy	3250.00
33. ☐	Walnut Lowboy	2000.00

All other woods such as Oak, Elm, Ash, Pine, etc., are 1/2 or less than quoted Retail Prices.

Note: Prices on English made pieces are usually 1/2 quoted Retail Prices.

SIDEBOARDS OF AMERICAN MAKE*

34. ☐	Hepplewhite Inlaid Sideboard	2500.00
35. ☐	Hepplewhite Simple Sideboard	850.00
36. ☐	Sheraton Inlaid Sideboard	1500.00
37. ☐	Sheraton Simple Sideboard	450.00
38. ☐	Federal & Empire Sideboards	150.00

Size, woods, shapes may vary the quoted prices considerably.

Note: English pieces are usually 1/2 of quoted Retail Prices.

Serpentine & Block Front Desks are more valuable.

SLANT FRONT DESK

1.

SLANT FRONT SERPENTINE DESK

KNEEHOLE DESK

DESKS OF AMERICAN MAKE*

Item & Description   **Prices Quoted Are Basic Retail Prices.**

	Item & Description	Retail
	SLANT FRONT DESKS	
1. ☐	Chippendale Desk (Illus.)...................................	750.00
2. ☐	Hepplewhite Desk...	600.00
3. ☐	Sheraton Desk...	350.00
4. ☐	Victorian Desk...	150.00
	FLAT TOP KNEEHOLE DESKS	
5. ☐	Chippendale..	850.00
6. ☐	Hepplewhite..	700.00
7. ☐	Sheraton..	500.00
8. ☐	Victorian..	150.00
	BUREAU DESKS (BUTLERS)	
9. ☐	Hepplewhite..	500.00
10. ☐	Sheraton..	300.00
11. ☐	School Master Desks (Comes in a variety of woods)	150.00
12. ☐	Roll Top Victorian Desks (Comes in a variety of woods)...	150.00

> *NOTE:*
> *Size plays an important part in price. Generally a smaller scaled desk will command a higher price.*
>
> *Price influenced by location of sale.*

***Desks of English make are 1/2 Retail Prices quoted.**

FRENCH & ITALIAN DESKS OF THE LOUIS XV & XVI PERIODS

13. ☐	Flat Top Kneehole Desk.....................................	1500.00
14. ☐	Drop Front or Slant Desk...................................	600.00
15. ☐	Roll Top (Cylinder) Desk...................................	500.00

SOFAS, SETTEES OF AMERICAN MAKE*

Item & Description	Retail
1. ☐ Sheraton Sofa. Mahogany wood	600.00
2. ☐ Chippendale Mahogany Sofa. Serpentine back with rolled arms, loose down cushion, grooved square legs joined and reinforced by underbrace..	750.00
3. ☐ Queen Anne Sofa	3500.00
4. ☐ Queen Anne Settee	1800.00
5. ☐ Chippendale Sofa (Illus.)	2750.00
6. ☐ Chippendale Settee	1500.00
7. ☐ Hepplewhite Sofa	850.00
8. ☐ Hepplewhite Settee	475.00
9. ☐ Sheraton Sofa (Illus.)	600.00
10. ☐ Sheraton Settee	350.00
11. ☐ Empire Sofa	100.00
12. ☐ Empire Settee	100.00
13. ☐ Early Victorian Sofa	175.00
14. ☐ Early Victorian Settee	125.00
15. ☐ Late Victorian (Also called Eastlake)	100.00
16. ☐ Late Victorian (Also called Eastlake) Settee	75.00

Prices on English made pieces are usually 1/2 quoted Retail Prices.

SOFAS & SETTEES OF FRENCH MAKE*

17. ☐ Louis XV Sofa	750.00
18. ☐ Louis XVI Settee	500.00
19. ☐ Louis XVI Sofa	750.00
20. ☐ Louis XVI Settee	500.00
21. ☐ Directoire Sofa	450.00
22. ☐ Directoire Settee	300.00
23. ☐ Empire Sofa	300.00
24. ☐ Empire Settee	200.00

Italian make sofas and settees of the same period are usually 20% less than quoted prices.

LOVE SEATS

25. ☐ Louis XV Wing Back Sofa (Love Seat)	700.00
26. ☐ Eastlake—Late Victorian	100.00
27. ☐ Victorian Transitional Sofa (Empire-Victorian)	75.00-300.00
28. ☐ Victorian Period, fine grape & leaf carvings on front and top	150.00

SHERATON SOFA
1.

CHIPPENDALE SOFA
5.

LOUIS XV
WING BACK
25.

TRANSITIONAL
VICTORIAN EMPIRE
27.

VICTORIAN
LOVE SEAT
28.

26.
EAST LAKE LOVE SEAT

·These are the 4 Prime Woods used in making all furniture
LISTED BY VALUE
1. Mahogany   2. Maple   3. Cherry   4. Walnut

FURNITURE (TABLES)

TABLES OF AMERICAN & ENGLISH MAKE

All Prices are for Good Condition Unless Otherwise Noted.

Item & Description	Retail American	English
1. ☐ Queen Anne Drop Leaf (Swing Legs)....................	750.00	300.00
2. ☐ Chippendale Drop Leaf Table..............................	750.00	300.00
3. ☐ Heppelwhite Drop Leaf Table..............................	350.00	200.00
4. ☐ Sheraton Drop Leaf Table.................................	300.00	175.00
5. ☐ Empire & Victorian Drop Leaf Table.......................	75.00	75.00
6. ☐ Curled Birch Gate Leg Table. Six legs with high dropleaf..	180.00	180.00

CARD & GAME TABLES

7. ☐ Chippendale Card & Game Tables.........................	850.00	350.00
8. ☐ Heppelwhite Card & Game Tables........................	700.00	250.00
9. ☐ Sheraton Card & Game Tables............................	450.00	200.00
10. ☐ Federal & Empire & Victorian Card & Game Tables	75.00	75.00
11. ☐ French Backgammon Louis XVI Card & Game Tables	750.00	

TILT TABLES (3 LEGGED)

12. ☐ Queen Anne Tilt Tables.................................	850.00	300.00
13. ☐ Chippendale Tilt Tables................................	800.00	300.00
14. ☐ Heppelwhite Tilt Tables................................	350.00	175.00
15. ☐ Regency & Federal Tilt Tables..........................	100.00	100.00

OCCASIONAL TABLES

16. ☐ Heppelwhite Occasional Tables...........................	250.00	150.00
17. ☐ Sheraton Occasional Tables.............................	150.00	100.00
18. ☐ Victorian Occasional Tables............................	100.00	60.00
19. ☐ American Pine Occasional Table. Oblong top above square legs tapered to base........................	50.00	

These are the 4 Prime Woods used in making all furniture
LISTED BY VALUE
1. Mahogany   2. Maple   3. Cherry   4. Walnut

6.

GATE LEG
TABLE

CARD
TABLE

8.

11.

BIRD
CAGE

BACKGAMMON
TABLE

13.

CHIPPENDALE
TILT
TABLE

3. CHIPPENDALE
DROP LEAF

QUEEN ANNE

1.

CHIPPENDALE

2.

FEDERAL

4.

2.
GEORGIAN

MIRRORS OF AMERICAN MAKE

Size, woods, shapes, ornamentation vary the Retail Prices quoted.

		Retail
1. ☐ Queen Anne Mirror (Illus.)		750.00
2. ☐ Chippendale (Georgian) Mirror (Illus.)		650.00
3. ☐ Federal, Empire, Regency, Standard Mirrors		150.00
4. ☐ Convex Mirrors (Federal Period)		500.00

Note: English mirrors are usually 1/4 to 1/2 of quoted prices.

Courtesy: Hammond-Harwood House.

Produced in huge quantities during last half of 19th century in hundreds of patterns and shapes. Early ware was made of lead glass which has a distinctive bell-tone ring. Today, these are sought after as collectors items. Some patterns were produced in colors. These carry a premium of 50% to 200% over clear ones. Blue is usually the highest priced.

Quotations listed on Pattern Glass are **retail prices** in clear glass for pieces in **perfect condition**. A fair offer for purchase by a dealer would be 25% to 40% of the stated retail price for ORIGINAL pieces in perfect condition.

A WORD ABOUT REPRODUCTIONS

The widespread interest in collecting of Pattern, or Pressed Glass, has created both high prices and scarcity of supply of original pieces, consequently reproductions and substitutes are being made. Be very cautious when buying Pattern Glass. A reputable dealer should be willing to guarantee the authenticity of any piece he sells.

ACKNOWLEDGEMENTS

Mr. John Hotchkiss — Hotchkiss House, 89 Sagamore Drive 1, Rochester, N.Y. For editing, compiling and pricing.

Mr. Serry Wood — Editor — Century House, Watkins Glen, N.Y. For permission to use illustrations from "WOOD-KAMM ENCYCLOPEDIA OF PATTERN GLASS, VOLUMES I & II."

Miss Virginia Desmond — Kamm Publications, P.O. Box 6813, Grosse Pointe, Michigan. For permission to use illustrations from "KAMM BOOKS ON PATTERN GLASS" (8 VOLS.)

We recommend the above books as the definitive works on the subject.

BIBLIOGRAPHY

RUTH WEBB LEE'S HANDBOOK OF EARLY AMERICAN PRESSED GLASS PATTERNS
EARLY AMERICAN PATTERN GLASS — ALICE HULETT METZ
CONFUSING COLLECTIBLES — DOROTHY HAMMOND

ACTRESS   AMBERETTE

CREAMER

CREAMER

CREAMER

ACTRESS (NON-FLINT)

	Retail
Cake Stand	$38.00
Compote, Open, 9½"	35.00
Creamer	25.00
Goblet	28.00
Pitcher, Milk	75.00
Sauce, Flat	8.00
Spooner	18.00

Reproduced

AMBERETTE (KLONDIKE) (NON-FLINT)

Butter Dish	$75.00
Compote, Covered. 8" high, standard	125.00
Goblet	75.00
Pitcher, Water. Frosted	100.00
Sauce, Footed, Frosted	25.00
Spooner	45.00
Sugar & Creamer, Set	150.00
Syrup	95.00
Tumbler	60.00

This pattern with stained light amber band has become a high priced, very speculative item subject to wide price fluctuation.

PATTERN GLASS

BABY-FACE

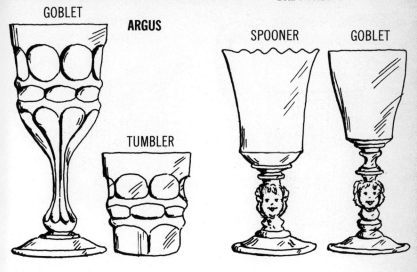

ARGUS (FLINT GLASS)

	Retail
☐ Ale Glass	$24.00
☐ Butter Dish	26.00
☐ Creamer	32.00
☐ Decanter, Quart	42.00
☐ Goblet	20.00
☐ Sauce	12.00
☐ Tumbler, Water	18.00
☐ Wine	18.00

BABY-FACE (NON-FLINT)

☐ Butter Dish	$48.00
☐ Compote, Small, Covered	40.00
☐ Creamer	45.00
☐ Goblet	50.00
☐ Pitcher	75.00
☐ Spooner	22.00
☐ Wine	35.00

Reproduced in most pieces.

PATTERN GLASS

BELLFLOWER

PITCHER
(WATER)

PITCHER
(WATER)

BELLFLOWER (FLINT)

		Retail
☐	Bowl, Berry, 8"..	$50.00
☐	Butter Dish..	42.00
☐	Celery, Banded...	60.00
☐	Compote Covered, 8", High Standard............................	90.00
☐	Compote Open, 8" Diam..	40.00
☐	Creamer..	60.00
☐	Decanter, Quart..	65.00
☐	Dish, Sauce..	14.00
☐	Egg Cup..	18.00
☐	Goblet...	45.00
☐	Lamp, All Glass..	42.00
☐	Lamp, Marble Base..	40.00
☐	Pitcher, Syrup...	60.00
☐	Pitcher, Water...	80.00
☐	Tumbler..	30.00
☐	Wine...	24.00

SUGAR BOWL (BANDED)

COIN (U.S.)

CAKE STAND

EGG CUP

CREAMER

BUCKLE (FLINT & NON-FLINT)

	Retail
] Butter Dish...	$20.00
] Cordial..	10.00
] Creamer..	17.00
] Egg Cup..	10.00
] Goblet..	10.00
] Pitcher, Water..	30.00
] Spooner..	10.00
] Tumbler..	8.00
] Wine..	10.00

th Flint & Non-Flint are old. Add 50-75% to above prices for Flint items.
ttern also comes with a band, same prices.

COIN (U.S.) (NON-FLINT)

] Bowl, Berry, Half-Dollars..	$180.00
] Butter Dish, Half-Dollars..	375.00
] Cake Stand, Half-Dollars..	300.00
] Compote, Quarters..	350.00
] Creamer, Half-Dollars..	175.00
] Goblet, Half-Dollars...	220.00
] Lamp, 20 Cents...	162.00
] Sauce, Quarters..	80.00

any reproductions. U.S. Coin made in Dimes, Quarters and Halves. Colum-
an coin pattern about 1/3 to 1/4 above values. Unfrosted glass about 30% less

PATTERN GLASS

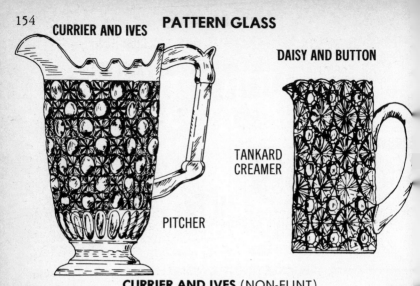

CURRIER AND IVES

DAISY AND BUTTON

TANKARD CREAMER

PITCHER

CURRIER AND IVES (NON-FLINT)

Retail

☐	Butter Dish	$24.00
☐	Decanter, Quart	15.00
☐	Goblet, knobbed stem	10.00
☐	Pitcher, Large	18.00
☐	Sauce	5.00
☐	Sugar Bowl	22.00
☐	Wine	8.00

DAISY AND BUTTON (NON-FLINT)

☐	Bowl, Berry	$10.00
☐	Butter Dish	18.00
☐	Canoe	10.00
☐	Celery	12.00
☐	Cruet	12.00
☐	Egg Cup	7.00
☐	Goblet	10.00
☐	Hat, or Toothpick Holder	8.00
☐	Inkwell	7.00
☐	Mug	6.00
☐	Sauce	4.00

Many shapes and colors have been reproduced. For authentic colored pieces add up to double above figures.

PATTERN GLASS

DAKOTA   **DIAMOND POINT**

CREAMER   DECANTER

TUMBLER   PITCHER

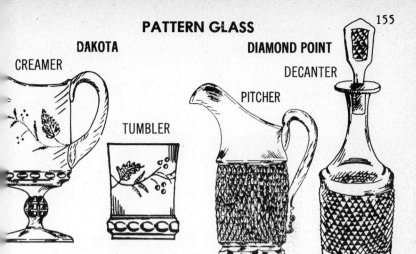

DAKOTA (BABY THUMBPRINT) (NON-FLINT)	**Retail**
Butter Dish, Covered..	$25.00
Compote, Covered, 5″, 6″..	27.00
Goblet..	15.00
Mug..	12.00
Sauce, Flat...	
Sauce, Footed..	8.00
Footed...	9.00
Spooner..	12.00
Tumbler..	10.00
Wine..	13.00

r etched leaf design add 50%. In Ruby etched, double above figures.

DIAMOND POINT (FLINT)	
Bowl, Berry, 8″...	$25.00
Butter Dish...	30.00
Castor Bottle..	9.00
Compote, High Standard...	60.00
Creamer..	45.00
Decanter, Bar Lip, Pint...	30.00
Egg Cup..	18.00
Goblet..	18.00
Sauce..	8.00

any variations of this pattern. Some in Non-Flint.

PATTERN GLASS

FINE RIB

GARFIELD DRAPE

PITCHER

COMPOTE

GOBLET

FINE RIB (FLINT AND NON-FLINT)

Reta

☐ Bowl, Berry, 8"...	$35.0
☐ Butter Dish...	35.0
☐ Compote, Open, 10"..................................	35.0
☐ Decanter, Pint.......................................	26.0
☐ Egg Cup, Double, Covered...........................	28.0
☐ Goblet..	18.0
☐ Lemonade Glass......................................	18.0
☐ Plate, 7"...	27.0
☐ Sauce..	6.0
☐ Tumbler, Water......................................	18.0
☐ Wine...	15.0

GARFIELD DRAPE (NON-FLINT)

☐ Butter Dish...	$25.0
☐ Creamer..	16.0
☐ Egg Cup..	12.0
☐ Honey Dish..	6.0
☐ Pitcher, Milk..	25.0
☐ Sauce, Footed.......................................	7.0
☐ Spooner...	9.0
☐ Sugar Bowl..	25.0

PATTERN GLASS

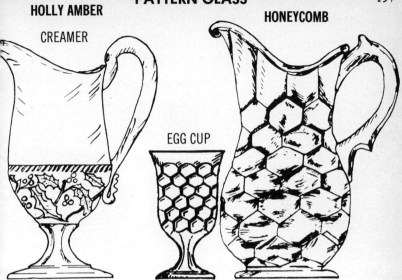

HOLLY AMBER   CREAMER

HONEYCOMB

EGG CUP

HOLLY AMBER (GOLDEN AGATE) (NON-FLINT)

	Retail
Butter Dish	$750.00
Cake Stand	800.00
Compote, Open	700.00
Pitcher, 10"	1000.00
Plate, 7½"	350.00
Sauce	150.00
Toothpick	150.00
Tumbler	250.00

This distinctive opalescent amber colored glass was made for a short period about 1900 in Greentown, Ind.

HONEYCOMB (FLINT AND NON-FLINT)

Bowl, 8"	$10.00
Compote, Covered, High Standard	25.00
Decanter, Quart	20.00
Egg Cup	8.00
Goblet	8.00
Lamp	15.00
Tumbler	6.00

Flint prices double above. This pattern made in many variations. Some very poor quality.

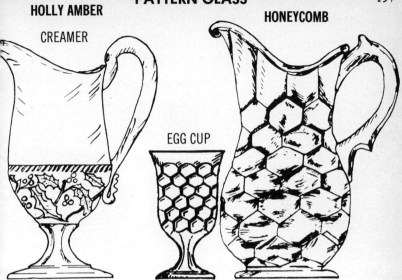

PATTERN GLASS

HORN OF PLENTY

CREAMER

SPOONER

LINCOLN DRAPE

BUTTER DISH

HORN OF PLENTY (FLINT)

		Ret
☐	Butter Dish	$50.
☐	Celery	60.
☐	Compote, Open	70.
☐	Decanter, Quart	40.
☐	Goblet	30.
☐	Honey Dish	12.
☐	Pitcher, Milk	125.
☐	Tumbler, Water	30.
☐	Wine	24.

Pattern has been reproduced in Non-Flint glass. Also reproduced in modern colors.

LINCOLN DRAPE (FLINT)

☐	Butter Dish	$35.
☐	Creamer	50.
☐	Decanter	40.
☐	Egg Cup	15.
☐	Goblet	25.
☐	Sugar Bowl	40.
☐	Tumbler	20.
☐	Wine	15.

Prices the same for pattern with tassel. *Reproduced*

COMPOTE
(HIGH STANDARD)

PATTERN GLASS

LION

CREAMER

MOON
AND
STAR

PITCHER

BOWL

LION (NON-FLINT)

	Retail
Celery, Footed...	$35.00
Compote, Open, High Standard..........................	40.00
Creamer..	27.00
Goblet...	30.00
Spooner, Footed...	25.00
Tumbler..	18.00
Wine...	35.00

Reproduced in most pieces.

MOON AND STAR (NON-FLINT)

Bowl, Berry, 8"...	$16.00
Celery...	20.00
Creamer..	40.50
Egg Cup..	20.50
Goblet...	20.00
Pitcher, Water..	45.00
Sauce, Flat...	8.00
Spooner..	14.00
Toothpick...	12.00
Tray...	25.00
Wine...	15.00

Pattern has been reproduced many times in clear and various colors.

ONE HUNDRED ONE   OVAL STAR

CREAMER   CREAMER

GOBLET

ONE HUNDRED ONE (NON-FLINT)

		Retail
☐	Bowl, Berry	$20.00
☐	Celery	17.00
☐	Goblet	12.00
☐	Lamp, Hand	15.00
☐	Sauce, Flat	4.00
☐	Spooner	10.00
☐	Tumbler	15.00

OVAL STAR (NON-FLINT)

☐	Bowl, Berry, 8"	$12.00
☐	Goblet	8.00
☐	Pitcher, Water	15.00
☐	Sugar, Bowl	12.00
☐	Tumbler, Water	5.00
☐	Wine	33.00

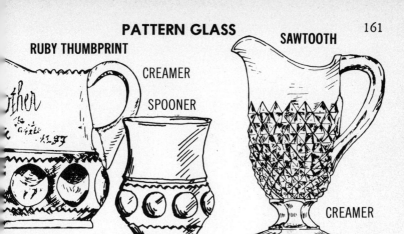

PATTERN GLASS

RUBY THUMBPRINT

SAWTOOTH

CREAMER

SPOONER

CREAMER

Y THUMBPRINT ("KING'S CROWN" IN CLEAR) (NON-FLINT) Retail

|---|---|
Bowl, Berry, 8"	$24.00
Compote, Open, High Standard	35.00
Cordial	14.00
Creamer	20.00
Goblet	18.00
Sauce	10.00
Spooner	15.00
Tumbler	15.00
Wine	16.00

being made today in lighter Ruby. Prices for "Red Block" pattern about same as above. *Reproduced in most pieces.*

SAWTOOTH (FLINT)

|---|---|
Bowl, Berry, 8"	$35.00
Butter Dish	45.00
Compote, Covered, 8", High Standard	50.00
Creamer	40.00
Decanter, Quart	45.00
Egg Cup	20.00
Goblet	25.00
Honey Dish	12.00
Pitcher	75.00
Tumbler, Water	11.50

made in Non-Flint. Deduct one-third for this type.

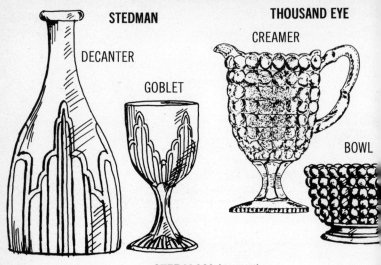

STEDMAN

DECANTER

GOBLET

THOUSAND EYE

CREAMER

BOWL

STEDMAN (FLINT)

R

☐ Bowl, Berry, 8"...	$2
☐ Butter, Covered...	2
☐ Celery..	
☐ Compote, Covered, High Standard..................	5
☐ Egg Cup...	
☐ Goblet..	2
☐ Sauce...	
☐ Tumbler..	1

THOUSAND EYE (NON-FLINT)

☐ Bowl, Berry, 8"...	$1
☐ Butter Dish, Covered......................................	2
☐ Celery..	2
☐ Compote, Open...	2
☐ Creamer..	2
☐ Goblet..	1
☐ Pitcher, Water...	
☐ Sauce, Footed..	
☐ Tumbler..	1

Also comes in Amber (add 25%), Blue, Green (add 50-75%).
Reproduced in most pieces.

THUMBPRINT

BOWL
AND
COVER

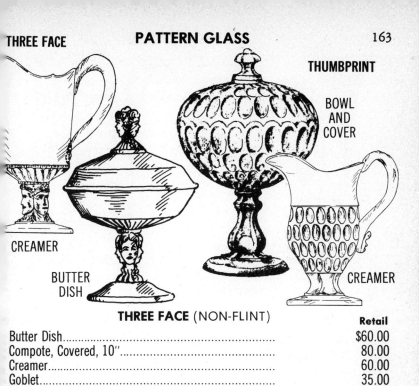

CREAMER

BUTTER
DISH

CREAMER

THREE FACE (NON-FLINT)

	Retail
Butter Dish	$60.00
Compote, Covered, 10"	80.00
Creamer	60.00
Goblet	35.00
Lamp	100.00
Spooner	25.00
Syrup Jug	40.00

ttern reproductions have restrained prices.

THUMBPRINT (FLINT)

Bowl, 8"	$40.00
Cake Stand, 10"	70.00
Compote, Covered, 10", High Standard	75.00
Decanter, Quart	60.00
Goblet, Knob Stem	27.00
Honey Dish	8.00
Pitcher, Water	85.00
Tumbler, Water	20.00
Wine	20.00

ttern made in many variations. Later ones Non-Flint (50% of above figures).
produced in most pieces.

PATTERN GLASS

TREE OF LIFE   **WAFFLE**

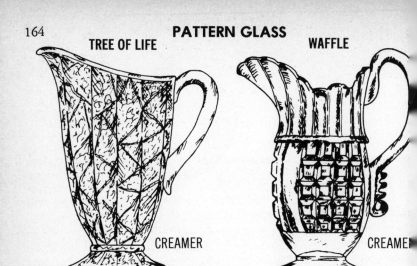

CREAMER   CREAMER

TREE OF LIFE (NON-FLINT)

Re

☐	Bowl, Berry, 8"	$15
☐	Butter Dish	30
☐	Celery	18
☐	Creamer	25
☐	Goblet	20
☐	Sauce	6
☐	Tumbler	10

WAFFLE (FLINT)

☐	Bowl, Berry, 8"	$25.
☐	Celery	30.
☐	Creamer	40.
☐	Decanter	35.
☐	Egg Cup	12.
☐	Goblet	20.
☐	Spooner	14.
☐	Sugar Bowl	25.
☐	Wine	15.
☐	Sauce	6.
☐	Tumbler	10.
☐	Wine	15.

Later variations made in Non-Flint (use 60% of above figures)..

ALL ABOUT GLASS

165

Letter from JOHN HOTCHKISS

HOTCHKISS HOUSE
COLLECTOR'S BOOKSHELF
89 SAGAMORE DRIVE · ROCHESTER, N. Y. 14617

...ace again it is a pleasure to contribute from my experience ...a collector, author, and appraiser in further expanding and ...dating this glass section to reflect the 1971/72 market.

...ce last year some new stars have appeared in collecting heavens. Perhaps ...brightest is Depression Glass which was produced during the thirties ...d forties of this century. It has now been discovered by the "now genera-...n" of collectors. It is now one of the fastest growing fields, along with ...tles, carnival and cut glass.

...other of the celestial celebrities that continues to shine brighter is Heisey ...ass with prices on the rarer pieces now going into orbit. Much authorita-...e new published information has focused the interest on this constellation.

...s also remarkable how some of the old standbys like pattern glass have ...reased their following in the fifty or more years it has been collected. ...ything remotely connected with the Art Nouveau movement of the early ...rs of the century is still spirally upwards. Some of the rarer Tiffany lamps ...e doubled in value in less than two years and cut glass, Steuben, French ...neo glass are also maintaining their popularity.

...ce again the opportunities for acquiring interesting collections which will ...bably later prove to have been shrewd investments are undiminished. To ...ist in this effort we have included a short bibliography of the best books ...glass out of the more than 1,000 titles we carry in stock on all types of ...iques and collectibles.

Cordially yours,

...H:jb

John F. Hotchkiss

BIBLIOGRAPHY OF BOOKS ON GLASS

...ERICAN ART NOUVEAU GLASS — Revi
...ERICAN CUT & ENGRAVED GLASS — Revi
...ERICAN ART GLASS — Barret
...ERICAN GLASS — George & Helen McKearin
...´ COLORED & CAMEO GLASS — Whitlow
...T GLASS NOVEAU — Grovers
...T GLASS PRICES — Hotchkiss
...ON BOTTLE HANDBOOK & PRICE GUIDE — ...Western Collector
...TTLE RUSH U.S.A. — Blumenstein

CARNIVAL GLASS PRICE — Hotchkiss & Hand
COLLECTING FRUIT JARS — Vols. I, II, III — Burris
CUT GLASS PRICE GUIDE — Hotchkiss
INSULATOR GUIDE — Stuart 2nd Ed.
JIM BEAM BOTTLES — Cembura
19th CENTURY ART GLASS — Revi
LUXARDO BOTTLES — Cembura
STEUBEN GLASS & PRICE GUIDE — Rochkwee & Hotchkiss

Pictures courtesy Rockwell Gallery, Corning Museum of Glass and Chrysler Art Museum.

AGATA GLASS

A single-layered shaded opaque glass ranging from deep raspberry at the t
to a rich cream at the base but characterized by irregular splotches of dark g
to black caused by an alcohol treatment in the finishing operation.

AMBERINA GLASS

A shaded, two-toned crystal 19th century glass from the New England Gl
Company. The deep fuschia to rich amber was produced by a second h
treatment of the fuschia portion. Also known as heat sensitive glass, it v
made again in the Twenties by Libbey Glass Company. Also see Baccarat.

APOTHECARY BOTTLES

Usually in clear, transparent glass, Apothecary bottles appeared in a wi
variety of shapes and sizes. They were used in 19th century drug stores
contain everything from candy to cough syrup. Genuine bottles are n
highly prized by collectors.

AURENE GLASS

Best known of all the Steuben ware produced by Carder. The name is deriv
from the Latin word for gold but this beautiful iridescent opaque glass v
produced in both a rich gold and brilliant peacock blue iridescence.

BACCARAT GLASS

This famous French glass works has been producing glass for more than
hundred years. Known for fine clear crystal tableware, colorful paperweigh
and an Amberina that shaded from a red-orange to clear.

BOHEMIAN GLASS

Bohemian glass is made in hundreds of varieties but the term is generally appli
to a rich, ruby glass that has been decorated by engraving through the ou
red layer to form elegant scenes and motifs. This area is now Western Czec
slovakia where skilled makers are still producing old patterns and new.

BRISTOL GLASS

Usually these pieces are semi-opaque, thin white glass, frequently decorat
with enameled flowers. Sometimes refers to an acid finished glass with d
surfaces.

BURMESE GLASS

ade in the United States first and then later under license in England as ueen's Burmese, it is an opaque shaded glass of light rose color at the top to pale yellow at the bottom. Later reproduced in the 1920's by Gunderson.

CAMEO GLASS

lso known as Acid Cut Back, this beautiful glass was first made by hand rving away a top layer of one color to produce a contrasting design in the base lor. These designs were later produced by masking and acid dipping. See allé.

CARNIVAL GLASS

form of iridized glass produced early in the Twentieth Century by pressing a mold to create the shape and design and treated to imitate the iridescence Aurene and Tiffany. Produced in hundreds of patterns and shapes, this once eap glass now ranges from a few dollars to many hundreds for one piece.

CRANBERRY GLASS

ght red transparent glass made by many factories over a great number of ars. Available in great many shapes and very collectable. Difficult to deter- ine exact age of some pieces. Still being produced.

CUSTARD GLASS

amed for its similarity to the color of baked custard. Color varies to very ght cream. Made by several American factories in identifiable patterns. Often rther decorated with gold.

CUT GLASS

sually refers to pieces made from 1880 to 1914 during the "Brilliant Period." eeply cut in all-over patterns in heavy lead crystal blanks. Has distinct bell ne when struck. Made in many shops, some of which marked some of their eces for a short period with a trademark.

CUT VELVET GLASS

Acid finish satin glass with a slightly raised pattern. The raised portion usually a darker tone than the depressed lower areas. Always has a dull velve appearance.

DEPRESSION GLASS

DURAND GLASS

Several types of Art Glass produced by a company of this name. Their g and blue iridescent pieces may be confused with Steuben and Tiffany un signed. Made in a number of characteristic shapes and patterns such as King 1

ENAMELED GLASS (MARY GREGORY)

Anti transparent or opaque glass that was decorated by hand using enam that were fired on. (See Mary Gregory for typical example.) Produced by m: different companies in the U. S. and on the Continent.

END OF DAY (SPATTER WARE) GLASS

Articles made up of random pieces of various colored glasses left over in glass shop at the end of the day. Sometimes called Spatterware.

GALLE GLASS

Most famous French maker of Cameo Glass. Gallé was an accomplished ar and his fine pieces were often three or four different colored layers of gl carefully etched back with acid to produce attractive scenic designs. Many oth French factories like Daum-Nancy produced similar wares.

HONESDALE GLASS

A scarce cameo or acid cut back glass made in Honesdale, Pa. by the Dorflin Co. and decorated by a subsidiary. The designs were often stained in gree and yellows. Red is especially scarce.

HEISEY GLASS

KEW BLAS GLASS

Another type of Art Glass contemporary with Steuben and Tiffany having own characteristic shapes, designs and colors. Frequently this ware has loop designs of different color. Not always signed.

LALIQUE GLASS & GLASS MUGS

...med for another French Glass artist and still being made today. Characterized
a frosted or satin finish produced by a special acid treatment. Recently
965) they introduced an annual glass plate in limited editions that have
...preciated rapidly in price.

LIBBEY GLASS

...ccessor of the New England Glass Company, they produced fine cut glass
...aring their signature and a later amberina glass that is also sometimes signed.
...ey made other types of fine glass which are not common.

LOETZ GLASS

...n Austrian glass sometimes confused when not signed with American
...descent products. Their peacock feather blue iridescent is highly prized.

LUTZ TYPE GLASS

...his term is usually applied to any piece of finely threaded or striped glass,
...me of which was made by a famous glassmaker by this name at Sandwich.
...me similarity to Venetian glass of the same style.

MARY GREGORY GLASS

...decorator at the Boston & Sandwich Glass Company who applied white
...amel figures of boys and girls on clear or colored crystal. This type decoration
...still produced in quantity in Venice and Czechoslovakia.

MILK GLASS

...ny opaque white glass article that usually has a pattern of some type impressed
...the outer surface. First made in the 19th century in hundreds of shapes and
...atterns, it is still being produced today by at least two American glass firms,
...enton and Westmoreland.

MILLEFIORE GLASS

...efers to the technique of impressing in hot glass, discs that have been sliced
...rom bundles of multicolored rods. Each disc may produce the effect of a flower
...ence the name "Thousand Flower." Used extensively in paperweights.

OVERLAY GLASS

Most commonly refers to Victorian glass vases which are decorated with contrasting colored glass in the form of fruits and flowers, interconnected wi vines or stems making an elaborate and ornate finished product.

OPALINE GLASS

Although, while on the surface there is a strong resemblance to milk gla when held to a light, Opaline glass has high iridescence and a variety of col which distinguishes it from its more common counterpart. From its creati in the late 1880's, Opaline has enjoyed great popularity.

PAPERWEIGHTS GLASS

Solid, domed shaped pieces of glass several inches in diameter that were us to hold papers on a desk but now because of their price and rarity are used decorative display. Made for over one hundred years in a large variety techniques by highly skilled glass workers. Some of the contemporary weig made today by a few American artists and Baccarat are equal in quality to t old ones. Others are much cheaper imports from Venice and Japan.

RUBINA - RUBINA VERDE GLASS

Two types of shaded glass. The first is a deep cranberry red at the top of t article shading down to a clear glass at the bottom. The second is the same the top but shades to a light transparent green color at the bottom.

SANDWICH TYPE GLASS

Products of the Boston & Sandwich Glass Company which covered a span sixty years from 1826 and covered many types such as blown, pressed, lacy, an overlay. Today many lacy glass, pattern glass and other types made at an number of glass shops are loosely called "Sandwich."

SATIN GLASS

Articles made of opaque glass in white or color that have been treated wi acid to form a smooth, dull surface are referred to as Satin Glass. Many these pieces are shaded from a darker tone at the top to a lighter shade at t bottom. Blue, orange, red are some of the colors. Mother of Pearl is a speci top layer satin glass. A pattern (diamond quilting, thumbprint, rain drop an others) are impressed in first layer. The second layer traps air in the low plac which shows through the finished piece as a pearly iridescence. Usually calle M.O.P. Satin Glass.

SILVER DEPOSIT (OVERLAY) GLASS

form of decoration applied to pieces of glass by painting the glass with a
nducting surface in the desired decoration. This is then placed in a bath
ere silver was deposited electrically only where coated.

STEUBEN GLASS

ass articles made by the Steuben Glass Company and the Steuben Division
the Corning Glass Company from 1902 to 1932. These should more properly
called Carder Steuben as they were all designed by the ounder, Frederick
rder. Mr. Carder was creating new designs until 1955. He died in 1964 at
e age of 100. There are about twenty different named types such as Aurene,
lcite, Iverene, Verre de Soie. Since 1932 the Steuben Division has produced
ly clear crystal articles that are also being collected.

TIFFANY GLASS

uis Comfort Tiffany, an accomplished artist produced various forms of art
ass from about 1895 to 1920. They fall into a number of different categories
ch as Gold Iridescent, Blue Iridescent, Paperweight, Agate, Cameo, Intaglio,
va, Millefiore. Many of the pieces are signed "Favrille-LCT." The variety in
lors, shapes, forms and sizes, all artistically done was tremendous. One of
e most sought after and highest priced items are lamps. The lampshades are
ade in beautiful floral forms of small pieces of various colored stained glass.
he shades and bases were signed.

VENETIAN GLASS

enetian Glass has been made on the island of Murano in Italy since about
350. In all these years they have produced outstanding pieces of art glass and
bleware. Typical is the work of the 19th and 20th Centuries is the fine
ligree white and colored twisted spirals. The use of gold or bronze powder
the glass is also typical. Still being made in a wide range of qualities, some
f it very inexpensive and gaudy.

VERRE DE SOIE GLASS

ne of the forms of Steuben Glass translated means "Glass of Silk." It is a
lear glass frosted and iridized by special treatments to produce the beautiful
himmering iridescence of silk.

Cruet

PITCHERS

VA

**All Prices shown are for Good Condition
and Fine Color**

Item & Description	*A.B.P.	Reta
☐ Pitcher 4½″ high. With handle and fine color............	800.00	1000.
☐ Pitcher 5″ high. With acid finish and fine color..........	800.00	1000.
☐ Celery	600.00	800.
☐ Mottled Cruet, Fine Color (Illus.).................................	750.00	900.
☐ Mottled Finger Bowl	450.00	750.
☐ Milk Pitcher. Blue and gold mottling. Rose to pale pink shadings. With hollow-reeded Agata handle	900.00	1500.
☐ Sugar Bowl. Over 4½″ high	850.00	1100.
☐ Toothpick holder. Variable top	325.00	500.
☐ Tumbler (Water) deep color	425.00	550.
☐ Vase. 3¼″ wide, 4½″ high. Surried top, rich blue hue	400.00	700.
☐ Vase, Morgan on Stand, 8½″	1800.00	2500.
☐ Whisky tumbler	400.00	600.
☐ Vase. 6″ high. Rich mottling, pinched top	800.00	1000.
☐ Vase, lily shape, 8″ deep color (Illus.)....................	750.00	900.

*A.B.P.—Average Buying Price see pg. 5

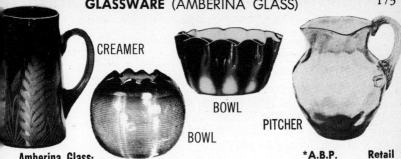

CREAMER

BOWL

BOWL

PITCHER

Amberina Glass:	*A.B.P.	Retail
Bottle. 8" high. Inverted thumbprint design...............	60.00	100.00
Bowl. Blown with base. Light color 8" diam...............	65.00	140.00
Bowl, finger. Deep fuschia color............................	90.00	175.00
Bowl. Inverted thumbprint pattern with floral designs.	90.00	160.00
Bowl. For serving punch. Complete with cover, cups and ladle. Inverted thumbprint pattern	180.00	400.00
Butter Dish. Thumbprint pattern with insert	125.00	180.00
Creamer. Red reeded handles and square top............	81.00	165.00
Cruet, vinegar...	90.00	180.00
Cup. For holding punch. Inverted thumbprint, Fuschia....	50.00	75.00
Decanter. For liquor or wine. Applied handle	125.00	200.00
Flower Vase. 5" high. Multi-colored gradients	75.00	110.00
Lamp. Small electrified base with shade	220.00	280.00
Lamp Shade. Large turned-down fluted scallops	70.00	120.00
Mustard Container. Has metal top	80.00	115.00
Pitcher. 7" high. Blown in "eye" pattern	270.00	325.00
Pitcher. 8" high. For milk. Curved rope handle...............	225.00	300.00
Pitcher. For gravy. Rich color, silver handles	175.00	225.00
Salt & Pepper Containers. With metal tops. Pair	80.00	120.00
Sugar Bowl & Creamer. Amber handles with squared tops.	175.00	250.00
Tumbler. Inverted thumbprint pattern	50.00	65.00
Tumbler. For lemonade with low handle......................	70.00	85.00
Tumbler. With hand-painted floral design	60.00	80.00
Vase. 4½" high. Floral pattern.................................	80.00	100.00
Vase. 10½" high. Curved neck with swirl pattern	90.00	150.00
Vase. 15¼" high. Large with flat base, signed "Libbey"	150.00	300.00
Vase. 16" high. Wide neck with floral designs............	100.00	200.00

*Average Buying Price

GLASSWARE (APOTHECARY-AURENE-BACCARRAT)

(see following page for illustrations)

All Prices shown are for Good Condition and Fine Color

Item & Description	*A.B.P.	Ret
Apothecary Bottles:		
1. ☐ 12" high. Has ground glass stopper for top	9.00	15.0
2. ☐ 11" high. Broad bottle with wide mouth	8.00	14.0
3. ☐ 9¼" high. Smoothly finished. With black lettering	15.00	20.0
4. ☐ 8½" high. Wide mouthed, inscribed bottle	6.00	10.0
5. ☐ 8" high. Tinted glass with stopper	9.00	12.0
Aurene Glass:		
6. ☐ Bottle. 6¼" high. Wide stopper, gold	120.00	150.
7. ☐ Basket, gold, signed	200.00	275.0
8. ☐ Candy Dish. Rich blue	200.00	250.0
9. ☐ Candlesticks. Twisted stem, pair	200.00	275.0
10. ☐ Cup and plate. Both signed, gold	100.00	120.0
11. ☐ Dish. For fruit. Carries Steuben mfg. marks, gold, 8"..	80.00	125.0
12. ☐ Goblet. For wine. Gold, twisted stem	120.00	150.0
13. ☐ Liquer Tumbler. 5½" high, gold	50.00	75.0
14. ☐ Perfume Container. 6½" high. Fluted. Pair, gold	125.00	175.0
15. ☐ Vase. 7" high. Opaque with iridescent pattern of red, gold and green. Both opaque and metallized decorations.	80.00	120.0
16. ☐ Vase. 6" high. Rose-colored overtones, gold	70.00	100.0
17. ☐ Wine Decanter. 4½" high. Signed, gold	150.00	185.0
Baccarrat Glass:		
18. ☐ Bottle. 6½" high. Multi-colored sides and cut stopper ..	30.00	45.0
19. ☐ Bowl. 6" diameter. Fluted sides	50.00	80.0
20. ☐ Carafe. For water. Complete in swirling design	45.00	60.0
21. ☐ Ginger Jar. Variable coloring with brass cover. Signed ..	50.00	80.0
22. ☐ Jelly Jar. Swirl pattern. Signed	30.00	45.0
23. ☐ Paperweight, Kennedy, Single 1964	175.00	240.0
24. ☐ Paperweight, Kennedy, Overlay. Red, white & blue	600.00	800.0
25. ☐ Paperweight, G. Washington, Single	120.00	175.0
26. ☐ Perfume or Cologne Container, 5½" high. Excellent cond.	20.00	35.0
27. ☐ Tumbler. Aqua swirl design	20.00	35.0
28. ☐ Vases. 6" high. Ornately cut. Pair	75.00	125.0

*****Average Buying Price**

APOTHECARY

AURENE

BACCARRAT

GLASSWARE (BREAD PLATES-BOHEMIAN)

BREAD
PLATE

DECANTER

BOWL

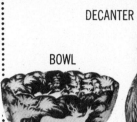

Item & Description All prices are for Good Condition	*A.B.P.	Reta
Bread Plates: CLEAR GLASS, PRESSED:		
☐ Faith, Hope, and Charity motto	16.00	25.0
☐ Frosted Bird	21.00	35.0
☐ General Ulysses Grant. Commemorative	15.00	25.0
☐ Horseshoe	18.00	30.0
☐ Liberty Bell in Philadelphia	18.00	27.0
☐ Little Red Riding Hood	16.00	25.0
☐ Patriotic Scene. Lexington	17.00	25.0
COLORED AND TINTED PATTERNS:		
☐ Beaded Green	26.00	40.0
☐ Centennial Blue	21.00	35.0
☐ Floral Amber	16.00	25.0
☐ Hobnail Amber	16.00	25.0
Bohemian Glass:		
☐ Beaker. For liquids. Rose with floral design	38.00	60.00
☐ Bell. 4½" high. Woodland scene painted on exterior	31.00	45.00
☐ Box. For powder. Forest scene. With cover	27.00	40.00
☐ Cordial Set. Blown glass in floral pattern	50.00	75.00
☐ Finger Bowl. Ornately hand-painted leaves	41.00	60.00
☐ Lamp. 12" high. Rich blue overpainting	62.00	90.00
☐ Mug. For coffee. With transparent handle	18.00	27.00
☐ Perfume Container. 7" high. Smoothly enameled	21.00	35.00
☐ Pitcher. For Water. Heavily decorated with flowers	61.00	90.00
☐ Sugar Jar. Woodland scene handpainted on exterior	64.00	95.00
☐ Tumbler. For water. Transparent with red overlay	23.00	35.00
☐ Vase. 12" high. Robins and flowers on exterior	37.00	55.00

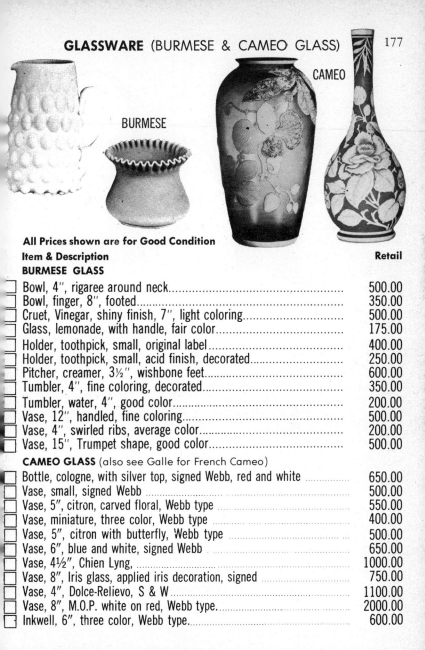

CAMEO

BURMESE

All Prices shown are for Good Condition

Item & Description	Retail

BURMESE GLASS

Bowl, 4", rigaree around neck	500.00
Bowl, finger, 8", footed	350.00
Cruet, Vinegar, shiny finish, 7", light coloring	500.00
Glass, lemonade, with handle, fair color	175.00
Holder, toothpick, small, original label	400.00
Holder, toothpick, small, acid finish, decorated	250.00
Pitcher, creamer, 3½", wishbone feet	600.00
Tumbler, 4", fine coloring, decorated	350.00
Tumbler, water, 4", good color	200.00
Vase, 12", handled, fine coloring	500.00
Vase, 4", swirled ribs, average color	200.00
Vase, 15", Trumpet shape, good color	500.00

CAMEO GLASS (also see Galle for French Cameo)

Bottle, cologne, with silver top, signed Webb, red and white	650.00
Vase, small, signed Webb	500.00
Vase, 5", citron, carved floral, Webb type	550.00
Vase, miniature, three color, Webb type	400.00
Vase, 5", citron with butterfly, Webb type	500.00
Vase, 6", blue and white, signed Webb	650.00
Vase, 4½", Chien Lyng,	1000.00
Vase, 8", Iris glass, applied iris decoration, signed	750.00
Vase, 4", Dolce-Relievo, S & W	1100.00
Vase, 8", M.O.P. white on red, Webb type.	2000.00
Inkwell, 6", three color, Webb type.	600.00

PITCHER

VASE

**All Prices shown are for Good Condition
and Fine Color**

Item & Description	*A.B.P.	Reta
Custard Glass:		
Bowl. Berry, Chrysanthemum	75.00	150.0
Bowl. Covered with floral panelling	100.00	175.0
Butter Dish. Winged scroll pattern	70.00	120.0
Celery Dish. Argonaut shell	90.00	120.0
Compote, Louis XV	65.00	90.0
Creamer and Sugar Bowl with cover, Argonaut	75.00	140.0
Cruet. Ornate scroll design	85.00	160.0
Pitcher, Water. Chrysanthemum Sprig. Fine gilt edge	100.00	180.0
Plate. 8″ diameter. Signed Northwood	30.00	45.0
Sauce Dish. Chrysanthemum	30.00	50.0
Spooner, Louis XV	35.00	55.0
Sugar Bowl. With Chrysanthemum Sprig. Signed	60.00	90.0
Sugar Shaker. Melon-ribbed	30.00	45.0
Toothpick or Match Holder. "Bee" pattern. Square	40.00	70.0
Tumbler. Chrysanthemum Sprig pattern. Gold overlay	25.00	45.0

*Average Buying Price

PITCHER

PITCHER

EPERGNE

All Prices shown are for

Cranberry Glass:	Good Condition and Fine Color	*A.B.P.	Retail
Basket. Metal handle and frame with hand-painted floral decor		50.00	75.00
Bottle. 8″ high. Narrow neck with crystal stopper		40.00	60.00
Bowl. 3″ deep. Beautiful deep color. Applied finish with rough rim		25.00	35.00
Bowl. 5½″ deep. Floral decorations		35.00	55.00
Box. With hinged top and miniature painting		20.00	40.00
Butter Dish. Enamelled flowers with crystal finial. Resilvered footed plate base		45.00	75.00
Castor. For pickles. With enamel floral decor and colorful foxes applied to frame		90.00	140.00
Creamer. 5¼″ high. Pontil flared cover		18.00	30.00
Creamer. 3″ high. Leaf top		25.00	40.00
Epergne. Lily shape, spiral decorated			200.00
Finger Bowl. Sculptured sides		20.00	35.00
Milk Container. 5″ high		60.00	80.00
Pitcher. Water. Floral decoration with clear handle		65.00	100.00
Pitcher. 6″ high. Tall, tapering neck with clear applied handle. Ornate white floral decorations		45.00	60.00
Pitcher. 4″ high. Clear handle with white overlay		20.00	40.00
Spanish Lace Rosebowl. 4″ high. Ornate decor		36.00	51.00
Syrup Container. Applied finish		45.00	65.00
Tumbler. With fluted sides		20.00	30.00
Vase. Floral designs		25.00	40.00
Vase. Scalloped design with wide neck		30.00	45.00

GLASSWARE (CARNIVAL GLASS)

WATER SET
Pitcher
Tumblers
$125.00

Item & Description All prices are for Good Condition	*A.B.P.	Retail

Carnival Glass:

	Item	*A.B.P.	Retail
1. ☐	Apple & Pear Banana Boat. 12½" long	12.00	17.00
2. ☐	Automobile Flower Holders. 7" high. For interior of touring cars. Pair	16.00	22.00
3. ☐	Bushel Basket. White glass. Marked N. Rests on four curved pedestal feet. Basketweave. Noticeable irridescence. Open handle	65.00	93.00
4. ☐	Berry Set. Leopard-shaped with bowl & dishes	58.00	83.00
5. ☐	Bowl. White glass. Rose Show	54.00	77.00
6. ☐	Bowl. 9" diameter. Chinese motif	25.00	35.00
7. ☐	Bowl. 9" diameter. Peacock at fountain. Hand-painted	43.00	61.00
8. ☐	Bowl. 9" diameter. Marigold. Painted clinging vines	14.00	20.00
9. ☐	Butter Dish. Birds on branches on exterior	33.00	47.00
10. ☐	Carnival Duck Powder Jar	12.00	17.00
11. ☐	Candlestick. 8½" high. Green glass with jeweled base	12.00	17.00
12. ☐	Candlesticks. Narrow stems, flat bases. Pair	26.00	37.00
13. ☐	Candy Dish. Lacy basketweave	8.00	11.00
14. ☐	Compote. 6½" x 4½". White opalescent	10.00	14.00
15. ☐	Compote. Amethyst Stippled Rays. Stemmed	15.00	21.00
16. ☐	Cracker Jar. Grape Cable. Coverless	33.00	47.00

FRUITS &
FLOWERS
BERRY BOWL . . .$65.00

SUGAR &
CREAMER
$45.00 ea.

GRAPE & CABLE
PUNCH BOWL . . . $165.00

	Item & Description All prices are for Good Condition	*A.B.P.	Retail
17. ☐	Creamer. 6" x 7". Peacock at Fountain with Battenburg Lace patterned base, Blue	32.00	45.00
18. ☐	Decanter. 1 ft. high. Orange thumbprint pattern	30.00	40.00
19. ☐	Dish. Colonial Marigold	7.00	10.00
20. ☐	Dish. 4½" Kittens' sauce container, Marigold	25.00	35.00
21. ☐	Goblet. Floral design	18.00	25.00
22. ☐	Mug. Orange Tree	9.00	12.00
23. ☐	Mug. Marsh scene. Overlayed purple	40.00	50.00
24. ☐	Nappie. Pansy. Quilted exterior	8.00	12.00
25. ☐	Nut Dish. Louisa ftd	17.00	22.00
26. ☐	Pitcher. Marigold Star Medallion, Marigold	10.00	15.00
27. ☐	Pitcher. Maple Leaf. Purple. With tumblers	70.00	100.00
28. ☐	Pitcher. Chirping birds on branch	45.00	60.00

*Average Buying Price — See Page 5

GLASSWARE (CUT GLASS)

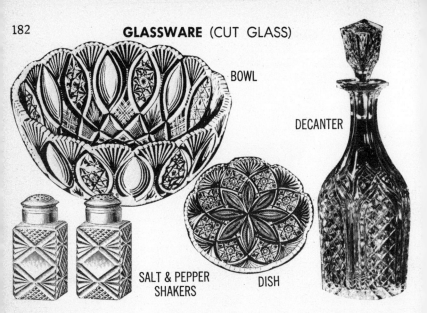

BOWL

DECANTER

SALT & PEPPER
SHAKERS

DISH

Cut Glass: Prices are for Good Condition	*A.B.P.	Retail
☐ Basket, Scrolls on sides, Pinwheel	75.00	125.00
☐ Basket. Floral pattern	60.00	90.00
☐ Bell. Glass deep all over cut	30.00	45.00
☐ Bowl. 10" high. Swirls of diamonds and cane-cut, large hobstar center, signed "Hawkes"	75.00	125.00
☐ Bowl. 8¼" high. Hobstars and diamonds with scrolled sterling rim	50.00	80.00
☐ Bowl. 8½" high. Hobstars and cane pattern	30.00	50.00
☐ Bowl. 8". Floral pattern	25.00	40.00
☐ Box. Cigarette, 3" x 7", Russian cut		100.00
☐ Butter Dish. Glass dome with floral cutting. 7"	55.00	85.00
☐ Bucket. For ice. Large Harvard-cut. 2 heavy handles	75.00	120.00
☐ Candlesticks, 10" pr. All over cut		175.00
☐ Celery Dish. 12" long oval, heavy cut		35.00
☐ Champagne Tankard. 11½". Blue cut to clear	125.00	200.00

*A.B.P. — Average Buying Price

Incising glass with an abrasive wheel became extremely popular in Europe during the late 1700's. The glass was forced against a revolving grinding wheel and slowly rotated to form the design. The Brilliant Period 1880-1914 produced pieces with heavy overall cutting and combination of motifs. True old cut glass is becoming extremely rare. European imports in imitation of old patterns are being sold today.

Item & Description — Prices are for Good Condition	*A.B.P.	Retail
☐ Cheese Dish. With cover, Hobstar design, 9"	95.00	160.00
☐ Creamer & Sugar. Pedestal bases	30.00	90.00
☐ Cruet. Pyramid-shaped. 7½" high. Diamond cut	30.00	50.00
☐ Decanter. 8" high. Harvard cut	30.00	60.00
☐ Dish. 8" diameter. Flat, light cut	20.00	45.00
☐ Finger Bowl and Plate. Rayed star pattern	15.00	35.00
☐ Goblet. Panel and prism-cut. 6"	40.00	50.00
☐ Goblets. 2 prism-cut goblets signed Hawkes, ea	30.00	70.00
☐ Goblet. Spiral pinwheel pattern	20.00	35.00
☐ Inkwell. 2" high with hinged sterling lid	15.00	25.00
☐ Lamp, Table. 18" Mushroom shade	320.00	500.00
☐ Mustard Container. Handled with hinged cover	12.00	20.00
☐ Muffineer. Sterling cone shaped with top	15.00	30.00
☐ Nappie. Deep cut, 7" diam	30.00	40.00
☐ Pitcher. Water. Hobstars and cross-hatchings	65.00	100.00
☐ Punchbowl. 12" high. Brazilian pattern. Signed	350.00	600.00
☐ Punchbowl. 14" high. On separate stand. Large hobstars, panels of diamonds and large fan swirls. Very ornate	220.00	750.00
☐ Salt & Pepper Shakers. 6" high. Pair	15.00	25.00
☐ Smelling Salts Bottle. 4" high. Cut ball stopper	15.00	20.00
☐ Toothpick Holder. Miter and diamond cut	18.00	25.00
☐ Tumbler, Water. All over cut	5.00	12.00
☐ Vase. Corset style. Banded on top with ribbed etchings	30.00	50.00

CUT VELVET GLASS

	*A.B.P.	Retail
☐ Vase, 11", Stick shape in Amethyst Diamond Quilting	123.00	185.00
☐ Vase, 9", Blue with ruffle top. DQ.	105.00	160.00
☐ Vase, 6", Butterscotch, ribbed	70.00	125.00
☐ Bowl, 7", ribbed, Tan colored	70.00	110.00
☐ Vase, 8", Carafe shaped, Blue satin, Diamond Quilted	100.00	160.00
☐ Vase, 8" double gourd, Green satin, Diamond Quilted	135.00	200.00

*Average Buying Price

American Glassware made by machine molding during the late twenties and thirties of this century. Especially characterized by the pastel shades of rose, sky blue, light apple green and similar shades all given a variety of named colors by their makers. The other feature usually to be found in the glassware is a pattern of some kind. Frequently it is pressed. Othertimes it is etched or a combination of both.

Made of non-lead glass it does not have the bell tone ring of earlier hand made glassware that disappeared from the market with soaring material and labor costs of the late twenties. The patterns are as varied as the manufacturers and their designers. Some patterns like English Hobnail are similar to the same patterns pressed in inexpensive glassware before the turn of the century. Like this earlier glassware, the most sought after pieces today are the colored ones. Some of the highest priced ones are in the less frequently used dark colors like Cobalt Blue and Amber.

PRICES ON DEPRESSION GLASS

Depression Glassware is found in more than a hundred different patterns and hundreds of different shapes and uses. With such great variety it would seem like an endless task to master the prices. Not so today. General rules can be followed with discretion. Most of the more common pieces in clear transparent crystal like plates, tumblers, saucers, tea cups, cereal bowls can be expected to range in price from *one to two dollars* per piece. Less common pieces like salad bowls, cake plates, and salt and pepper shakers can be found from *two to four or five dollars* in most shops and sales. Covered pieces like cookie jars, two piece covered butter dishes, pitchers and carafes will again be double the above prices ranging from around the *eight to ten to twelve dollar* range.

Colors generally speaking bring more than clear pieces. If a clear piece is *one dollar* the colored piece might well be *one fifty or even two dollars.* Some of the exceptions are a few patterns produced in the darker colors. Because of low production originally and high demand at present some of these may be as much as *five or more dollars.* Since the market for this new popular collectible has not yet stabilized the prices mentioned above might be considered safe. As collecting levels off sometime in the future, high priced specialties will appear. Some of the over pricing that will probably occur will result in some later decreasing price.

MAKERS MARKS ON DEPRESSION GLASS

LIBBEY GLASS CORPORATION   A. H. HEISEY GLASS COMPANY   IMPERIAL GLASS CORPORATION   CORNING GLASS WORKS

ANCHOR HOCKING GLASS COMPANY   THE FEDERAL GLASS COMPANY   WESTMORELAND GLASS COMPANY

DEPRESSION

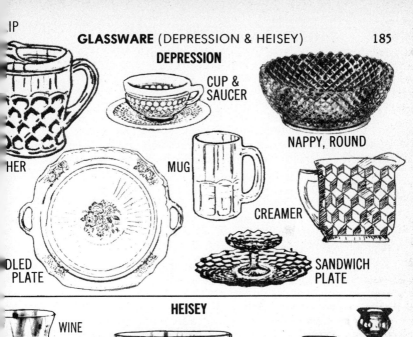

.IP

CUP & SAUCER

NAPPY, ROUND

HER

MUG

CREAMER

DLED PLATE

SANDWICH PLATE

HEISEY

WINE

BOWL

CANDLESTICKS

CUSTARD

DECANTER

PITCHER

FOOTED ICE TEA

The A. H. Heisey & Company made glassware of all types from it's found in 1895 to it's closing in 1956. Pressed, pattern, etched, cut, colored, engraved glass was produced, in popular forms such as Bowls, Dis Pitchers, Candlesticks, Goblets, Baskets, Salts, Tumblers, Ash Trays, Cru etc. Also humorous animal figures of all types in crystal glass. Most of He glass of this period is marked with the distinctive "H" in the diamond outl This gives assurance to the collector that he has authentic pieces.

In 1958 the Imperial Glass Company of Bellaire, Ohio, acquired the orig Heisey patterns, trademarks, molds, and tools. Imperial has reissued a n ber of pieces. These reproductions are marked with the symbol "IG", as as the Heisey "H" in the diamond. The reissues are very attractive and themselves collectible, but should never be bought as original Heisey. Bew of ground off "IG" hallmark.

Prices are still relatively reasonable for many types and patterns of glassw Baskets are scarce and will range from **twenty** to **forty dollars**. Plain cry bowls may be found as low as **three dollars** but the larger and better examp will be as much as **forty dollars**. Candlesticks from **ten** to **fifty dollars** a p with ornate candelabra going **over a hundred**. Plates and other ordin pieces of tableware will bring from **two dollars** to perhaps **six**. But the c ered pieces as in most other makes will be **at least double**, ranging up **twelve** to **fifteen dollars**. The same applies to pitchers. Tumblers are pri from **two** to **five dollars** and goblets will usually be **about double** this. O more the better the grade, the lower the production, and the use of color hand finishing the higher the price range. The clear simple, utilitarian pie in plain or simple patterns will be at the lower end of the scale.

1895-1956   *After 1958*

1906-1956

*The Original Heisey
Logo & Hallmark*   *The Combination
Heisey & Imperial Glass
Hallmarks.*

This glass was derived and named for the fact that glassblowers would n the contents of the glass pots after work was through and use the remain-material to blow glass objects of their own design and fancy. End-of-Day ss comes in many forms and each item is as different as the craftsman who e it. It is also known as Spatterware. Popular in the 1880's, Spatterware is made today.

JAR

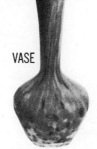

VASE

VASE

Item & Description: All Prices are for Good Condition	*A.B.P.	Retail
Barber Bottle with red & white spots	33.00	50.00
Basket, 8", w/white lining, thorn handle	35.00	60.00
Boot. Multi-colored glass variations	45.00	70.00
Bowl, 10" spatter coloring, pleated top	50.00	75.00
Candlesticks. Matched pair, random splotches	37.00	60.00
Carafe with Tumbler, red, white & yellow	35.00	55.00
Jar, 6" covered, brown coloring	58.00	85.00
Lamp. Sculptured. Highly colored	37.00	60.00
Perfume Bottle	24.00	35.00
Pitcher. White, red and blue satin finish	73.00	120.00
Pitcher. Water, 8" multi-color spatter on blue	56.00	85.00
Syrup Jug. Pewter top	45.00	70.00
Shoe, miniature 3", high type, good color spatter	12.00	20.00
Tumbler. Yellow and blue	18.00	75.00
VASES:		
5-1/4" high, elongated spots	27.00	35.00
7-1/2" high, reds, yellows and amber	58.00	75.00
10-1/2" bottle shape, blues & purples, signed	96.00	150.00

B.P. — Average Buying Price

GLASSWARE
(GALLE, HONESDALE & KEW BLAS)

HONESDALE

KEW BLAS

GALLE

All Prices shown are for Good Condition and Fine Color

Re

GALLE GLASS

☐ Bowl, 10", diam. Scenic design		27!
☐ Goblet, 8", blue, floral, Galle		27!
☐ Vase, 5½", browns and gold floral, Galle		12!
☐ Vase, 12", barrel shaped scenic with mountains, Galle		35(
☐ Vase, 10", scenic with mountain goats, Galle		55(
☐ Vase, 10", grape cluster design, Galle		15(
☐ Vase, 16", stick vase, grape and berry decoration, Galle		17!
☐ Vase, 16", floral design in three colors, Galle		20(
☐ Tumbler, 4", water, forest scenes, Galle		14(

HONESDALE GLASS

☐ Bowl, 8 diam. heavy cameo design in green scrolls		16(
☐ Goblet, 7", embossed gold border, gold design, Heisey blank		3!
☐ Vase, 9", bulbous, green cameo scrolls, gold decoration		18(
☐ Vase, 7", flared top, yellow cameo mums outlined in gold		16(
☐ Vase, 4", yellow cameo scrolls, on iridescent crystal		25(
☐ Vase, 12", acid finish with white enamel scrolls, green beads		25(
☐ Vase, 10", cameo yellow crystal outlined in gold		17!

KEW BLAS GLASS

☐ Tumbler, 4", gold with feather decoration		20(
☐ Compote, 4", low footed, gold iridescent, signed		32(
☐ Vase, 8", cylindrical calcite and gold with feather design, signed		22!
☐ Vase, 8", dark blue iridescent, white looped decoration, signed		40(
☐ Compote, 6", gold iridescent, unsigned		20(
☐ Candlestick, 9", calcite and gold with green feather, unsigned		15(

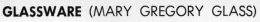

GLASSWARE (MARY GREGORY GLASS)

WINE CONTAINER

PITCHER

VASE

Item & Description — All prices are for Good Condition	*A.B.P.	Retail
Mary Gregory Glass:		
Ale Mug. Figure of girl hand-painted	23.00	35.00
Barber Bottle. Pale green with white enamel decorations and hand-painted figure of young boy on side	33.00	50.00
Box. Powder. 4″ high with cream and red decorations	33.00	50.00
Inkwell. 1¼″ sq. Swirl pattern	8.00	12.00
Kerosene Lamps. Ca. 1880. Covered squat bowls. Pair	100.00	150.00
Pitcher. Water. 8″ high. Clear with white enamelled overlay	38.00	60.00
Pitcher. Cream. 6½″ high. Light green with curved handle	29.00	45.00
Plaque. 10″ high. Young girl in woodland scene	70.00	110.00
Stein. 15″ high. Pale amber glass with tall lid of burnished pewter. Hand-painted figure of girl	75.00	115.00
Sugar Bowl. Cream colored with figure of girl	14.00	25.00
Tumbler. Water. 4″ high. Cream and amber enamelling	14.00	25.00
Vase. 8″ high. Green with rigaree and enamel decorations	60.00	100.00
Vase. 5¼″ high. Cobalt blue. Hand-painted white figure	23.00	35.00
Vases. 5½″ Deep, rich green. With figures of small boy and girl hand-painted on enamelled sides. The pair	61.00	100.00
Wine Container. Sculptured, rounded bowl with narrow neck and cut stopper. Thumbprint pattern	58.00	85.00

.B.P.—Average Buying Price see pg. 5

GLASSWARE
(LIBBY, LOETZ, LUTZ GLASS & MILLEFIORE)

All Prices shown are for Good Condition

Item & Description	Re
LIBBY GLASS	
Vase, 12" corset shaped, amethyst overlay cut to clear, signed	22!
Basket, 7", cut glass with florals and geometrics, signed	18(
Vase, 10", Amberina Jack-in-the-Pulpit, signed Libbey	27!
Vase, 16", Loving cup with two handles, footed, signed	40(
Bowl, 2½", cream colored satin, decorated, signed.	42!
Tazza, 6", crystal and shades of blue, signed.	36(
Candlestick, 6", crystal stem, red feather top, signed, pair	34(
LOETZ GLASS	
Vase, 8", bronze iridescent, pedestal base	6(
Vase, 10", fine iridescence with heavy silver overlay	19(
Basket, brides, red with enamel decoration, silver holder	20(
Candlestick, 10", red and green fern decoration, pair	8(
Epergne, four green trumpet lillies and small baskets	20(
Vase, 8", green iridescent	75
Vase, 12", dark and light blue iridescent,	35(
Vase, 6", blue iridescent pinched sides	22(
Vase, 7", feather design, signed Loetz	19(
LUTZ GLASS	
Set, washbowl and pitcher, Wheeling type, some documentation	550
Jar, 14", covered, applied decoration, footed, attrib. Lutz	800
Vase, 12", white and applied bosses, filigree handles	260
Bowl, finger and plate, red and white filigree striping	65
Tumbler, water, 4", twisted blue and white threading	110
Cup and saucer, 4" filigree white and light blue	125
MILLEFIORE GLASS	
Vase, 8", double handled on lavender background (Venetian)	40
Lamp, 7", miniature with dome shade and base in millefiore	120
Tumbler, 4", overall millefiore in blues and greens	85
Paperweight, 3", crowned allover design, modern	15
Vase, 10", urn shaped, excellent regular pattern	125
Cruet, 5", complete millefiore including handle and stopper	170
Vase, unusual dragonfly design with netting, signed.	375
Pitcher, cream, 4", scattered millefiore on white ground.	220
Vase, 8", double handle laid millefiore in rows.	175
Vase, 8", random millefiore on blue background.	320

GLASSWARE (OVERLAY GLASS)

LIBBEY

LOETZ

LUTZ TYPE

MILLEFIORE

OVERLAY

All Prices shown are for Good Condition and Fine Color

Item & Description	Retail
OVERLAY GLASS	
Vase, 11", Wheeling type glass, floral overlay applied decoration	125.00
Vase, 8", cased blue over white, applied clear decoration	75.00
Vase, 12", red over white, applied leaves and flowers	85.00
Basket, 12", white and shaded red, amber feet, amber decoration	175.00
Jar, covered, 14", elaborate decor., attributed to Sand.	250.00
Vase, 10", rose inside, white outside with amber overlay	100.00
Vase, 7", signed Steven & Williams, amber.	350.00
Vase, 9½", shaded rose, pine cone overlay.	290.00
Vase, 11", strawberry overlay.	275.00
Basket, 9", shaded blue, red and yellow flowers overlaid	225.00
Bowl, 12", centerpiece, rose and white, elaborate overlay	300.00

GLASSWARE (MILK GLASS)

BOWL & COVER

CRIMPED BOWL

BOWL

CAKE PLATE

CANDY JAR

ROSE BOWL

Item & Description Prices are for Good Condition	*A.B.P.	Retail
Milk Glass:		
☐ Atlas Compote. White glass with scalloped edge. Flaked.	44.00	70.0
☐ Bowl. 7" high. Openwork finish	11.00	18.0
☐ Bread Tray. Basketweave pattern. Signed and dated	21.00	35.0
☐ Cake Plate. Footed with openwork edge	13.00	20.0
☐ Cake Plate. Opaque finish	11.00	16.0
☐ Dog Dish. With cover	22.00	35.0
☐ Dog Dish. Rich blue with cover. Unmarked Vallerystahl	14.00	25.0
☐ Egg Cup. Blackberry coloring	11.00	15.0
☐ Fish Figurine. Sculptured	5.00	10.0
☐ Goblet. tapered base	11.00	18.0
☐ Hen Figurine. White with blue head, sculptured feathers	13.00	20.0
☐ Lion. Sculptured mane	12.00	20.0
☐ Lamp. Painted pastoral scene with wide metal base	10.00	18.0
☐ Platter. Hand-painted scene of retriever with bird	54.00	90.0
☐ Sugar Bowl. Marked 1870. Excellent condition	12.00	20.0
☐ Vase. 9" high. Dark brown with yellow and white. Floral design on exterior	16.00	25.0
☐ Vase. Hobnail with ruffled edge. Tall	21.00	35.0

_INE

BACCARAT

ONYX

GEOMETRIC

	*A.B.P.	Retail
Onyx Glass (Findlay):		
Bowl, crimped top, silver	185.00	300.00
Cream Pitcher. Silver	140.00	275.00
Cream Pitcher. Cinnamon and white	240.00	400.00
Tumbler. Cream color, silver inlay	130.00	225.00
Tumbler. Raspberry, white flowers	550.00	900.00
Opaline Glass:		
Basket. With hen, gold trim	26.00	50.00
Dish. Ruffled with strawberry design	12.50	25.00
Finger Bowl. Threaded with ruffled top. Light blue	18.00	30.00
Lustres 17" high. Tall brass feet, cut-glass prisms. Pair	120.00	200.00
Marriage Basket. Green and white.	19.00	40.00
Syrup Container. Tapered neck, squat body	16.00	30.00
Tumblers. 6½" high. Threaded Vaseline color. Pair	20.00	30.00
Vase. 8" high. Pink ribbed with tapering body	21.00	35.00
Paperweights: BACCARAT		
Snake. Green with brown markings on rockwood ground	2000.00	3000.00
Spoked-wheel. Shows cogs within wheel mechanism	350.00	600.00
Spray of Flowers. Includes a very rare burgundy-red flower with two rows of heart-shaped petals beside a pansy with 2 purple petals and three yellow-petals		
Above surrounded by clematis flowers with red centers	1500.00	2500.00
Virgin of Lourdes. Statue of famous religious figure	100.00	175.00
GEOMETRIC		
Blue and white with sharp enamelled decorations	110.00	160.00
Green with yellow enamelled decorations	90.00	150.00
Rose-colored with ten sides. Sharply chiseled	95.00	160.00
Turquoise Blue. Twelve-sided	120.00	175.00

A.B.P. — Average Buying Price

RUBINA

SILVER
DEPOSIT

VERRE DE SOIE

**All Prices shown are for Good Condition
and Fine Color**

Item & Description

Re

RUBINA GLASS

- Bowl, 7″, scalloped top and fine gold enamel designs 100
- Bowl, 8″, good color and shading, fine enamel designs in gold 100
- Candlesticks, 9″, pair, deep cranberry to clear, twisted design.... 125
- Carafe, water, 8″, cranberry to clear, see color illustration.......... 65
- Pitcher, 9″, water, thumbprint design, typical colors.................. 140
- Tumbler, water, 4″, gradual, shading, good color...................... 25
- Tumbler, water, 4″, deep cranberry to clear, enamel decoration...... 35
- Tumbler, water, 4″, panelled and good colors................................. 30
- Vase, 8″, good shading, with applied crystal leaves........................ 95

SILVER DEPOSIT GLASS

- Bottle, cologne, 4″, silver and monogram on crystal 45
- Vase, 6″, scrolls in silver on green glass 100
- Pitcher, 6″, heavy silver with cupid on crystal,.................. 185
- Bottle, dresser, 5″, silver on green Verre de Soie, signed Alvin 225

VERRE DE SOIE GLASS

- Decanter, 8″, white iridescent with matching stopper 175
- Candlestick, 10″, twisted stem, signed F. Carder, pr........................ 200
- Vase, 12″, stemmed flower form, green VDS, signed F. Carder........ 250
- Compote, 6″, covered fruit finial, unsigned 150
- Sherbet, with plate signed F. Carder 120
- Vase, 8″, intaglio cut floral design, unsigned 120

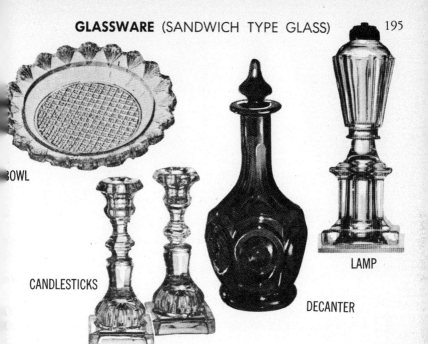

BOWL

CANDLESTICKS

DECANTER

LAMP

Item & Description All prices are for Good Condition	*A.B.P.	Retail
Sandwich Type Glass		
Bowl. 6¼" diameter. Floral design with fancy lacing	45.00	75.00
Bowl. Industrial mixing. Ruffled edge, uneven finish	20.00	35.00
Candlesticks. Tapered bases with highly fluted columns. Pr.	90.00	150.00
Candlesticks. Sculptured column, wide base, pr.	70.00	120.00
Dish. 11" diameter. Colored feathers forming pattern	65.00	125.00
Lamp. 9" high. Burnished amber finish	175.00	250.00
Plate. 7" diameter. Large and flat	35.00	60.00
Plate. With ornate floral designs and leafy borders	60.00	100.00
Salt Container. Lavender in royal pattern	70.00	125.00
Sugar Bowl. Ornate floral designs. With cover	45.00	80.00
Tray. 7" across. Hand-painted decorations on border	25.00	50.00
Vase. Bright yellow. Widely flared neck. Heavy base	55.00	100.00

*Average Buying Price

ROSALINE

AURENE

VERRE
DE SOIE

Steuben Glass 1903-1933   **All prices are for Good Condition**   Retai

ROSALINE:

1. ☐ Bowl. Shrimp. 14". Alabaster footed. Inset glass compartment for crushed ice. Signed by Carder................ 900.0
2. ☐ Vase. 10½" high. Amphora-shaped with white alabaster handles. Signed with fleur de lis 300.00
3. ☐ Vase. 10" high. Flared sides. ACB design.................... 275.00

VERRE DE SOIE:

4. ☐ Bottle. Cologne. Melon ribbed, with rich ruby stopper 75.00
5. ☐ Bottle. Perfume. 7½" high. With feet and tear-shaped stopper 100.00
6. ☐ Candlestick. 10" high. Twisted stem. Signed. Pair........ 200.00
7. ☐ Pitcher. Silver collar, rose petal stopper...................... 175.00
AURENE:
8. ☐ Decanter. 8" high. Gold iridescent with stopper, Aurene 200.0
9. ☐ Sherbet. With plate signed "F. Carder", Calcite............ 135.00
10. ☐ Vase. 12" high. High stemmed flowers. Signed, Blue .. 275.00
11. ☐ Vase. 11½" high. With 7" gold iridescence swirl bowl 160.00
12. ☐ Vase. 8" high. Intaglio-cut flowers. Peacock blue........ 375.00

COLORED GLASS:

13. ☐ Bottle. Perfume or cologne. Ruby red with stopper 95.00
14. ☐ Bowl. 7½" high. Ivory. Excellent condition 300.00
15. ☐ Bowl. 9" high. Heavy ribbing. Signed "Steuben", Gold Ruby 175.00
16. ☐ Candlesticks. 4" high. Sharp tear-drop crystal. Signed. 120.00
17. ☐ Goblet. Wine. 5" high. Stem crystal. Signed 35.00
18. ☐ Vase. 9½" high. Rich green crystal. Signed "Steuben" 160.00

Item & Description	All Prices shown are for Good Condition and Fine Color	Retail

Steuben Glass: 1903-1933

ACID-CUT BACKS:

] Compote. 8". Blue cut to alabaster...............................		350.00
] Vase. 12" high. Ivory cut to black. Signed "F. Carder"		1000.00
] Vase. 10" high. Green to alabaster. Signed............		400.00

AURENE:

] Bottle. For Perfume or cologne. Rich blue. Signed		220.00
] Bowl. 5" high. Rich blue Iridescence		275.00
] Centerpiece Dish. 10" diameter. Gold iridescent		175.00
] Vase. 12" Blue Aurene...		300.00
] Vase. Decorated Red Aurene. Signed Carder, 8"..........		2600.00

ACID
CUT
BACK

AURENE

CLUTHRA

DECORATED
AURENE

CLUTHRA:

] Lamp. 10½" high. Shaded		350.00
] Vase. Rose, alabaster handles...................................		400.00
] Vase. 10". Blue with curved handles. Signed		375.00
] Vase. 5". Canary yellow to off-cream color		325.00

JADES:

] Bottle. Perfume. 8" high. Green. Signed......................		125.00
] Cup, saucer and matching plate. Curved handle of alabaster on cup. The set		100.00
] Glass. Champagne. Alabaster stem and curved foot		80.00
] Vase. 14" high. Green with alabaster feet. Signed		200.00
] Vase. 6" high. Blue threaded pattern		175.00

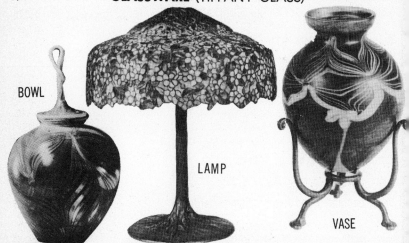

BOWL

LAMP

VASE

Item & Description Prices are for Good Condition	Retail
☐ Bottle. Cologne. 6" high. Rich blue iridescent. Signed	200.0
☐ Bottle. 6" high. Blue-green iridescent. With lily pads. Signed	500.0
☐ Bowl. Miniature. 2" high. Pastel rose. Signed	275.0
☐ Bowl. 3½" high. Blue iridescent. Good coloring	375.0
☐ Bowl. 6" high. Panelled sides. Gold and turquoise. Signed	250.0
☐ Candlesticks. 4" high. Mulberry and gleaming opal. White feet. Signed. "L.C.T.". The pair	850.00
☐ Candle Lamps. 10" high. Three piece shade. Tubular base. Brass attachments. Signed. The pair	450.00
☐ Centerpiece. Complete with floral design and flower holder	300.00
☐ Chalice. 11" high. Rich gold iridescent with green leaves. Variable pattern. Signed	600.00
☐ Champagne glass. Hollow stemware. Signed. "L.C.T."	120.00
☐ Compote. Rich gold. Signed	170.00
☐ Cordial Glass. 1½" high. Iridescent gold. Signed	85.00
☐ Decanter. 9" high. Dark brown agate. Vertical cream lines run length of piece. Signed "L.C.T."	600.00

Item & Description	Prices are for Good Condition	Retail
] Desk Calendar. Studio-type. Mounted bronze		40.00
] Dish. Heavy metal frame with four legs. Unsigned		100.00
] Dish. Salt. Iridescent gold. Signed		75.00
] Finger Bowl. With plate. Rich gold with fluted edges. Signed "L.C.T."		150.00
] Glass. Liqueur. 2" high. Pinched sides. Signed		125.00
] Goblet. 6" high. Gleaming pastel blue. Signed		250.00
] Lamp. 10" high. Candle-operated. Gold. Signed		250.00
] Lamp. Table. 11½" high. Mushroom-shaped. Signed		450.00
] Lamp. Table. 29" high. Jewelled with dragonflies. Signed. Excellent condition		4500.00
] Lamp. Table. Tulips. Signed "L. C. Tiffany"		2500.00
] Parfait. 5". Cream and lavender. Signed		220.00
] Pitcher. Water. Floral and intaglio design. Signed		350.00
] Plate. 6" high. Bird of Paradise design. Signed		750.00
] Salt Dish. Master. Fluted sides. Unsigned		100.00
] Shade. Lamp 4" high. Panelled and signed		50.00
] Shade. Lamp. 7" high. Panelled in gold and green		75.00
] Tumbler. 4" high. Gold iridescent. Pinched. Signed		100.00
] Tumbler. Signed "L.C.T.". Intaglio design		150.00
] Vase. 15½" Horn-shaped with large floral design in forest green and rich amber. Heavy base		1,200.00
] Vase. 14" high. Flower form with flat top. Signed		650.00
] Vase. 14" high. Cream and green cameo decor. Signed		2,000.00
] Vase. 13" high. Tulip-shaped. Patterned and signed		700.00
] Vase. 11" high. Cream iridescent. Millefiore pattern. With leaves and floral designs. Signed		1000.00
] Vase. 9½" high. Dark iridescent Cypriote. Signed. "L.C.T."		2000.00
] Vase. 5" high. Rich blue and glossy black iridescent. Signed		700.00
] Vase. 4" high. Ruby red iridescent. Silver decorated Signed		2500.00
] Vase. 4" high. Blue and black iridescent. Pinched and signed		600.00

GLASSWARE (SATIN GLASS)

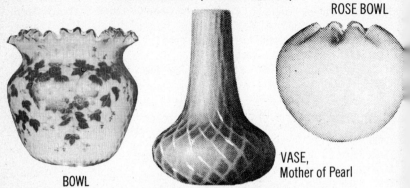

ROSE BOWL

VASE,
Mother of Pearl

BOWL

Item & Description All prices are for Good Condition Unless Otherwise Noted.	*A.B.P.	Reta
Satin Glass:		
☐ Bride's. Basket. 12". Blue to white, silver holder..........	180.00	250.0
☐ Bowl. Blue to silver finish with quilted design	160.00	225.0
☐ Bowl. Rose MOP...	60.00	175.0
☐ Bowl. Blue to white satin glass.................................	35.00	60.0
☐ Cracker Container. Rose-colored with quilted MOP	65.00	180.0
☐ Cruet. Shaded blue glass. Excellent............................	50.00	75.0
☐ Ewers. Decorated blue glass with camphor handle. Pair	100.00	160.0
☐ Finger Bowl. With plate and fluted sides.....................	80.00	100.0
☐ Lamp. Gone-With-The-Wind Type. Blown shaded rose glass...	110.00	175.0
☐ Lamp. High pedestal of rose satin MOP	375.00	475.0
☐ Pitcher. Applied camphor curved glass handle. Mother-Of-Pearl Finish. Flared neck. Rare....................	275.00	350.0
☐ Salt and Pepper Shakers. Enameled, hand-painted finish	45.00	70.0
☐ Shaker. Sugar. 7" high. Ribbed decorated, blue satin	50.00	75.0
☐ Shaker. Silver top. Of pink satin glass. Dated...............	25.00	65.0
☐ Tumbler. Water. 4" high. Blue MOP............................	18.00	75.0
☐ Tumbler. Water. 4" high. Rose satin glass....................	18.00	50.0
☐ Vase. 18" high. Iris decoration with rich blue finish......	100.00	160.0
☐ Vase. 8" high. Rainbow MOP, quilted..........................	40.00	500.0
☐ Vase. 6-1/2" high. Blue MOP..................................	120.00	175.0
☐ Vase. 5" high. Raindrop MOP..................................	110.00	160.0

*A.B.P.— **Average Buying Price see pg. 5**

ZARA "MEDIEVAL PALACE"*
Pre-World War II—Extremely Rare

ZARA "FAENZA"*
Pre-World War II—Extremely Rare

* Reproduced—1952

ZODIAC DECANTER
Majolica Specialties

ARDO OWL
Venetian Glass Figural

Courtesy Mr. Hans Schonewald & Luxardo Co.

For Listing & Prices
see page 246

Photo: Den of Antiquity, MacDougal Street, N. Y. C.

LADIES ANTIQUE JEWELRY

Page 203

For Listing & Prices
see page 247

Photo: Den of Antiquity, MacDougal Street, N. Y. C.

ANTIQUE WATCHES, FOBS, CHAINS, SEALS & PINS

Page 204

For Listing & Prices
see page 248

For Listing & Prices
see page 249

THE COLORFUL WORLD OF ANTIQUE WATCHES...

Onion Watch
One Hand Center Wind
Last Half of 17 Century
Very thick movement
$750.00

Very thin Gold
& Enamel Watch
Circa: 1830
$400.00

Book Watch
Silver Case
Late 17 Century
$1,500.00

Day-Date-Visible Balance
Sweep-Second, Gold Case
Circa: 1800
$550.00

E. Howard
Gold Box Case
Circa: 1865
$275.00

Photo: Mr. Barnys', 1145 2nd Ave., N. Y. C.

iss Gold set with
quoise & Rubies
ate 18 Century
$400.00

Enamel surrounded
with Pearls.
Circa: 1820
Silver Gilt—$550.00
Gold—$850.00

Clock-Watch
Late 18 Century
Gilt Brass—$600.00
Gold—$850.00

Gold & Enamel
Circa: 1790
$350.00

Gold W/Enamel
Late 18 Century
$400.00

COMIC & CARTOON CHARACTER TOYS (1920-40's)
For Complete Listing & Prices see pages 325-326

TOONERVILLE TROLLEY—TIN
German—1922   **75.00-100.00**

BUCK ROGERS ROCKET   **75.00-1(**
Louis Marx—ca. 1935

FELIX ON SCOOTER   **25.00-50.00**
Nifty Toys—ca. 1932

CHARLIE McCARTHY CAR   **2**
Louis Marx—ca. 1935

SUPERMAN "ROLL-OVER" TANK
Louis Marx—ca. 1939   **25.00-50.00**

AMOS & ANDY FRESH AIR TAXI
Louis Marx—ca. 1932   **75.00-10**

COMIC & CARTOON CHARACTER TOYS (1920-40's)
For Complete Listing & Prices see pages 325-326

CHARLIE CHAPLIN   **over 100.00**
German—1920

HAPPY HOOLIGAN   **25.00-50.00**
Chein—ca. 1928

MICKEY MOUSE DRUMMER
Nifty Toys—1932   **75.00-100.00**

HAROLD LLOYD   **over 100.00**
Louis Marx—ca. 1928

COURTESY: SECOND CHILDHOOD, 283 Bleeker St., N.Y.C. 10014

STEAMER LOCOMOTIVE
English Manufacture
Circa 1910 . . . $75.00-$125.00

With Working Steam Boiler

TRAIN SET—PULL TOY
Made by Pratt & Letchworth
Circa 1900 . . . $175.00

STEAM FIRE ENGINE
Made by Stevens & Brown
Clockwork Mechanism
Circa 1880
$250.00-$300.00

Prices are for Excellent Condition—Good Color

FIRE PATROL WAGON—CAST IRON
Made by Wilkens
circa 1900 . . . $225.00-$250.00

STEAM FIRE ENGINE—CAST IRON
Made by Carpenter
Circa 1880 . . . $225.00-$250.00

HOSE REEL WAGON
CAST IRON
Made by Wilkens
Circa 1880 . . . $250.00

Prices are for Excellent Condition — Good Color

TOYS — TIN, IRON, WOOD

For Complete Listing & Prices see pages 327-334

CAST IRON FIRE HOSE WAGON
Hubley Manufacturing Co. 1906

PUNCH & JUD
With music box

SCHÖNHUT TIGER
Wood, 1908

TIN TRACKLESS TRAIN
American made, Late 1800's

Courtesy of New York Historical Society, N. Y. C.

TOYS — TIN, IRON, WOOD
For Complete Listing & Prices see pages 327-334

CAST IRON HANSOM CAB
Hubley Man Co. 1906

BATTLESHIP "MAINE"
Cast iron pull toy

JACK-IN-THE-BOX
Late 1800's

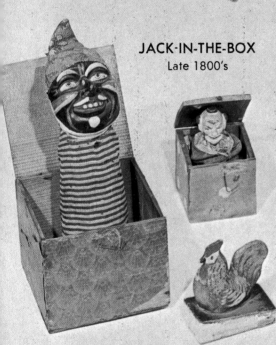

WOODEN CHICKEN
Squeeze toy with bellows

JENNY LIND DOLL
American, 1864

"AMERICA'S ANSWER TO THE
KAISER" — 1917 — 36" x 45"   60.00

"BOY SCOUTS LIBERTY BOND" —
1917 — 19" x 28"   50.00
By J.C. Leyendecker

"PRO PATRIA" — 1917   15.00
By Welsh — 26" x 40"

MOVIE POSTERS   30.00

"ON THE JOB"—1917—30" x 40" $30.00

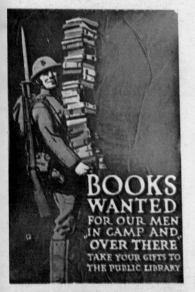

"BOOKS WANTED"—1917 $25.00
By C. B. Palls—25" x 38"

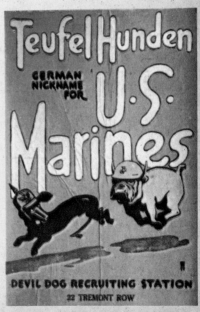

"U. S. MARINES"—1916 $25.00
18" x 27"

MECHANICAL BANKS

For Complete Listing and Prices see pages 16-21

OWL
#107......$50.00

LION AND MONKEYS
#86...............$150.00

TRICK PONY
#122............$150.00

TAMMANY (BOSS TWEED)
#145.....................$65.00

CABIN BA
#19......$50.

the early part of the Twentieth Century, manufacturers of candy created
ntainers in various interesting shapes, in order to create more sales for
eir product. Most were made of clear glass, however, they are also found
amber, red, blue, and milk glass.

s the name "candy containers" implies, they were used for holding candy
d were closed with a screw cap or metal strip to hold the candy in
later containers were closed with a cardboard strip). The candy containers
ere also used as toys and some of them had slotted openings so they could
used as a penny bank.

he condition of the candy containers as to original paint, original closing,
d completeness, determines the value of the container. Many of the early
ntainers were fully painted. Other containers were only partly painted. Any
rly container found in good original condition would be considered a
arce item. Since all containers were made of glass and very easily broken,
e collector should collect any duplicates also.

ome of the later containers are considered more scarce than others. This
epends on the number of the same type that is found in various collections.

eproductions are made.

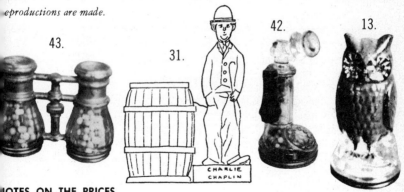

43.   31.   42.   13.

CHARLIE
CHAPLIN

IOTES ON THE PRICES

rices shown are for glass candy containers in good condition and complete with
losing.

Any early glass candy container found without the tin slide or cap closing should
cost about 10% less than the price shown.

Any later glass candy container found without the cardboard closing should cost
about 15% less than the price shown.

Any early or later glass candy container found with the original candy inside should
cost about $1.00 more than the price shown.

ourtesy: Mr. R. T. Matthews, Glenelg, Md. 21737 "Old Glass Candy Containers"

GLASS CANDY CONTAINERS

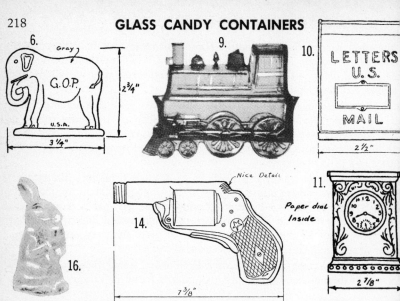

Item & Description Prices are for Good Condition:	*A.B.P.	Retail
1. ☐ Automobile. 4-1/2" long, open top (old-time)........	9.00	19.50
2. ☐ Baseball Player. Beside barrel (also a bank)..........	9.25	29.50
3. ☐ Battleship (modern)..	4.00	9.50
4. ☐ Dirigible. With name "Los Angeles"	9.00	18.50
5. ☐ Donkey. Pulling barrel-wagon with driver	9.50	20.50
6. ☐ Elephant. Republican Party symbol	9.50	19.50
7. ☐ Fire Engine. With metal wheels 5" long (old-time)	9.50	18.50
8. ☐ Liberty Bell of Philadelphia—clear glass	5.00	10.50
blue glass	8.00	15.00
9. ☐ Locomotive. 5" long. Clear Glass (two piece)........	9.00	17.00
10. ☐ Mailbox. 3-1/4" high...	9.00	17.50
11. ☐ Mantel Clock. 3-3/4" high..	7.00	14.50
12. ☐ Motorcycle. With sidecar & glass wheels	12.00	22.50
13. ☐ Owl. Sitting with Metal Screw Base	6.00	15.50
14. ☐ Pistol. Amber Glass	7.00	16.75
15. ☐ Pistol. With Metal Cap	4.00	8.00
16. ☐ Rabbit. With ears up. Clear Glass	4.00	9.75
17. ☐ Radio. With horn speaker	8.00	16.00
18. ☐ Santa Claus	7.50	17.50
19. ☐ Submarine. With Periscope (complete).................	15.00	28.50

Drawings by R. T. Matthews, Glenelg, Md. 21737

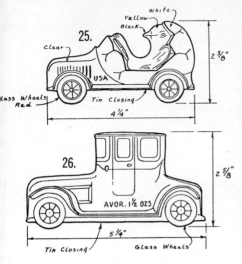

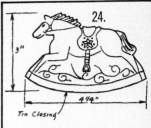

ROCKING HORSE

The rocking horse candy container is probably one of the finest designs ever made. The quality of the glass reminds one of the early type "Sandwich Glass".

	Item & Description Prices are for Good Condition:	*A.B.P.	Retail
20. ☐	Telephone. With wooden receiver 4½" high	5.00	12.00
21. ☐	Toonerville Trolley—painted.................................	15.00	30.00
22. ☐	Trumpet. Opaque Milk Glass	6.00	14.75
23. ☐	War Tank. 4" long (with man's head)	5.00	10.50
24. ☐	Rocking Horse	20.00	35.00
25. ☐	Baby Chick. In Shell Driving Auto	11.00	21.00
26. ☐	Auto. With Long Hood (old-time)	9.00	19.50
27. ☐	Greyhound Bus. With tin wheels........................	12.00	22.00
28. ☐	Duck. With Large Head	8.00	12.00
29. ☐	Running Rabbit. On Log	7.00	14.50
30. ☐	Spark Plug—painted...	12.00	22.50
31. ☐	Charlie Chaplin. Beside Barrel. 3-3/4" high..........	10.00	19.75
32. ☐	Revolver. Marked "Kolt"	9.00	18.50
33. ☐	Willys Jeep Auto	4.50	8.75
34. ☐	Auto. Station Wagon	4.50	8.75
35. ☐	World War I Tank—no chips.............................	10.00	21.50
36. ☐	Airplane. Marked "U. S. P-51"	4.00	8.00
37. ☐	Kewpie. Beside Barrel (also Bank)	12.00	24.50
38. ☐	Barney Google. Beside Barrel (also Bank)	14.00	24.50

*A.B.P.—Average Buying Price see pg. 5

Sketches by R. T. Matthews, Glenelg, Md. 21737

39.

KIDDIES DRINKING MUG

Opening Ribbed Outside

40.

THIS BOSTON KETTLE

Clear

Brown

Three Feet Stippled Base

41.

Red

PAPER SHADE

Red & Green Design

Metal Cap & Rod

Closing

Ribbed Inside

1½" dia

44.

1 5/8"

Glass Wheels

Cardboard Closing

45.

Glass Wheels

Cardboard Closing

46.

All prices are for Good Condition

Item & Description	A.B.P.	Retail
39. ☐ Kiddies Drinking Mug (with label)	5.00	12.50
40. ☐ Boston Kettle (with label)	4.50	11.75
41. ☐ Lamp With Decorated Paper Shade (complete)	14.00	26.50
42. ☐ Telephone With Dial on Base	3.75	8.50
43. ☐ Opera Glasses (all parts glass)	10.00	18.50
44. ☐ Auto. 4-1/2" long, Open Bottom (modern)	2.75	5.25
45. ☐ Fire Engine. 5", glass wheels (modern)	3.00	7.50
46. ☐ Miniature Baby Bottle, French Telephone, Lantern, and Hound Dog (all modern, 2"-3" high).	1.00	2.50 each

*A.B.P.— Average Buying Price see pg. 5

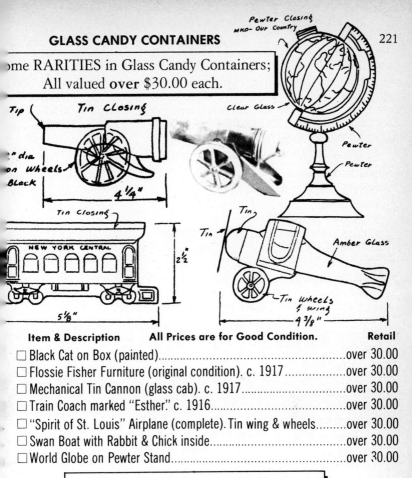

Some RARITIES in Glass Candy Containers;
All valued **over** $30.00 each.

Item & Description	All Prices are for Good Condition.	Retail
☐ Black Cat on Box (painted)		over 30.00
☐ Flossie Fisher Furniture (original condition). c. 1917		over 30.00
☐ Mechanical Tin Cannon (glass cab). c. 1917		over 30.00
☐ Train Coach marked "Esther." c. 1916		over 30.00
☐ "Spirit of St. Louis" Airplane (complete). Tin wing & wheels		over 30.00
☐ Swan Boat with Rabbit & Chick inside		over 30.00
☐ World Globe on Pewter Stand		over 30.00

· Some Helpful Notes For Collectors ·

...andy containers can still be found in out-of-the way shops, antique shows
...nd mostly at flea markets.

...Before you pay a big price for a container, make sure first, that the container
...s a scarce one. Do not *overpay* for a container that is plentiful.

...Unlike most antiques, it is possible for a *SCARCE* candy container that is
...hipped or partly broken to be a saleable item.

...n the candy container field, prices in California and surrounding areas have
...een slightly higher.

POST CARDS

Cards made for mailing purposes originated in the U.S. in the 1860's. Th
original use was primarily for business and advertising purposes. In 1898
change in the postal laws enabled the production of souvenir view cards. Po
cards were produced in the following types: **VIEWCARDS, GREETIN**
CARDS, COMICS, EXPOSITIONS, "ART" TYPES, NOVELTIE
ADVERTISING CARDS.

All prices are for Good Condition

Item & Description:	*A.B.P.	Ret
☐ Aircraft. Early (Pre World War I**)	.30	1.
☐ Angels flying	.05	
☐ Automobiles (until 1930's)	.30	
☐ Boats and other sailing vessels (Side Wheeler**)	.15	
☐ California. Early west	.15	
☐ Chickens and chicks—Bunnies	.06	
☐ Christmas (Kewpie Postcards—5.00 ea.)	.06	
☐ Detroit	.12	
☐ Disasters (Hurricanes, Floods, Fires) (San Francisco**)	.15	
☐ Easter birds—Easter crosses	.10	
☐ Embossed and airbrush type	.20	.4
☐ Expositions (19th Century)	.12	.6
☐ Fairs (1800-1899)	.12	.6
☐ Floral Designs (Bouquets, flower garlands, etc.)	.06	.1
☐ Flower Letters	.10	.2
☐ Gelatin	.20	.4
☐ Greetings, Birds—Children	.05	.1
☐ Hall Manufacturing Co. Holidays, July 4th, etc.	.15	.3
☐ Horseshoes	.10	.2
☐ Leather	.20	.4
☐ Newspaper comics, Mutt & Jeff, etc.	.30	.7
☐ Parades and floats before 1910	.20	.6
☐ Patriotic Theme. (Flags, Map of U. S. etc.)	.12	.6
☐ Presidents. Before Woodrow Wilson (1915)	.25	1.0
☐ Santa Claus. (Various designs)	.12	.5
☐ Saint Patrick	.12	.2
☐ Sunbonnet Baby	.75	1.5
☐ Thanksgiving (Pilgrims, Religious)	.06	.1
☐ Train Wrecks	.25	.6

*A.B.P. — Average Buying Price   **Double Price

PATRIOTIC

BOATS & SHIPS

SUNBONNET
BABIES

FLORAL

EXPOSITIONS
- FAIRS

COMIC - MUTT & JEFF

EARLY AIRPLANES

Pictures Courtesy N. Y. Historical Society-Landauer Collection

The original machine was patented by Thomas A. Edison in 1878. Before advent of electrically operated machines, millions of these spring wound driven phonographs were produced, in a great variety of models from the "Toy Graphophone" of 1898 that sold for $1.50, to the Edison Amb Model 75 with built in storage cabinets for holding dozens of cylinders. S of the more popular company names involved in production of phonogr: were: Edison, Columbia, Bettinni, Berliner, Victor (RCA Victor), P: Excelsior, National Gramophone, Murdoch, some of these companies are in existence.

*Courtesy: Mr. Walter Engel, Mr. Leslie Gould
AGC, 52 1st St., Hackensack, N. J. 07601*

"Toy Graphophone"

1.

**All prices shown are for
Very Good, Playable Condition**

Item & Description	*A.B.P.	Re
1. ☐ COLUMBIA "EAGLE" GRAPHOPHONE — 1898-1900 Model B. Plays 2 minute records. Nickel horn, key-wind	90.00	175
2. ☐ COLUMBIA GRAPHOPHONE — 1897 MODEL Q* Plays 2 minutes. Wax Cylinders. Metal Horn *Produced before Edison.	100.00	200.
3. ☐ COLUMBIA GRAPHOPHONE — 2nd Series 1898 Plays 2 minute records. Metal Horn Key Wind	70.00	130
4. ☐ EDISON CONSOLE — 1910-1916 Plays 15 records to each winding. Diamond Stylus	175.00	300.
5. ☐ EDISON FIRESIDE EDITION — Model "A" 1910-1914 Plays 2 minute Cylinders. Wooden Cygnet Horn. Diamond Stylus	100.00	200.
6. ☐ EDISON FIRESIDE PHONOGRAPH — 1906-1910 Plays 2 and 4 minute records. Wood base. Morning Glory Horn and Crane	135.00	235.

2.

3.

4.

5.

GRAMOPHONES — PHONOGRAPHS

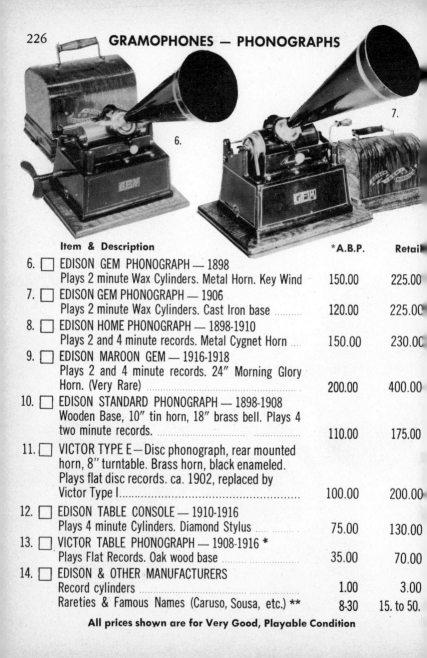

6.

7.

Item & Description	*A.B.P.	Retail
6. ☐ EDISON GEM PHONOGRAPH — 1898 Plays 2 minute Wax Cylinders. Metal Horn. Key Wind	150.00	225.00
7. ☐ EDISON GEM PHONOGRAPH — 1906 Plays 2 minute Wax Cylinders. Cast Iron base	120.00	225.00
8. ☐ EDISON HOME PHONOGRAPH — 1898-1910 Plays 2 and 4 minute records. Metal Cygnet Horn	150.00	230.00
9. ☐ EDISON MAROON GEM — 1916-1918 Plays 2 and 4 minute records. 24" Morning Glory Horn. (Very Rare)	200.00	400.00
10. ☐ EDISON STANDARD PHONOGRAPH — 1898-1908 Wooden Base, 10" tin horn, 18" brass bell. Plays 4 two minute records.	110.00	175.00
11. ☐ VICTOR TYPE E — Disc phonograph, rear mounted horn, 8" turntable. Brass horn, black enameled. Plays flat disc records. ca. 1902, replaced by Victor Type I	100.00	200.00
12. ☐ EDISON TABLE CONSOLE — 1910-1916 Plays 4 minute Cylinders. Diamond Stylus	75.00	130.00
13. ☐ VICTOR TABLE PHONOGRAPH — 1908-1916 * Plays Flat Records. Oak wood base	35.00	70.00
14. ☐ EDISON & OTHER MANUFACTURERS Record cylinders	1.00	3.00
Rareties & Famous Names (Caruso, Sousa, etc.) **	8-30	15. to 50.

All prices shown are for Very Good, Playable Condition

Pictures Courtesy Mr. Walter Engel

	Retail
With Outside Morning Glory Horn	250.00
Most Rare are Teddy Roosevelt Speeches (3)	ea. 50.00

INKWELLS — INKSTANDS

Containers for ink have been used for hundreds of years. Many of th
have been ornately decorated, proving that an object need not necessarily o
be functional when it can also be made quite attractive.

SILVER PLATE
& GLASS
$50.00

BRASS
& GLASS
$40.00

Item & Description: All prices are for Good Condition	*A.B.P.	Re
☐ Brass sea animal. 6½" high. Heavy cover	10.00	2i
☐ Brass. Head of deer. Glass insert container	8.25	1(
☐ Brass. Heavy solid brass	9.75	1!
☐ Bronze. Cat. Excellent coloring and condition	14.00	28
☐ China. Fruit and flowers	9.50	1!
☐ China. German forest scene	8.00	1(
☐ Cloisonne. Sculptured tray and well	16.00	3.
☐ Delft. Brass with ornate design	17.00	3!
☐ Glass. Admiral Dewey. Transparent cover	18.50	3;
☐ Glass. Large round top	7.50	1!
☐ Glass. With embossed silver top	6.50	12
☐ Glass. Swirled glass with identical lid & tray	8.00	16
☐ French Gold Plate. Horse with horseshoe base	9.00	18
☐ Iridescent. Green glass. Brass lid. 3½" high	12.50	25
☐ Iron. Crab. Black lacquered enamel	7.50	15
☐ Iron. Cast. Camel figure	9.50	19
☐ Milky glass. Double Dogs. Cast iron stand and base	31.25	62
☐ Porcelain. Flower and leaf design. Removable insert	20.00	40
☐ Pottery. Frog	5.50	11
☐ Pottery. Lion	12.50	25
☐ Racing Car. Driver and mechanic wearing goggles. Two inkwells under hood of vehicle	32.50	65
☐ Reindeer. With fawn and doe. Transparent well	8.25	17
☐ Rockingham. Bird in nest with eggs. Snake below	34.00	68
☐ Satin Glass. Blue hue swirl	34.50	70
☐ Staffordshire. Sculptured greyhound on base	15.00	31
☐ Staffordshire. Hinged type with alternating floral stripes	12.00	25
☐ Tiffany. Silver and copper interspersed with iridescent green glass	52.00	100

*A.B.P. — Average Buying Price

pricing of gadgets, tools, instruments and curios, depends on the merit of individual item and such factors as whether or not it is hand made; age, uty of decoration, and design and the fame or reputation of the maker, if : is known.

nanufactured broad axe of the mid or late 19th Century might sell for 15 20 dollars while a hand forged, decorated 17th Century axe of beautiful ign will sell for many times this amount. Prices herein are quoted to cover range of quality and condition.

the case of instruments, one made by a known 18th Century maker could for several hundred dollars, while an equally good instrument of unknown ;in might be bought for 85 to 90 dollars. We have, therefore, given a wide ge in this general pricing. **A fair offer for purchase by a dealer would be % to 50% of stated Retail value, for items in "Good" condition.**

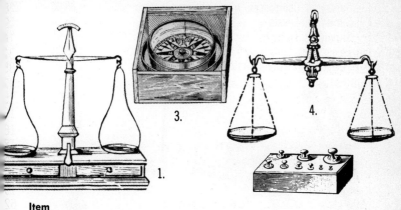

Item	RETAIL	
INSTRUMENTS (Nautical and Scientific)	From	To
☐ Apothecary Scales (with or without weights) used in drug stores	35.00	100.00
☐ Binnacles (Container Holding a Ships' Compass) usually brass	125.00	250.00
☐ Compasses, in case, on gimbals	50.00	100.00
☐ Gold Scales (with small weights)	35.00	100.00
☐ Guinea Scales (English Scale used to weigh gold coins)	35.00	60.00

urtesy of: Sydney Strange, Antiques for Men. 855 2nd Ave., N. Y. C. 10017

A fair offer for purchase by a dealer would be 35% to 50% of stated Retail va
for items in "Good" condition.

		From	RETAIL
6. ☐	Hydrometers, in case with Weights and Thermometer	35.00	5
7. ☐	Ivory or Boxwood Rules (used for measuring & drafting)	10.00	2
8. ☐	Microscopes	85.00	40
9. ☐	Octants (Hadley Quadrant) Ebony, in case (used for Ships' Navigation)	150.00	30(
10. ☐	Pocket Scales	15.00	5(
11. ☐	Sextants (brass, in case) late 19th to 20th Century	100.00	22!
12. ☐	Ship's Telegraph	175.00	25(
13. ☐	Slide Rules	35.00	12!
14. ☐	Sovereign Scales (English Scale used to weigh coins)	15.00	3(
15. ☐	Surveyors' Compasses, with sight bars in case	85.00	25(
16. ☐	Surveyors' Levels	85.00	25(
17. ☐	Surveyors' Transits	50.00	75(
18. ☐	Telescopes (Long Glass)	150.00	15(
19. ☐	Telescopes on Stand (Astronomical)	275.00	150(

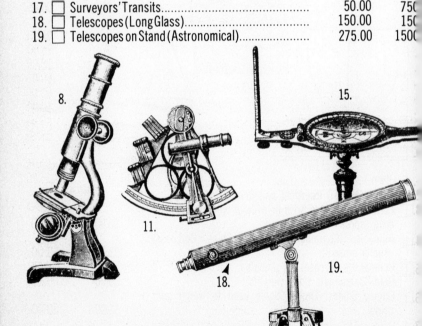

8.

15.

11.

18.

19.

fair offer for purchase by a dealer would be 35% to 50% of stated Retail value, for items in "Good" condition.

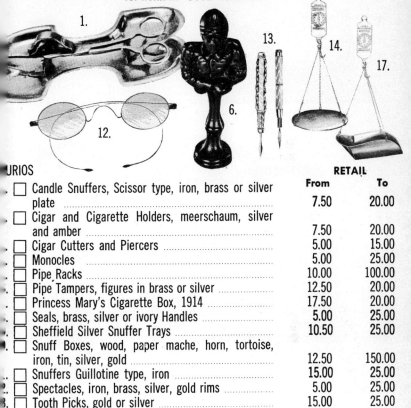

CURIOS

		RETAIL	
		From	**To**
□	Candle Snuffers, Scissor type, iron, brass or silver plate	7.50	20.00
□	Cigar and Cigarette Holders, meerschaum, silver and amber	7.50	20.00
□	Cigar Cutters and Piercers	5.00	15.00
□	Monocles	5.00	25.00
□	Pipe Racks	10.00	100.00
□	Pipe Tampers, figures in brass or silver	12.50	20.00
□	Princess Mary's Cigarette Box, 1914	17.50	20.00
□	Seals, brass, silver or ivory Handles	5.00	25.00
□	Sheffield Silver Snuffer Trays	10.50	25.00
□	Snuff Boxes, wood, paper mache, horn, tortoise, iron, tin, silver, gold	12.50	150.00
□	Snuffers Guillotine type, iron	15.00	25.00
□	Spectacles, iron, brass, silver, gold rims	5.00	25.00
□	Tooth Picks, gold or silver	15.00	25.00
	SCALES		
□	Circular Fish Scales, used in stores and markets for weighing fish	15.00	25.00
□	Letter Scales, Victorian, used to weigh letters for postal charges	25.00	40.00
□	Standing Tradesmen Scales (balance type), iron or brass, wood base, English or American	65.00	100.00
□	Store Scales (Brass Scoop), used in General Stores	20.00	50.00

A fair offer for purchase by a dealer would be 35% to 50% of stated Retail val
for items in "Good" condition.

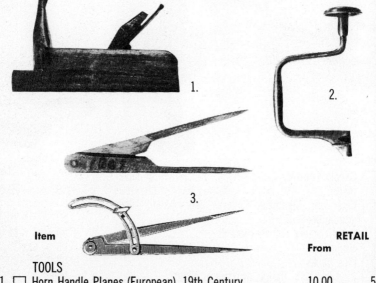

Item		RETAIL	
		From	T
TOOLS			
1. ☐	Horn Handle Planes (European), 19th Century	10.00	50.
2. ☐	Iron Bit Braces, manufactured, 19th Century, American or European	15.00	25.
3. ☐	Large Wood or Iron Dividers	35.00	100.
4. ☐	Mauls, (Heavy hammer w/wooden head) wood or burl, 19th Century	10.00	25.
5. ☐	Moulding Planes, mid 19th Century to late	4.00	10.
6. ☐	Primitive Wood Bit Braces, 17th-18th Century, American or European	45.00	125.
7. ☐	Smoothing Jack Jointer Planes, 19th Century	7.00	12.
8. ☐	Spokeshaves, 19th Century	7.50	15.
9. ☐	Sun Planes	40.00	65.
10. ☐	Unusually Shaped Screwdrivers, 18th-19th Century	10.00	20.
11. ☐	Wood Bit Braces, manufactured, 19th Century, American or European	15.00	30.
12. ☐	Wood and Brass Bit Braces, 19th Century	25.00	65.
13. ☐	Treadle operated Jig Saw on Cast Iron stand	50.00	100.

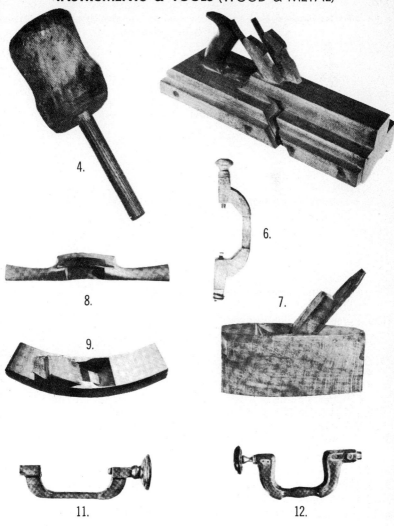

4.

6.

8.

9.

7.

11.   12.

A fair offer for purchase by a dealer would be 35% to 50% of stated Retail value, for items in "Good" condition.

Item	RETAIL	
	From	To
TOOLS		
19. ☐ Adjustable Plow Planes, 19th Century	25.00	40.00
20. ☐ American Broad Axe, 18th-19th Century, Hand Wrought	20.00	40.00
21. ☐ American Broad Axe, 19th Century, mid to late, manufactured	25.00	65.00
22. ☐ Blacksmiths' Tongs		
23. ☐ Bow Saws	20.00	35.00
24. ☐ Carpenters' or Shipwrights' adzes (Long Handle) 19th Century	25.00 25.00	75.00 50.00
25. ☐ Carriage Makers Planes	15.00	40.00
26. ☐ Compass Planes (Cooper's)	25.00	60.00
27. ☐ Coopers' Adzes, 19th Century	15.00	25.00
28. ☐ Coopers' Adzes, Early 17th-19th Century	25.00	50.00
29. ☐ Croze, and, or Howell, Plane for inside Barrel (used Coopers)	30.00	60.00
30. ☐ Drawknives, 19th Century	5.00	15.00
31. ☐ Early European Planes, 17th-18th Century, Decorated or Dated	40.00	150.00
32. ☐ Early Hammer Heads, 17th-18th Century	10.00	25.00
33. ☐ Ebony and Heavy Brass, reinforced Marples (bit brace), Sheffield, England	75.00	90.00
34. ☐ English Poleless Broad Axe, 18th Century, Hand Wrought	30.00	65.00
35. ☐ European Highly Decorated Iron Dividers, 17th-18th Century	75.00	150.00
36. ☐ Froes (Shingle Splitter)	12.00	20.00
37. ☐ German Goose Wing Broad Axe, 17th-18th Century, Hand Wrought, Decorated	125.00	250.00
38. ☐ German Goose Wing Broad Axe, Penn-Dutch or Mid Europe, 18th-19th Century, Hand Wrought	90.00	125.00
39. ☐ Hammers	5.00	10.00
40. ☐ Chamfer Knife used by Cooper for cutting staves	20.00	30.00

19.

20.

24.

25.

33.

30.

36.

Pictures Courtesy Shelburne Museum, Shelburne, Vermont

Courtesy of: Sydney Strange, Antiques for Men. 855 2nd Ave., N.Y.C. 10017

Medical equipment, kits, tools, glassware, etc., are much sought after today. These items have a special appeal to members of the medical professions.

All items listed here were used in actual medical practice.

Prices are for good condition.

BLEEDING KNIVES, FLEAMS OR PHLEBETOMES

Item	RETAIL From	To
SHOCKING COIL		
1. ☐ Hand Cranked	35.00	50.00
2. ☐ Battery Operated	20.00	30.00
BLEEDING KNIVES		
3. ☐ Fleams or Phlebetomes	25.00	40.00
4. ☐ Scarifiers and Spring loaded Fleams	50.00	100.00
5. ☐ Bleeding Cup, Blown Glass	8.00	16.00
6. ☐ Nursing Bottle, Blown Glass, has Glass Nipple, 19th Century	15.00	25.00
7. ☐ Breast Pump, Blown Glass, Early 19th Century	15.00	25.00

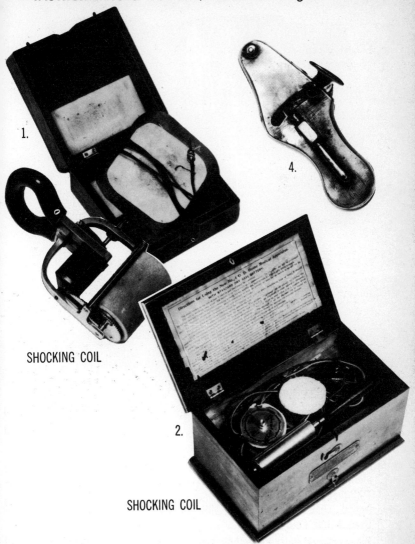

1.

4.

SHOCKING COIL

2.

SHOCKING COIL

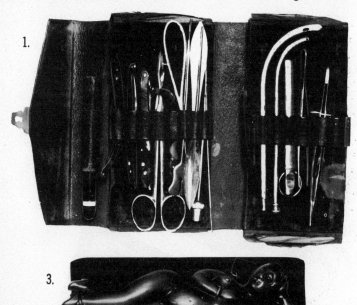

All items listed here were used in actual medical practice.
Prices are for good condition.

Item	RETAIL	
FIELD SURGICAL KITS	From	To
1. ☐ Early to Mid 19th Century	90.00	125.00
2. ☐ Wood Cased Fitted Surgical Kits 18th or Early 19th Century	150.00	500.00
3. ☐ Chinese Doctors Ivory Medical Doll	175.00	250.00
4. ☐ 19th Century Ophthalmoscopes	20.00	35.00
5. ☐ Dental Cabinet, Wood w/glass, 19th Century	35.00	65.00
6. ☐ Dentist Drill, Foot Driven	30.00	60.00
7. ☐ Wood or Wood and Ivory Stethoscope	50.00	90.00
8. ☐ Wooden stethoscope, made of Wood, or Wood and Ivory	40.00	100.00

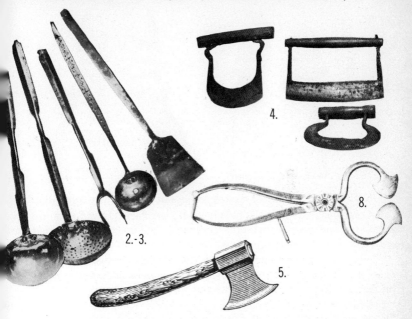

2.-3.

4.

8.

5.

fair offer for purchase by a dealer would be 35% to 50% of stated Retail value, for items in "Good" condition.

Item	RETAIL From	To
TOOLS (Kitchen)		
1. ☐ Butchers' Steels (Knive Sharpeners)	10.00	20.00
2. ☐ Ladles, Skimmers, Forks, 18th Century, Decorated iron or brass or copper Bowls	25.00	45.00
3. ☐ Ladels, Skimmers, Forks, Hand Wrought, 18th-19th Century	12.50	30.00
4. ☐ Meat Choppers, Hand Wrought, 18th-19th Century	5.00	15.00
5. ☐ Meat Cleavers, Hand Wrought	10.00	25.00
6. ☐ Meat Rockers	12.50	25.00
7. ☐ Roasting Jack (key, bracket and meat hanging wheel complete)	75.00	100.00
8. ☐ Sugar Cutters	20.00	35.00
9. ☐ Wall Match Safes, tin or cast iron	3.00	10.00

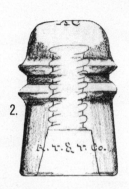
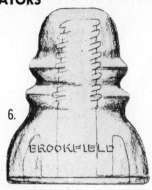

S. F. B. Morse, father of the telegraph, was also midwife to the insulator.

Companies making glass objects would use their leftover glass in variou colors (carnival, green, cobalt blue, dark amber and others) for making colore insulators. This material was known as "end of the day glass."

Like other glass pieces, the older the insulator, the more desirable an higher priced it is. A prime example is an old, non-thread, pin-hole insulator — this means it is over a 100 years old and valuable.

Often insulators on the same pole are different in both size and color The reason is that the telephone companies are using insulators in stock sinc they are planning on putting all telephone and telegraph lines underground

Pictures courtesy: "Stuart's Insulator Guide,"
P.O. Box 862, Gilbert, Arizona.

20.   22.

All Prices are for Excellent Condition

Item, Description & Size	Retail
1. ☐ Am. Tel. & Tel. Co., Green, Single Skirt—2⅜" x 3⅞"	2.00
2. ☐ Am. Tel. & Tel. Co., Aqua, Single Skirt—2½" x 3¾"	3.00
3. ☐ Armstrong's #5, Clear, Double Petticoat—3⅛" x 3¾"	2.00
4. ☐ Barclay, Aqua, Double Petticoat—3" x 4¼"	15.00
5. ☐ Brookfield, Green, Double Petticoat—3-3/16" x 3⅝"	3.00
6. ☐ Brookfield, Dk. Olive Green, Double Petticoat—3¾" x 4"	6.50
7. ☐ Cable, Aqua, Single Skirt—3¼" x 5¼"	13.00
8. ☐ California, Lt. Green, Double Petticoat—3¾" x 4"	3.00
9. ☐ Gayner, Green, Double Petticoat—3-3/16" x 3⅞"	8.00
10. ☐ H. G. Co., Amber, Double Petticoat—3¼" x 3¾"	10.00
11. ☐ Hemingray #9, Aqua, Single Skirt—2¼" x 3½"	3.00
12. ☐ Hemingray #10, Clear, Single Skirt—2⅝" x 3½"	3.00
13. ☐ Hemingray #16, Green, Single Skirt—2⅞" x 4"	3.00
14. ☐ Hemingray #19, Aqua, Double Petticoat—3¼" x 3"	3.00
15. ☐ Hemingray (Beehive), Green, Double Petticoat—3⅛" x 4⅜"	10.25
16. ☐ Lynchburg, Aqua, Single Skirt—2¼" x 3⅝"	3.00
17. ☐ Maydwell #9, Clear, Single Skirt—2¼" x 3½"	3.00
18. ☐ McLaughlin #9, Green, Single Skirt—2¼" x 3⅝"	3.00
19. ☐ Pyrex, Clear, Double Threads—2⅝" x 4"	4.00
20. ☐ STAR, Aqua, Single Skirt, Pony—2⅜" x 3½"	3.00
21. ☐ W.F.G. Co., Green, Single Skirt—2⅜" x 3⅝"	4.00
22. ☐ Whitall Tatum, #3, Aqua, Single Skirt—2⅜" x 3¼"	4.00

IRONWARE

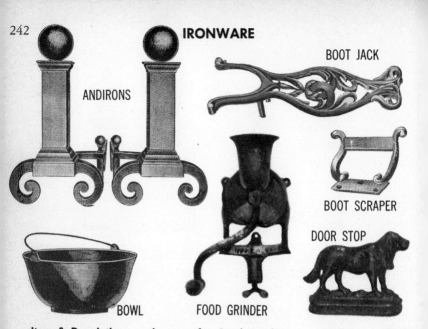

ANDIRONS

BOOT JACK

BOOT SCRAPER

DOOR STOP

BOWL

FOOD GRINDER

Item & Description: prices are for Good Condition	*A.B.P.	Retail
ANDIRONS:		
☐ 15" High. Carved Heads	15.00	30.00
☐ 14" High. Sculptured knobs. Pair	17.50	35.00
☐ 14" High. George Washington (Head of Washington) Pr.	30.00	60.00
☐ Bean Pot. (7" H. With cover	16.00	32.00
☐ Bread Peel. With rams head handle and curler	20.00	40.00
☐ Boot Jack. Foliate design	6.50	13.00
☐ Boot Scraper. Sculptured ends	6.00	12.00
☐ Bowl. Cast Iron. With wire handle	8.00	16.00
☐ Bullet Mold. 7" long. Early 19th century	25.00	50.00
☐ Calipers. 12" long. Double points	14.50	29.00
☐ Cane Sugar Hammer. 8" High	10.00	20.00
☐ Candle Snuffer. Scissors type. Marked "J.S.F." on handle	15.00	30.00
☐ Cannon. Navy model miniature	26.00	52.50
☐ Eagle. In diving position, wings out, 40 lbs	50.00	100.00
☐ Dolphin Figurines. Handsome lines. Pair	30.00	60.00
☐ Door Stop. Iron dog. 7-1/2" tall, 10" wide	4.75	9.50
☐ Flatiron Miniature	5.00	9.50
☐ Flatiron Figurine. Jockey with hat	7.00	14.00
☐ Food Grinders. Hand Crank. 14" High	11.00	22.00

*Average Buying Price

Item & Description:	*A.B.P.	Retail
FIREPLACE ITEMS:		
] Crane with arm..	35.00	70.00
] Kettle. 13" dia. x 8" deep with two handles.................	5.00	10.00
] Kettles. 12" diameter. Cast iron. Set of three................	10.00	20.00
] Pokers. Assorted shapes....................................	6.00	12.00
] Pokers. Shovel and tongs. Marked "King" on blade......	15.00	30.00
] Scale w/brass pan and 4 iron weights. 17" tall............	16.50	33.00
] Tongs and brush. Set.......................................	9.50	19.00
] Trammel. 24" long. Hooked with bolt & ring for kettle..	20.00	40.00
] Waffle Iron. Musical instruments adorn lid.................	11.00	22.00
] Waffle & pancake mold. Double handles & safety catch	13.00	26.00
] Foot Scraper. Attached to fluted dish........................	7.50	15.00
] Hand branding iron. For cattle marking. Letter "M" with circle and bar. Late 19th century.........................	25.00	50.00
] Harpoon. Whaling type with barbed iron head.............	25.00	50.00
] Hitching Post. 1880's.......................................	60.00	120.00
] Hand Cuffs. Old-style with chain joint, screw release....	15.00	30.00
] Ladle. Large, used for soup....................................	5.00	10.00

HITCHING POST

HAND CUFFS

FOOTSCRAPER

KETTLES

WAFFLE MAKER

HORSE & RIDER DOORSTOP

IRONWARE

All Prices Shown are for Good Condition:

Item & Description	*A.B.P.	Reta
IRONS:		
☐ Branding Iron. Reinforced handle. Marked "Dennison"	15.00	30.0
☐ Branding Iron. Leather wrapped handle. "Dawson"......	17.00	34.5
KETTLES:		
☐ Small...	5.00	10.0
☐ Medium...	7.50	15.0
☐ Large...	9.00	18.0
☐ Lamp. Iron ornate frame. With brackets......................	12.50	24.0
☐ Lamp. Hanging type..	15.00	30.0
☐ Lamp. Sconce type. Fluted columns............................	20.00	40.0
☐ Lantern. English bird cage. Opaque glass....................	16.00	32.0
MATCH HOLDERS:		
☐ Hanging with hinged cover. Late 1860's......................	6.00	12.0
☐ Table-type. With extensive hand decorations................	10.00	20.0
☐ Mortar & Pestle. Cast iron...	8.00	16.0
☐ Monkey Bank. Hanging from tree. Slot in base..............	10.00	20.0
☐ Pistol. Toy. Shoots corks...	7.00	14.0
☐ Pot. With cast iron curved feet.....................................	10.00	20.0
☐ Plate. For serving roasts..	5.00	10.0
☐ Plaque. General Grant with life dates...........................	40.00	80.0
☐ Skillet. Reinforced handle. 12" diameter.......................	8.00	16.0
☐ Sling swivels. From 19th century rifle...........................	4.00	7.0
☐ Spurs. From Civil War period.......................................	7.50	5.0
☐ Stove. Original pot belly. Cast iron with one lid............	30.00	60.0
☐ Stove. Pot-belly with set of five pans. Orig. condition....	50.00	100.0
TEA KETTLES:		
☐ Curved feet with cover...	7.50	15.0
☐ Flat covered with recessed base..................................	8.50	17.0
☐ Squat shape with curved handle. Dent in spout............	6.00	12.0
TRAPS:		
☐ Bear Trap. Drag hooks and chains................................	25.00	50.0
☐ Bobcat Trap. With interlocking teeth............................	11.00	22.0
☐ Fox Trap..	10.50	21.0
☐ Small game trap. Single spring action. With tether hooks	15.00	30.0
☐ Wolf Trap. Broken bar..	5.00	10.0
☐ Wolf Trap. Double-spring...	7.00	14.5
☐ Wolverine Trap. Marked "Sutter Inc." Ca. 1880. New Eng.	10.00	20.0

*A.B.P. — Average Buying Price

LAMP
FRAME

CHARCOAL
IRON

SADIRONS

GARDEN FURNITURE

SCALE

CIVIL
WAR
SPURS

LADIES ANTIQUE JEWELRY
See Page 202 for Color Picture

The Jewelry items listed below are for the pieces shown in full color
page 202. The prices quoted are current RETAIL PRICES. These prices a
to jewelry in good to fine condition. A dealer's offer of 25% to 40% of Sta
Retail Price, would be quite fair, for this type of jewelry, in good to fine conditi

	Item & Description	Re
1.	☐ Silver West Indian bangles	12
2.	☐ 18K Woven mesh flexible bracelet	125
3.	☐ Group Victorian 14K bracelets	ea. 30.00 to 6C
4.	☐ 14K hairpin	6
5.	☐ Star shape amethyst, and 18K pendant	120
6.	☐ Amethyst neacklace, heart shaped center 4 pearls on necklace chain	60
7.	☐ 18K turquoise and pearl locket, Victorian design, and gold chain	150
8.	☐ Hungarian silver pendant and chain. Pearls and semi-precious stones	125
9.	☐ 14K Art Nouveau locket, wave form design	24
10.	☐ Jade earrings, silver gilt setting	35
11.	☐ Stone cameo earrings. Fine carvings, classic head	60
12.	☐ 14K locket with pearls, Victorian motif, arrows & wreath	60
13.	☐ Seed pearl earrings, Spanish design	40
14.	☐ Florentine mosaic earrings, rectangular shape	40
15.	☐ Florentine mosaic pin, 18K oval setting	60
16.	☐ Set of coral carved earrings and pin, rose & leaf	46
17.	☐ Carved coral necklace, with carved head pendant	80.

Courtesy: Den of Antiquity. 106 MacDougal St., N.Y.C.

Prices quoted below are for jewelry shown in color picture.

RINGS—GEM STONES

		Retail
.	☐ Carved agate cameo............................	30.00
2.	☐ Genuine sapphire diamonds............................	150.00
3.	☐ Opal, rubies, pearls, and chips............................	60.00
4a.	☐ 1 Diamond, 2 pearls............................	60.00
b.	☐ 2 Diamonds, 2 pearls............................	100.00
c.	☐ 2 Diamonds, 3 pearls............................	200.00
.	☐ Lapis-Lazuli and pearls............................	60.00
6.	☐ Sapphires, pearls............................	30.00
7.	☐ Genuine ruby, and old mine diamonds............	160.00
8.	☐ Lapis-Lazuli and pearls............................	48.00
9.	☐ Turquoise with diamond center............................	80.00
0.	☐ Diamond cluster, old mine diamond center..........	80.00
1.	☐ Jade heart gold setting............................	70.00
2.	☐ Enamel and pearl beetle. Gold setting..............	200.00

PINS, PENDANTS, BRACELETS, EARRINGS

3.	☐ Enamel (Art Nouveau pendant), with gold chain (circa 1910)............	35.00
4.	☐ Florentine mosaic pendant with gold chain..........	60.00
5.	☐ Enamel and pearl pin with diamond (circa 1859)..	65.00
6.	☐ Enamel pin, Victorian star design (circa 1870-80)	25.00
7.	☐ Garnet pin (low carat) sunburst shape..............	60.00
8.	☐ Bracelet Victorian design no stones..............	45.00 to 60.00
9.	☐ Crescent pin, Art Nouveau............................	16.00
0.	☐ Pendant, star shape pearls with center diamond..	45.00
1.	☐ Jade earrings, 2 pearls, 12 diamonds..............	125.00
2.	☐ Slide, 2 pearls on enamel............................	15.00
3.	☐ Enamel portrait pin hand painted, gold setting......	45.00
4.	☐ Earrings with enamel hands, 2 pearls..............	250.00
5.	☐ Dragon fly pin. Open work gold with turquoise......	80.00
6.	☐ Cameo classic head, malachite background..........	80.00
7.	☐ Hollow dangle pin, Victorian design..............	26.00
8.	☐ Tiger tooth with gold fittings............................	30.00
9.	☐ Cameo—carved boy on dolphin, gold setting........	60.00
0.	☐ Hungarian silver pin, turquoise with garnets........	60.00
1.	☐ Small gold flower pin, pearls with center diamonds	30.00
2.	☐ Real beetle, petrified and set in filigree gold..........	45.00

(See Page 204 for Color Picture)

The Watches and Watch Jewelry items listed and priced below are for th
pieces shown in full color on page 204. The prices quoted are current RETAI
PRICES. These prices apply only to watches in good to fine condition in *goo*
working order, and to watch jewelry in good to fine condition.

	Item & Description	Retai
1a.	☐ Watch pin, brass and enamel..............................	6.0
	☐ As above in gold..	30.0
b.	☐ Ladies gold filled lapel watch, enamel back..........	40.0
2.	☐ Man's gold filled watch fob, with charm and attachment................................	12.0
	As above in gold..	40.00 to 60.0
3.	☐ Man's 18K gold key wind watch. Gold face with scene (circa 1830)......................	85.0
4.	☐ Georgian gold and Carnelian cut seal fob.............	40.00 to 80.0
5.	☐ Gold watch chain with garnets, lightweight...........	30.0
6.	☐ White gold Waldemar chain.................................	35.0
7.	☐ Ladies open face Waltham gold filled watch. Transition from lapel to wrist watch (circa 1912)..	30.0
8.	☐ Man's hunting case watch. Vacheron Constantine 18K (circa 1900)..............	200.0
9.	☐ Ladies heartshaped pearls and turquoise watch pin (hook behind). May be worn on pendant or as a watch pin..	60.0
10.	☐ Ladies 14K fleur-de-lis watch pin.......................	15.0
11.	☐ Men's 18K watch chain with baroque pearl pin attachment..	60.0
12a.	☐ Coin silver hunting case watch. Engraved cover....	50.0
b.	☐ Silver chain with silver charm............................	20.0
13.	☐ Ladies gold face "O" size watch.........................	140.0
14.	☐ Men's 18K hunting case key wind watch (ca. 1860)..	135.0
15.	☐ Ladies 14K, blue enamel face watch, (lapel or pendant)..	80.0
16.	☐ Men's 14K hunting case watch. Made by Elgin........	120.0
17.	☐ Man's 14K gold 15 minute chime repeater..............	300.0
18.	☐ Gold repeater (Chime watch telling time to 1 minute	450.00 to 2000.0

Courtesy: Den of Antiquity, 106 MacDougal St., N.Y.C.

Prices quoted below are for jewelry shown in color picture.

Retail

MEN'S GOLD RINGS — GENUINE STONES

1.	☐ Agate Cameo, classic face	100.00
2.	☐ Carnelian seal (18th Century)	180.00
3.	☐ 6 Rose diamonds in gold band	70.00
4.	☐ Victorian stone cameo, Cavalier head	75.00
5.	☐ Gold seal 14K	45.00
6.	☐ Russian Lapis-Lazuli incised Lion seal	60.00
7.	☐ Gold seal (elaborate) incised coat of arms	60.00
8.	☐ Persian seal on gem stone, gold inlay	60.00

MEN'S GOLD STICKPINS

9.	☐ Sword — Carved hilt and handle, enamel and gold	35.00
10.	☐ Sword & scabbard with pearls on handle & scabbard	45.00
11.	☐ Crystal with hand painted animal carving	24.00
12.	☐ Gold knot with diamond in center	15.00
13.	☐ Enamel flower with oriental pearls	35.00
14.	☐ Etruscan work with sapphire in recessed center	20.00
15.	☐ Enamel with pearls — Victorian design	24.00
16.	☐ Gold dog or other animal, 3 dimensional	20.00
17.	☐ Garnets, 3 leaf clover shape	15.00
18.	☐ Gold ladies leg with garter, 3 dimensional	15.00
19.	☐ Genuine pearls in acorn pin	35.00
20.	☐ Mosaic bug, gold setting	20.00

BAR PINS

21.	☐ Sculptured foxhead with ruby chip eyes	35.00
22.	☐ Riding crop and stirrup	35.00
23.	☐ Tie clip in gold, with horses head	20.00
24.	☐ Georgian watch seal	40.00
25.	☐ Watch fob (locket type). Brooklyn Bridge engraved on front	45.00
26.	☐ Cigar cutter, gold filled	18.00
27.	☐ Gold toothpick (retractible)	12.00

CUFF LINKS

28.	☐ Red enamel dragon in gold setting	75.00
29.	☐ Victorian designed front, gold	45.00
30.	☐ Blood stone, large round front	30.00
31.	☐ Gold with diamond chip, sculptured edges	18.00
32.	☐ Double agate with gold embossed inset	15.00
33.	☐ Double amethyst round stones, set in gold	45.00
34.	☐ Sterling silver match safe, mermaid & sea serpent	40.00

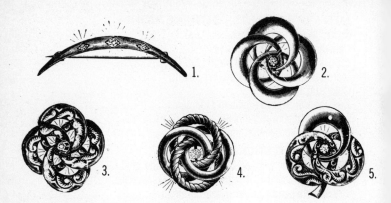

Brooches were made in a tremendous variety of designs and motifs. Floral, circular, curlecue, insect, star, and shell shapes are the most common. They were made in solid gold, rolled gold, silver, Onyx, crapestone, coral, and other materials. The gold pins were often studded with precious stones, such as diamonds, pearls, opals, and rubies. Semi-precious stones, such as rhinestone, cultured pearls, etc. were also used on the rolled gold and silver brooches.

Item & Description	*A.B.P.	Ret.
DIAMOND:		
1. ☐ Bow-shaped. Large diamond in center, two smaller diamond settings on either side	30.00	60.
2. ☐ Four Circle. Smooth gold cluster with center diamond	35.00	70.
3. ☐ Four Circle. Engraved gold cluster with diamond in center	35.00	67.0
4. ☐ Four Circle. Gold cluster; two circles of smooth gold finish, two circles of rope twisted gold finish. Diamond in center	35.00	68.0
5. ☐ Three Leaf Clover design. Top leaf of smooth gold, two side leaves ornately embossed. Diamond in center	35.00	72.0

*A.B.P. — Average Buying Price — See Page 5

6.
7.
8.
9.
10.
11.
12.
13.
14.

Item & Description	*A.B.P.	Retail
ROLLED GOLD PLATE:		
6. ☐ Bow-shaped. Openwork design. Large stone in center	5.00	12.00
7. ☐ Butterfly Figure. Elaborate detailing on wings and body	6.00	15.00
8. ☐ Circular Leaf design. Open center. Seven stones	3.00	8.00
9. ☐ Crisscross Figure Eights. Elaborately engraved. Stone in center	5.00	12.00
10. ☐ Eye-shaped design. Three stones	6.00	12.00
11. ☐ Fan-shaped design. Stone in center	3.50	9.50
12. ☐ Five Loop Bow design. Engraving on Loops. Five stones in center of loops. One larger stone set in center	4.50	10.00
13. ☐ Flower in center of Crescent. Stone constitutes Flowerbud	4.00	9.50
14. ☐ Flower-shaped pin with stem. Dark shaded gold in center. Stone in center	4.00	9.50

Item & Description	*A.B.P.	Re
SOLID GOLD:		
15. ☐ Double Heart. Elaborately embossed	10.00	19
16. ☐ Eight Leaves on circular pin with eight gold knobs between each leaf	10.00	19
17. ☐ Filigreed Leaf design. Ornately carved. Stone in center	11.00	30.
18. ☐ Heart-shaped. Elaborately embossed	8.00	16.
19. ☐ Intertwined Loops. Ornately engraved	11.00	30.
20. ☐ Intricate Openwork design on textured gold. Pearl in center	11.00	22.
21. ☐ Ivy Leaf. Heart-shaped	9.00	15.
22. ☐ Ivy Leaf Wreath design	9.00	26.
23. ☐ Ornately designed Openwork pattern. Diamond in center	11.00	35.

15.

16.

17.

18.

19.

2

21.

22.

23

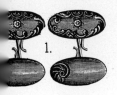
1.

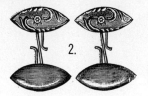
2.

3.

Item & Description	*A.B.P.	Retail
DIAMOND:		
☐ Comparable front and back Oval shape. Ornate scrollwork on front corner. Scrollwork on back. Textured 14 kt. Gold, with center diamond setting	16.00	32.00
☐ Eye-shaped front and back. Ornate designing on front with center diamond set in 14 kt. textured gold. Smooth gold finish on back	17.00	35.00
☐ Oval-shaped. Textured 14 kt. Gold. Dot trimmed edge. One small diamond in Star-engraved center	16.00	22.00

4.

4a.

5.

6.

GOLD FILLED FRONT:		
4. ☐ Circular-shaped. Ornately embossed design in shape of reverse halfmoon	3.00	6.00
4a.☐ Horseshoe-shaped. Head of Horse in center of engraved Horseshoe	4.00	8.00
5. ☐ Scalloped design. Pattern of Leaves and Flowers. Smooth, plain gold-filled finish	4.00	7.00
6. ☐ Square-shaped, embossed Fan design in lower left corner. Picture of Butterfly in upper right corner. Textured finish	3.00	6.00

7. 8. 9. 10. 11.

Item & Description	*A.B.P.	Ret
ROLLED GOLD PLATE:		
7. ☐ Circular-shaped. Five-Petal Flower design around edge. Center stone embedded in textured rolled-gold plate	4.00	8.5
8. ☐ Circular-shaped. Textured finish. Stone in center	3.00	6.0
9. ☐ Oval-shaped. Ornate embossing on left side. Stone setting to the right. Textured finish	3.00	6.0
10. ☐ Round-shaped. Engraving of Insect on Plant. Textured finish	3.00	7.0
11. ☐ Square-shaped. Ornate Flower and Leaf design around edge. Center stone. Textured finish	4.50	8.6

12. 13. 14.

SOLID GOLD:

12. ☐ Egg-shaped front and back. Ornate engraving on upper half of front link. Ornate engraving on lower half of back link	9.00	18.0
13. ☐ Rectangular-shaped face. Ornately engraved. Smaller rectangular shaped back link with some engraving	9.00	18.5
14. ☐ Smooth Finish. Round Face. Back link Oval-shaped with raised dotted design around edge	7.00	17.0

*A.B.P. — Average Buying Price — See Page 5

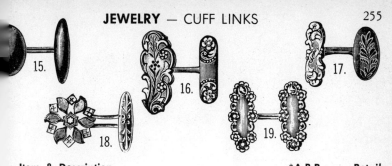

15.   16.   17.   18.   19.

Item & Description	*A.B.P.	Retail
SOLID SILVER:		
Egg-shaped front bob. Smooth textured Silver. Back link has elongated Oval shape	3.00	6.50
Elaborate Leaf-shaped front link, ornately embossed. Back, Oval-shaped and smaller than front. Flower embossed on upper and lower half of link	4.00	8.50
Figure Eight-shaped. Ornately carved front. Back, Egg-shaped. Line textured silver, with Leaf pattern	3.00	6.00
Filigree Diamond Leaf pattern. Back link elongated. Oval-shaped. Engraved design	3.00	6.00
Oval-shaped. Flowerbud pattern around outer edge. Front link slightly smaller with same designing on line textured silver	4.50	9.00

JEWELRY — CUFF OR BABY PINS

1.   2.   3.   4.

Item & Description	*A.B.P.	Retail
SOLID GOLD:		
Oblong-shaped. Flower design on either side of the word "PET"	2.80	5.75
Oblong-shaped. Smooth finish. 14 kt. Gold	3.00	6.00
Ornately engraved with floral pattern	3.50	7.00
Rectangular-shaped. Wheat design on one side	3.00	6.00
Very slim Pin with Rosebud. Stone in center of bud	3.00	6.00

.P. — Average Buying Price — See Page 5

Item & Description	*A.B.P.	R
GOLD PLATE: (PIERCED EAR)		
1. ☐ Flowerbud design. Tiny screw bob	3.00	
2. ☐ Crescent design on textured finish. Semi-precious stone hangs from top of Crescent	4.00	1
3. ☐ Heart-shaped. Acorn and Leaf engraving	3.00	
4. ☐ Horseshoe design. Round bob in lower center of Horseshoe. Semi-precious stone hangs from top of Horseshoe	3.50	
5. ☐ Twisted Intertwined Rope Loops	3.00	
SOLID GOLD:		
6. ☐ Bird in Flight. Pearl in each wing. Semi-precious stone in Bird's mouth	11.00	3
7. ☐ Embossed Leaf design on Three Leaf Clover. Stone in center. Tiny hanging knobs	9.50	1
8. ☐ Intertwined Loop. Pearl setting in center	10.00	1
9. ☐ Pearl in 14 kt. Gold setting. Screw-type bob	10.00	1
10. ☐ Pinwheel design. Small stone in center. Screw-type bob	10.50	2
11. ☐ Round-shaped. Textured 14 kt. Gold. Leaf engraved on Flat face. Tiny hanging gold knobs	9.00	1
12. ☐ Six Point Star. Six tiny pearls. Semi-precious stone in center	11.00	2
13. ☐ Solid Round Ball of 14 kt. gold	9.00	1
14. ☐ Three Leaf Clover design. Small stone in center	11.00	2

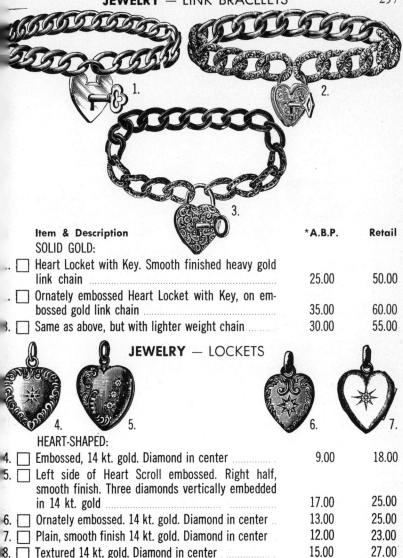

1.
2.
3.

Item & Description	*A.B.P.	Retail
SOLID GOLD:		
☐ Heart Locket with Key. Smooth finished heavy gold link chain	25.00	50.00
☐ Ornately embossed Heart Locket with Key, on embossed gold link chain	35.00	60.00
☐ Same as above, but with lighter weight chain	30.00	55.00

JEWELRY — LOCKETS

4.   5.
6.   7.

	*A.B.P.	Retail
HEART-SHAPED:		
4. ☐ Embossed, 14 kt. gold. Diamond in center	9.00	18.00
5. ☐ Left side of Heart Scroll embossed. Right half, smooth finish. Three diamonds vertically embedded in 14 kt. gold	17.00	25.00
6. ☐ Ornately embossed. 14 kt. gold. Diamond in center	13.00	25.00
7. ☐ Plain, smooth finish 14 kt. gold. Diamond in center	12.00	23.00
8. ☐ Textured 14 kt. gold. Diamond in center	15.00	27.00

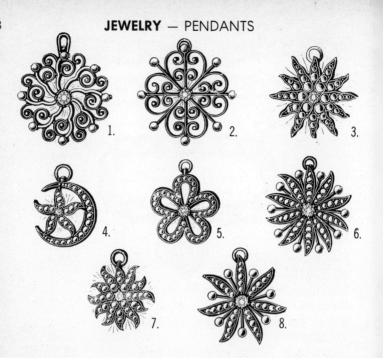

PENDANTS

The pendant was worn on a chain (usually gold) around the neck. The star and its' variations was the most popular motif. Crescents, cloverleafs, circles, curlecues, and wreathes. Silver and gold designs were decorated with diamonds and pearls, and sometimes with other precious stones. The same design was often made as a brooche with a clasp back.

WATCH CHARMS

These watch charms were worn hanging from watch chains during the "gay 90's" (and before and after). The most popular shapes were square, round, rectangular, and heart shape. The most popular motifs were stars, crescents, horseshoes (and horses), clover leafs, and large initials. Most charms were hinged, enabling the wearer to carry small photos of loved ones. The watch charms were usually made of gold, embedded with diamonds.

DIAMOND & PEARL:

		A.B.P.	Retail
☐	Filigree, ornately carved. Eight pearls. Large diamond in center	32.00	70.00
☐	Filigree. Eight Pearls. Diamond center	32.00	65.00
☐	Graduated Pearls in 12 Point Star Fish mount. Diamond in center	37.50	74.00
☐	Crescent with Starfish. Pearl studded. Diamond in center	32.00	65.00
☐	Cluster. Pearl studded. Diamond in center	32.00	70.00
☐	Large 10 Petal Flower shape. Petals are studded with Pearls, Large Diamond in center	38.50	76.00
☐	Pearl studded. 12 Point Starfish-shaped. Diamond setting	37.00	72.00
☐	Seven Petal Flower-shaped. Pearl studded. Pearl at the ends of seven spikes which are placed between each petal. Diamond in center	32.00	65.00

JEWELRY — WATCH CHARMS

9. 10. 11. 12.

Item & Description	*A.B.P.	Retail
GOLD WATCH CHARMS:		
9. ☐ Diamond-shaped. Textured gold. Center diamond setting	20.00	40.00
10. ☐ Round-shaped. Diamond mounted in center of textured gold	20.00	35.00
11. ☐ Round-shaped with Crescent in which are embedded three small diamonds; larger diamond centered in crescent. Textured finish	25.00	50.00
12. ☐ Square-shaped with four small diamonds set diagonally across textured 14 kt. gold	20.00	35.00

1.   2.   3.   8.   1:

Item & Description	*A.B.P.	Re
SOLID GOLD: (CAMEOS)		
1. ☐ Classic Face framed by reverse "S" design around outer edge. Design on either side of flat 14 kt. gold band	24.00	50.
2. ☐ Classic Face on smooth rounded gold band	23.00	35.
3. ☐ Large Square-shaped 14 kt. gold. Classic face design	25.00	55.
SOLID GOLD: (PEARLS & SEMI-PRECIOUS STONES)		
4. ☐ Cluster of four small Pearls and three semi-precious stones. Designing on either side of 14 kt. gold band	19.00	37.
5. ☐ Eight simulated pearls surround a smooth semi-precious stone. 14 kt. gold band	19.00	38.
6. ☐ Engraved 14 kt. gold band. Two Semi-precious stones on either side of Pearl	14.00	24.
7. ☐ Large Semi-precious center stone. Two smaller stones vertically set. Four Pearls; Two on either side of center stone	18.50	40.
8. ☐ Oval-shaped. Semi-precious stone surrounded by eight small pearls. Smooth 14 kt. band	18.00	35.
9. ☐ Smooth 14 kt. gold band. Two Pearls with center, semi-precious stone. Vertical setting	14.00	25.0
10. ☐ Star-shaped setting of six small pearls. Oval-shaped semi-precious stone in center. Smooth 14 kt. gold band	16.50	33.5
11. ☐ Two Semi-precious stones on left and right side of pearl. Smooth 14 kt. gold band	14.00	25.0
12. ☐ Two Semi-precious stones. Pearls set on top and bottom of stones. Smooth 14 kt. gold band	14.00	26.0

*A.B.P. — **Average Buying Price** — See Page 5

Item & Description	*A.B.P.	Retail
SOLID GOLD WITH PEARLS:		
☐ Bird with semi-precious stone in its' mouth. Two Pearls in each wing	13.00	29.00
☐ Bunny Rabbit sitting upright, holding Pearl to its' mouth	12.00	26.50
☐ Figure of Bat with outspread wings. Intricately carved	11.50	21.00
☐ Figure of Fish. Solid gold	10.50	20.00
☐ Figure of Fish with Pearl in open mouth. Four graduated Pearls in tail	14.00	26.50
☐ Figure of Fly with three small Pearls in each wing	12.00	27.50
☐ Frog with Semi-precious stone for body	12.00	28.00
☐ Lance with ornately engraved hilt. Pearl setting in center	9.50	21.00
☐ Saber Hilt has Crescent design. Six small graduated Pearls in Crescent	14.00	26.50
☐ Saber. Ornately engraved hilt. Two Pearls	13.00	25.00
☐ Saber with ornately engraved hilt	9.50	21.00
☐ Two Owls perched on Halfmoon. Seven tiny Pearls embedded in halfmoon	12.50	26.50
☐ Walking Cane encircled with Wreath. Six small Pearls in handle of cane	13.50	25.50

A.B.P. — Average Buying Price

LANTERNS

All prices shown are for Good-Working Condition.

	Item & Description	*A.B.P.	Ret
1. ☐	Auto lamp. Oil burning. Solid brass	25.00	45.0
2. ☐	Candle. 12" H. Tin with pierced gallery	20.00	40.0
3. ☐	Candle. 15" H. Three glass sides	27.50	55.0
4. ☐	Candle. 4-1/2" H. Brass saucer with chimney. Pat. 1873	10.00	20.0
5. ☐	Dietz Driving Lamp. For automobile	17.50	35.0
6. ☐	Magic Lamp. Three optical viewers, 19 colored slides.	29.00	60.0
7. ☐	Magic Lamp. "Venus E. M. & Co., U.S.A." stamped on side. Complete with 48 slides of the Spanish American War. Excellent and original	40.00	80.0
8. ☐	Magic Lamp. In box complete with transparent slides..	22.50	45.0
9. ☐	Ship's Lanterns. Brass. Set for use with batteries	35.00	70.0
10. ☐	Street Post Lanterns	70.00	140.0
11. ☐	U.S. Kerosene-type	18.00	36.0

*A.B.P.—Average Buying Price see pg. 5

LAMPS, ELECTRIC

263

5.   4.   13.   11.

Item & Description All prices are for Good Condition	*A.B.P.	Retail
☐ Aladdin Lamp. 14" H. Curved handles & polished base	25.00	50.00
☐ Amethyst Lamp. Cut clear glass globe with painted decorations	31.50	63.00
☐ Dual Study Lamp. 21" H. Burnished, polished brass withwith heavy base and clear bowls	45.00	90.00
☐ Egyptian-type Handel lamp. 30" high. Heavy bronze base and multi-colored art glass shade. Rare	60.00	120.00
☐ Floor Lamp. Large fringed fabric shade with hand-painted figures in sylvan scene. Raised and culptured base	100.00	214.00
☐ Floor Lamp. Heavy overlays on shade	46.00	92.50
☐ Gone-with-the-Wind Lamp. 26-1/2" high. Smooth rosy finish with matching high glass shade	60.00	120.00
☐ Hanging Hall Lamp. Metal frame with swag and chain. Egg-shaped globe	50.00	100.00
☐ Hanging Bristol-type Lamp. 13-1/2" high. Weights and elongated shade	37.50	75.00
☐ Hanging Lamp. Ball shade with emvossed floral decorations	85.00	170.00
☐ Monument Lamp. Boston & Sandwich Glass Company. Heavy overlay white engraved over deep rosy cranberry. With matching stem & original solid marble base	125.00	250.00
☐ Peg Lamp. Mounted on flint pedestal base	75.00	150.00
☐ Student Reading Lamp. Solid brass base with rounded shade. Excellent condition	82.50	140.00
☐ Tiffany Lamp. Mottled with green and yellow shade	250.00	400.00
☐ Tiffany Lamp. Signed bronze base and translucent glass shade	345.00	510.00

*Average Buying Price

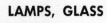

Item & Description All prices are for Good Condition	*A.B.P.	Retail
1. ☐ Chandelier-type Coal Lamp. 16" high. Sculptured bowl with glass pendants suspended from sides. Heavy metal re-inforced base....................................	48.00	79.0
2. ☐ Coal Lamp. 11-1/4" high. Sandwich glass with curved bowl..	40.00	60.0
3. ☐ Convex Reflector Lamp. Triangular-shaped lamp with metal reflector back. Convex backing. Burns either coal oil or kerosene. Metal handle. Very rare...............	92.00	155.5
4. ☐ Desk Lamp. 12" high. Rounded Satin glass bowl with taper stem. Brass feet...................................	35.00	52.5
5. ☐ English Street Lamp. 15" high. Four-paneled box-type lamp. Sturdy hardwood stand with cross members......	147.00	262.5
6. ☐ Footed Lamp. 13" high. Satin glass with ornate embossing surrounding metal base with 4 balled feet..	30.00	51.5
7. ☐ Hanging Lamp. With two matching opaque glass globes. Furled glass pendants and brass linked balance swag. Excellent condition. Late 19th century. Accepts oil or kerosene.....................................	300.00	415.0
8. ☐ Milk Glass Hand Lamp. 17" high. Cream-colored with floral decorations under opaque glass....................	38.00	60.0
9. ☐ Pair of Flint Glass Lamps. Pewter covers and elongated bowls. In excellent condition............................	115.00	186.5

*A.B.P.— Average Buying Price see pg. 5

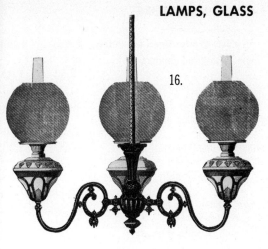

16.

18.

Item & Description	All prices are for Good Condition	*A.B.P.	Retail
10. ☐ Revere Lamp. 17" high. Reproduction of original oil burning lantern. Three glass sides. Ventilated top with handle.		80.00	126.75
11. ☐ Sculptured Lamp. 16" high. Coal burner with two angels playing at base. Oil container sculptured with cherub heads.		60.00	110.00
12. ☐ Sculptured Lamp. 11" high. Sandwich glass "Star" pattern. Hexagonal base with flat balled feet.		70.00	105.50
13. ☐ Suspended Reading Lamp. 26" high. Brass lamp fixture on metal stand. Rounded, serrated base. Adjustable stem.		50.00	88.00
14. ☐ Table Lamp. 22" high. Hand-painted scenic design on shade.		90.00	150.00
15. ☐ Tom Thumb Lamp. Cone-shaped brass lamp with hinged, removable cover and wick. With curved metal handle.		54.00	105.00
16. ☐ Triple Tier Coal Suspension Lamps. 38-1/2" high. Victorian metalwork branching to three oblong bowls and oil reservoirs.		80.00	125.00
17. ☐ Triple Light Lamp. Ornate shade with rich blue overlay. Base and shade signed.		375.00	500.00
18. ☐ Whale Oil Lamp. Cone-shaped with structural bowl.		20.00	32.50

*Average Buying Price

Item & Description All prices are for Good Condition	A.B.P.	Retail
1. ☐ Brass Saucer. 4-1/2" high. Sculptured chimney. Marked "1873"	8.50	15.00
2. ☐ Cosmos Lamp. 8" high. Multi-colored floral decorations	65.00	89.50
3. ☐ Golden Eagle. Orange body with gold and yellow trim....	36.00	62.75
4. ☐ Milk Glass. 8-1/2" high. Blue enamelled lillies in cream ground	100.00	135.00
5. ☐ Signed Tiffany acorn shade lamp and base	244.00	395.00
6. ☐ Pressed Clear Glass Hand Lamp. 5-3/4" high. Variant pattern. Scalloped shade base with nutmeg burning cylinder	92.00	137.50
7. ☐ Green Glass. 9-1/2" high. Chimney top. Pedestaled with fluted stem and embossed font	37.50	50.00
8. ☐ Brass Banquet Lamp. 10" high. Amethyst shade. Jewels on base. Glass. White and blue wildflowers and tendrils in relief	95.00	125.00
9. ☐ Mary Gregory Lamp. Chimney and base of ornate cranberry glass. Girl in woodland scene on base	95.00	140.00
10. ☐ Glass. Mount Washington and landscape in relief. Rich blue overlay	80.00	110.00
11. ☐ Cobalt Glass. 7-1/2" high. Chimney top with cover and handle	18.50	30.00
12. ☐ Elephant Lamp. Ivory-colored porcelain base. Matching beige and yellow shade. Burns nutmeg from cylinder mounted at top	46.00	78.75
13. ☐ Brass Skating Lamp. 8" H. Complete w/long link chain	30.00	55.50
14. ☐ Amethyst. Embossed base and slim, tapered chimney..	28.00	47.50
15. ☐ Bristol-type. Decorative figures on sides. Hexagonal base	40.00	68.00
16. ☐ Blue Glass. 4-1/2" H. Grimm's fairy tales hand-painted....	37.50	50.00
17. ☐ Milk Glass. 5-1/2" high. Chimney top. Fluted stem and footed base	24.50	43.00
18. ☐ Amberina Lamp. 7" high. Tinted glass with brass furnishings	50.00	86.00

3.

9.

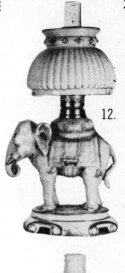

12.

19.

20.

Item & Description All Prices are for Good Condition	*A.B.P.	Retail
19. ☐ Burmese-type Lamp. White enamelled fruit and flowers decorations. Beautifully designed and painted..............	60.00	100.00
20. ☐ Custard Glass Bedroom Lamp. 6" high. Acorn burner with blue and gold decorations and trim. Shaded light blue, top...	41.00	75.00
21. ☐ Copper Candle. 3-1/2" high. Authentic reproduction of colonial piece..	20.00	35.00

*A.B.P.—Average Buying Price see pg. 5

Pictures Courtesy The Spinning Wheel

As long as men have had structures and buildings they've had to protect there have been locks and keys. Formed in every conceivable metal: iron, copper, brass, steel, etc., they've ranged from the simplest to the most complicated man could devise.

Used throughout the world and through the centuries of man's history, imagination and ingenuity have played a most vital role in the creation of these ingenious designs.

Even though the most valuable are the older and more intricate locks, the more current locks and keys used in the United States are becoming more desirable and collectors are introducing them into their collections.

Locks illustrated are in working order complete with original keys. Locks without keys are worth a fraction of quoted prices and are collected merely for decoration or for lack of an intact specimen in a collection.

Courtesy of: Sydney Strange, Antiques for Men. 855 2nd Ave., N. Y. C. 10017

LOCKS AND KEYS

Manufactured Locks Late 19th Century to Early 20th

Item & Description & Date All Prices are with Keys	Retail
1. ☐ Small Dragon Figural Lock. Manufactured late 19th Century	10.00
2. ☐ R. R. Lock. Late 19th Century	18.50
3. ☐ Brass Door Padlock. Late 19th Century U.S.A.	10.00
4. ☐ Cast Iron Store Padlock. These came in many sizes and were found in Europe and U. S. 1880 -1910	15-25.00 According to Size
5. ☐ Cast Iron Lever Lock. Late 19th Century-Early 20th Century	15.00
6. ☐ Brass 6 Lever Lock. Same as above	25.00
7. ☐ Cast Iron Store Padlock. Late 19th Century	25.00
8. ☐ Large Cast Iron Store Lock	30.00
9. ☐ Unusual German Patent Brass Lock with Cross Key. Late 19th Century	35.00
10. ☐ Cast iron Decorated French Lock. Late 19th Century	25.00
11. ☐ Patent Side Opener Keystone. Cast Iron Brass Hasp	20.00
12. ☐ Small Brass Decorated Eastern Lock. 19th Century	25.00

LOCKS AND KEYS
Small Locks

All Prices are with Keys

Item & Description & Date	Size	Retail
13. ☐ Eastern Brass Animal Locks. India 19th-20th Century	15"	25.00
14. ☐ Man Figure-Screw. Lock—Asiatic 19th Century. Removable Hasp	15"	125.00
15. ☐ French Heart Shape Wrought Iron 18th Century	1¾"	75.00
16. ☐ French Fish Shape Wrought Iron 18th Century	2½"	85.00

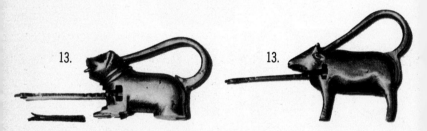

13. 13.

17th-18th Century Hand Locks and Keys
Locksmith Individually Made

All Prices are with Keys

Item & Description & Date	Retail
17. ☐ Nuremburg Lock 17th Century	125.00
18. ☐ Trick Opening French 17th Century	140.00
19. ☐ Trick Opening Austria 17th Century	165.00
20. ☐ Screw Lock. Mid-European 18th Century	75.00
21. ☐ Screw Lock. Mid-European 18th Century (Long Key)	75.00
22. ☐ Wrought Iron Chinese, 18th Century	175.00
23. ☐ Wrought Iron Morocco, Slide Key, 18th Century	85.00

LOCKS AND KEYS
Small Locks

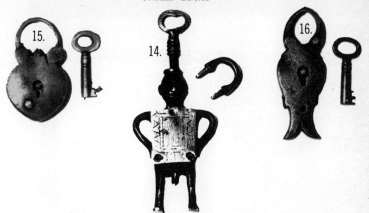

15.

14.

16.

17th-18th Century Hand Locks and Keys

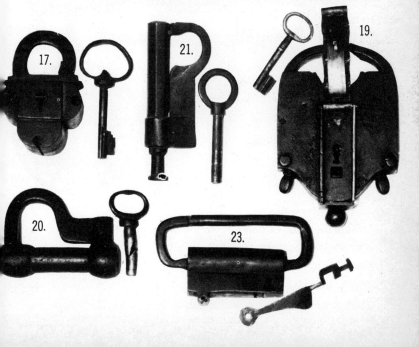

17.

21.

19.

20.

23.

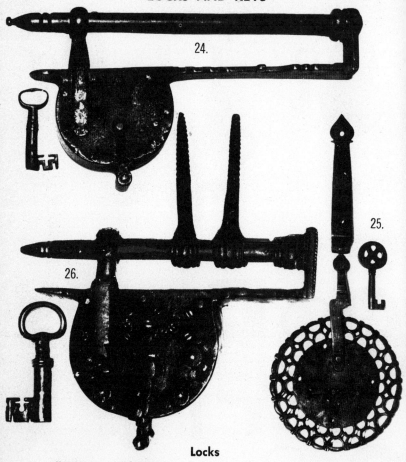

Locks

All Prices are with Keys

Item & Description & Date	Size	Retail
24. ☐ Spanish Gate Lock. 18th Century	16" Overall	250.00
25. ☐ Italian Chest Lock. 17th Century	6" Diameter	150.00
26. ☐ Dungeon Lock—Inquisition Madrid, Spain. 16th Century	15" Overall	600.00

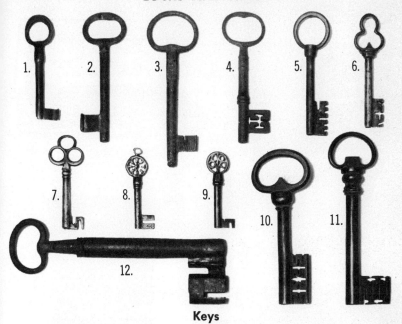

Keys

Item & Description & Date	Size	Retail
1. ☐ Common Primitive Spanish Wrought Iron. 18th-19th Century	4½"	2.00
2. ☐ Common Primitive Spanish Wrought Iron. 18th-19th Century	5½"	3.00
3. ☐ Common Primitive Spanish Wrought Iron. 18th-19th Century	7"	5.00
4. ☐ Georgian English Key Wrought Iron. 18th Century	5½"	10.00
5. ☐ Austrian. 17th Century	5¼"	15.00
6. ☐ Trefoil Box Austrian. 17th Century	4¾"	25.00
7. ☐ Trefoil Box Italian. 18th Century	4"	20.00
8. ☐ Chamberlain's Key Decorated Bow. Italian. Polished Steel. 17th Century	3½"	40.00
9. ☐ Chamberlain's Key Decorated Bow French. 17th Century	3½"	30.00
10. ☐ Austrian Chest Key. 18th Century	6½"	
11. ☐ Austrian Chest Key. 17th Century	7½"	60.00
12. ☐ Austrian Chest Key. 18th Century	10"	35.00

All Prices are for Good Working Condition

Item & Description	Retail
Cylinder-type:	
1. ☐ Blonde rosewood case. Plays six separate tunes..........	175.00
2. ☐ Enamelled case. Hand-painted cover. Plays 4 tunes. ca. 1860..	185.00
3. ☐ Hand-painted case. Lightly etched antique finish. Plays eight tunes...	180.00
4. ☐ Mermod Freres Box. 2, 8" Brass cylinders. Plays 12 tunes. Originally coin operated "Peerless Forte Piccolo"	475.00
5. ☐ Carved mahogany case. Three round bells with hammer strikers. Plays ten separate tunes.................	320.00
6. ☐ Drum and Bell Box. Polished inlaid rosewood case with drum and six fine-tuned bells with manual controls. 14" cylinder. Swiss made...	400.00

Courtesy: AGC, 52 First St., Hackensack, N. J. 07601.

Item & Description	All Prices are for Good Working Condition	Retail

Interchangeable Cylinder-type:

☐ Double-cylinder box. Beautifully polished and matched rosewood, walnut and ebony woods. Complete with dial, tune-selector and safety lock. Contains six separate tunes on each cylinder. 350.00

☐ Double-cylinder box. Multiple carvings on polished mahogany case. Wide, flared legs. Plays six tunes on each of two cylinders. Over 1 hour playing time 375.00

☐ Double Dawkins Cylinder Box. Seven separate cylinders. Each cylinder is brass and over 11" long. Hand-polished golden wood box has container for storage of spare cylinders. 1,500.00

◢. ☐ Twenty-Tune Cylinder Box. Large, polished mahogany box contains two 10" brass cylinders, each with ten separate tunes. Finest Swiss manufacture 300.00

Disc-Music Boxes:

◢. ☐ Adler Disc Music Box. Scrolled-Victorian case. 18¾" disc. Coin-operated. 625.00

2. ☐ Britannia Music Box. Lever-wound machine with 9¼" discs. Table model 275.00

3. ☐ Regina Table Model, 20-3/4" Discs, double comb, Mahogany case, short bedplate 1,395.00

4. ☐ Monopol Disc Music Box. Double-comb machine which plays Monopol 13" discs. Cabinet has drawer for storage of spare discs. Fine German manufacture 500.00

5. ☐ Olympia Disc Music Box. Single-comb table machine with 15½" disks. Contained in hand-carved mahogany grained case. 525.00

6. ☐ Polyphon Deluxe Bell Box. Hand-rubbed and polished walnut case surrounding precision machine playing 14-1/2" discs. Cover is richly inlaid in polished lighter wood. 12 tuned saucer bells, 18-1/2"x17"x25", ca. 1900 .... 950.00

7. ☐ Stella Disc Music Box. Mahogany-cased table model. Uses 9½" discs. 150.00

8. ☐ Symphonion Disc Music Box. Unusual design housed in lower portion of 7" x 12" clock. Top-mounted music box plays 4½" discs. 375.00

During the latter part of the Victorian period (1880-1900), mustache cup
grew increasingly popular. They differed from standard drinking mugs o
glasses, in that a separate piece was inserted along one rim of the cup to kee
the gentleman's facial decoration out of his tea. "Left-handed" cups made fo
left-handed men are the scarcest and most valuable. They can be worth a
much as $300.00

All prices are for Good Condition

Item & Description:	*A.B.P.	Retail**
1. ☐ Austrian-designed. Multi-colored floral decoration	18.00	40.00
2. ☐ Floral design. Gold, beaded edge and foot..............	12.00	26.00
3. ☐ Floral design. Lavender flowers (Carlsbad)............	10.00	22.50
4. ☐ Floral-design. Blue forget-me-nots and roses	15.00	35.00
5. ☐ Floral-design. Lavender and pink assorted flowers	9.00	20.00
6. ☐ Floral design. Red roses with gold trim on cup	10.00	22.50
7. ☐ Silver Plated cup & saucer set•.............................	12.50	25.00
8. ☐ Swirled Cup & Saucer "Papa" lettered on side........	9.00	20.00
9. ☐ Pink lustre ware cup & saucer. Inscribed panel......	20.00	40.00

• **Sterling or "Coin" double price**   **"Left-handed" cups, double price.**

NOTE: "Left-handed" and "right-handed" cups are being reproduced.

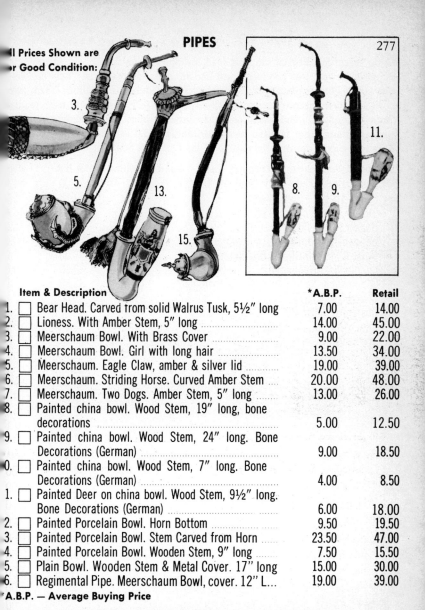

PIPES

All Prices Shown are for Good Condition:

Item & Description	*A.B.P.	Retail
1. ☐ Bear Head. Carved from solid Walrus Tusk, 5½" long	7.00	14.00
2. ☐ Lioness. With Amber Stem, 5" long	14.00	45.00
3. ☐ Meerschaum Bowl. With Brass Cover	9.00	22.00
4. ☐ Meerschaum Bowl. Girl with long hair	13.50	34.00
5. ☐ Meerschaum. Eagle Claw, amber & silver lid	19.00	39.00
6. ☐ Meerschaum. Striding Horse. Curved Amber Stem	20.00	48.00
7. ☐ Meerschaum. Two Dogs. Amber Stem, 5" long	13.00	26.00
8. ☐ Painted china bowl. Wood Stem, 19" long, bone decorations	5.00	12.50
9. ☐ Painted china bowl. Wood Stem, 24" long. Bone Decorations (German)	9.00	18.50
10. ☐ Painted china bowl. Wood Stem, 7" long. Bone Decorations (German)	4.00	8.50
11. ☐ Painted Deer on china bowl. Wood Stem, 9½" long. Bone Decorations (German)	6.00	18.00
12. ☐ Painted Porcelain Bowl. Horn Bottom	9.50	19.50
13. ☐ Painted Porcelain Bowl. Stem Carved from Horn	23.50	47.00
14. ☐ Painted Porcelain Bowl. Wooden Stem, 9" long	7.50	15.50
15. ☐ Plain Bowl. Wooden Stem & Metal Cover. 17" long	15.00	30.00
16. ☐ Regimental Pipe. Meerschaum Bowl, cover. 12" L...	19.00	39.00

*A.B.P. — Average Buying Price

PEWTER

Made from an alloy of tin and lead, or other metals: copper, antimony, bismuth. Pewter was produced and had its greatest popularity between 17! and 1850. Dinner plate was the chief article produced until about 1825, whe china began to replace pewter in homes. After 1825 pewter was used to mal other household items such as sugar bowls, coffee pots, flagons, tankare porringers and other familiar pieces. Britannia metal is considered to be pewte Britannia pieces are usually stamped "Jas Dixon & Son", or "Dixon".

Item & Description	Original Pieces—Good Condition	*A.B.P.	Ret.
Basin. Unmarked. Good condition. 6-1/2".................		26.00	64.0
Basin. 10-1/2" Unmarked**..		31.50	75.0
Beaker. Dixon & Son. Pint size.................................		19.00	48.0
Beaker. Griswold A..		32.50	75.0
Bedpan. Boardman. Good condition...........................		29.00	60.0
Bowl. 8". Danforth, S., Boardman, T........................		48.00	120.0
Candlestick. Dunham 6"..		30.00	60.0
Candlestick. Saucer-type 8", Gleason, pair..................		32.50	80.0
Charger. Unmarked..		19.00	40.0
Charger. English 20"...		45.00	125.0
Chocolate Pot. Swiss manufacture.............................		32.50	65.0
Coffee Pot. Wooden handle, Dixon & Son 10-1/2" H.....		26.00	80.0
Coffee Pot. 9", Leonard, Reed & Barton......................		32.50	85.0
Coffee Pot. Ohio-manufactured, Sellens & Co...............		39.00	65.0
Coffee Urn. Footed base, Reed & Barton, 14" H...........		45.00	91.0
Cuspidor. Oval-shaped..		42.00	84.5
Deep Dish. Good condition, Calder, Danforth...............		52.00	125.0
Flagon. Unmarked		48.00	97.0
Flagon. Gleason, 10" high		85.00	170.0
Foot Warmer. Oval-shaped		16.00	40.0
Ladle with wooden handle, 13" long...........................		15.00	38.0
Lamp. Porter Co.		39.00	90.0
Mugs. Curved handle. 19th century English		16.00	32.0
Mug. 6"		20.00	52.0
Plate. Austin & Co.		39.00	78.0
Plate. 8"		45.00	100.0
Plate. Wm. Calder		45.00	91.0
Plate. E. Danforth		45.00	91.0
Plates. Thomas Danforth		39.00	80.0

*Average Buying Price
**Basins made by Austin, Boardman, Danforth, Pierce—$125.00.

CHALICE

OFFEE POT

BOWL

TANKARD

PORRINGER

OTE: Reproductions are made.

Item & Description Prices are for Good Condition	*A.B.P.	Retail
] Plate. 13½". Unmarked	26.00	52.00
] Porringer. 3" Unmarked	26.00	62.00
] Porringer. 4½" Unmarked. Heart handle	45.00	91.00
] Porringer. Hamlin stamped. 5¼"	65.00	130.00
] Spoon. Crown and rose. Made in Holland	6.00	20.00
] Tankard with hinge cover, 16" High	34.00	68.00
] Teapot. Dunham, R. 7-1/2" high	39.00	82.00
] Teapot. 10". Savage	32.50	65.00
] Teapot. Shaw and Fisher. England	32.50	70.00

**Average Buying Price

Posters are, by their nature, a bold and dramatic reminder of the pas
a theatre production, a household product, a movie, a political campaign, a wa
in which our country was engaged.

The present popularity of the American poster more than compensate
for their former neglect. Enthusiasts will frame a tattered poster today in th
same spirit our ancestors encased an old fragment of worn lace.

It may be said that our early poster designers were ahead of their tim
so effectively did they combine illustration and type, so daringly did they preser
the figure of the American woman.

The affinity between old posters and today's pop art is apparent to th
casual observer. Consequently they not only blend with a traditional setting
but they also enhance a modern decor.

It should not be omitted that old posters are an American treasur
within the reach of any budget.

Pictures and information courtesy: SMOLIN PRINTS, Antique Center of America,
410 East 53 St., N.Y.C. 10022.

WAR

ADVERTISING

MOVIE

ADVERTISING POSTERS

4. / 5.

Originals Only

Item, Description & Date	*A.B.P.	Retail
1. ☐ Admiration—"The Cigar That Wins" 1930— poster has box of actual cigars in center Size 21 x 36	8.75	22.50
2. ☐ Bailey's Circus—Circus Scene Depicted 1890's Size 24 x 36	5.00	16.50
3. ☐ Chicago Chronicle—Ads for Newspaper 1895 (several different) Size 14 x 20	4.00	8.00
4. ☐ Coal For Sale—Orange & Yellow Size 16 x 22	12.50	30.00
5. ☐ Godey's Magazine—Blue, Red, White 1900 (several different) Size 14 x 20	10.00	20.00
6. ☐ Penfields Advertising Posters—(Penfield artist) 1895 Size 12 x 19	17.50	35.00
7. ☐ Pierce Arrow—Picture of car & couple admiring car 1910 Size 9 x 14	7.00	15.00
8. ☐ Scribner's Series—Magazine Posters—1900 Size 22 x 15	9.00	22.50
9. ☐ Sportsmans Show—Grand Central Palace—1907 (shows picture of moose) Size 29 x 44	17.50	35.00
10. ☐ Trommers Malt Beer—Embossed Metal Sign 1930 Size 10 x 13	8.00	18.50
11. ☐ Tuttles Horse Elixir—Red, White & Black 1890 Size 29 x 44	6.00	12.50

All Sizes are in Inches.

POSTERS — MOVIE

All Prices Shown are for Very Good Condition:
All Sizes are in Inches.

Item, Description & Date	*A.B.P.	Reta
1. ☐ "All Through The Night"—1930's with Humphrey Bogart Size 14 x 35	5.00	15.
2. ☐ "Angel"—1930's with Marlene Dietrich Size 40 x 80	20.00	40.
3. ☐ "The Harvey Girls"—1930's with Judy Garland Size 14 x 35	5.00	20.0
4. ☐ Hoot Gibson"—1935 with Hoot Gibson on Bucking Bronco Size 30 x 39	25.00	50.0
5. ☐ "The Loves of Carmen"—1948 with Rita Hayworth & Glenn Ford Size 14 x 35	5.00	15.0
6. ☐ "Palmy Days"—1930's with Eddie Cantor Size 27 x 40	10.00	30.
7. ☐ "Reckless"—1930's with Jean Harlow & William Powell Size 40 x 80	20.00	45.0
8. ☐ "A Scarlet Weekend"—1935 with Dorothy Revier Size 21 x 27	2.25	10.0
9. ☐ "Ship of Wanted Men"—1930's featuring Dorothy Sebastian Size 21 x 27	2.25	10.0
10. ☐ "St. Louis Woman"—1935 with Jeanette Loff Size 21 x 27	2.25	10.0

LOBBY CARDS

All Prices Shown are for Very Good Condition:

Item, Description & Date	From	To
1. ☐ Lobby Cards From Movies In color 11 x 14	1.50	4.50

8.

4.

9.

10.

All pictures and information courtesy: SMOLIN PRINTS

POSTERS—WORLD WAR I
See Pages 214-215 for Color Photos

With the outbreak of World War I (1914) the War Poster called men, money, and arms for the countries needs.

Whatever the cause, War Loans, Recruitments, War Funds, Charities of all types, the poster became the basic structure of persuasion.

ALL PRICES FOR ORIGINAL POSTERS
COURTESY: Tom & Eileen Gilman, N.Y.C.

Item & Description & Date	Condition	*A.B.P.	Retail
1. ☐ "America's Answer to the Kaiser"—1917 Vividly-Colored—36" x 45"	Good	40.00	60.00
2. ☐ "Boy Scouts Liberty Bond"—1917. 19" x 29"—J. C. Leyendecker—Perfectly reflects the mood of W.W. I	Good	30.00	50.00
3. ☐ "Down with Murderers. Up with Democracy" from Czechoslovakia Recruiting Office—by Vogtech Preissig Two soldiers in combat. Black & blue, simple graphics done in collaboration with 1917 American Artist—25" x 36"	Good	30.00	50.00
4. ☐ "Our Free Colors" from Czechoslovak Recruiting Office—by Vogtech Preissig in collaboration with American Artist, 1918. Soldiers carrying different national flags. Color Printed at Wentworth Institute, Boston, Mass. 25" x 38"	Good	30.00	series of 8 50.00
5. ☐ "Books Wanted" One of the most memorable posters by C. B. Falls. Soldier carrying tall stack of books. Colored 1917. 25-1/2" x 38"	Good	15.00	25.00
6. ☐ "For the Flag" For Victory/Subscribe to the National Loan" Famous French Poster by George Scott . . . inspired by the spirit of the French Revolution. Red, white & blue. 1917—12" x 17"	Good	45.00	very rare 75.00
7. ☐ "3rd National Defense Loan; Subscribe!" French poster by Jules Abel Faiure—executed in the Florid, classical manner. Colored—1917. 29" x 45"	Good	30.00	50.00

*A.B.P.—**Average Buying Price see pg. 5**

Item & Description & Date	Condition	*A.B.P.	Retail
8. ☐ "Theatre des Arts" French poster by Poulbot. Children sitting among village ruins. Brown & reds on white. 1918. 31" x 42"	Good	30.00	50.00
9. ☐ "A million boys behind a million Fighters" A small boy backing a soldier. Colored—1917. 12" x 21"	Very Good	10.00	15.00
0. ☐ "Save Serbia Our Ally" taken from French poster "Serbia Day" (same illust.) by Theophile Steinlen. Marching Serbian soldiers. Colored—1916. 24" x 36"	Good	15.00	25.00
1. ☐ "Albert, King of the Belgians" Drawn by E. V. Nodherny. Portrait of King Albert. Colored—1917. 15" x 18"	Good	5.00	10.00
2. ☐ "Welcome, Noble Belgians" Woman dressed in American Flag welcoming Belgian woman in Belgian Flag dress. Red, White & Blue & Yellow on white—1918. 20" x 40"	Fair	5.00	10.00
3. ☐ "Miss America reports for service, Sir" Miss America saluting Uncle Sam. National League for Womans Service. Colored—1917. 24" x 40"	Good	10.00	15.00
4. ☐ "Teamwork Wins". United States Shipping Board Emergency Fleet Corp. Men Fixing Ships with American Flag Flying. By Mibberd V. B. Kline. 1917. 26" x 40"	Good	15.00	25.00
5. ☐ "Nous les aurons". Buy More Liberty Bonds. French Poster. French girl dressed as a soldier standing in front of a French Flag. Colored—1918. 26" x 40"	Good	25.00	40.00
6. ☐ "Keep All Canadians Busy". Beavers Knawing a tree. Victory Bonds Poster. Colored—1918. 18" x 24"	Very Good	15.00	25.00
7. ☐ "A Stitch in Time". Uncle Sam stitching Germany on globe; by J. C. Fireman. 4th Liberty Loan Poster. Black on Brown—1917. 14" x 22"	Good	10.00	20.00
18. ☐ "Pro Patria". Join Army for Period of War. By: Welsh. Soldiers (two) on horseback carrying American Flag & "Italian" Flag. Colored—1917. 26" x 40"	Very Good	10.00	15.00

*Average Buying Price

	Item & Description & Date	Condition	*A.B.P.	Rete
19. ☐	"On the Job". U.S. Shipping Board. Artist (N.A.) Vividly Colored—Dock Scene. 30" x 40". 1917	Good	18.00	30.
20. ☐	"U.S. Marines"—1916. 18" x 27" Orange Background—Bulldog chasing a Dachshund	Good	15.00	25.0
21. ☐	"United War Work Fund". Lieillo (artist)—1917. 19" x 26". 2 Football players. Brown, Black, Red	Good	25.00	40.0
22. ☐	"Italian (Erneste Rossi)"—19" x 29" 3 Stage Story, Left to Right	Good	5.00	10.0
23. ☐	"Help The Women's Land Army"—24" x 40" Artist—Wilson, 1918 (Uncle Sam & Lady) Red, White, Blue	Good	10.00	15.0
24. ☐	"Men for the Army"—19" x 28" Colorful—Soldiers charging	Good	5.00	10.0
25. ☐	"Children's Year"—1918. 19" x 29" Artist—F. Luis Mora. Children marching in Row, Blue Background	Good	5.00	10.0
26. ☐	"Save Wheat". 24" x 40". Black Background—3 Women Tilling the Soil	Good	10.00	15.0
27. ☐	"Save Food". 13" x 20" Artist—F. Luis Mora. Green & Yellow Background	Very Rare Good	75.00	120.00
28. ☐	"United War-Work Campaign" (card) 11" x 21". Sponsored by Various Organizations	Good	3.50	7.00
29. ☐	"Defeat the Kaiser". 14" x 21". Dark Background with White & Red Letters	Good	10.00	20.00

*Average Buying Price   See Pages 214-215 for Color Photos

l Pottery depicted and priced on the following pages is herein described

COMMON POTTERY

…itarian pottery, or stoneware jugs, jars, and crocks, are found in most antique …ps today. Generally light gray in color they were often decorated with eagles, …, dogs, birds, in cobalt blue. The decorated pieces are the most valuable.

BENNINGTON POTTERY

…ht pottery covered with a slight salt glaze was originally made in England. …he mid-1780's, a factory was established in Bennington, Vermont produc-…the same pottery. Bennington is easily recognized by its smooth, mottled …wn finish. In its later type in which a large number of Toby Jugs were …duced, Bennington took the form of a lighter, dull-finished parian. This …tery was also known as Bennington-Ware.

BUFFALO POTTERY

…he first decade of the 20th century, a large quantity of hand-tinted under-…zed jugs were produced by the Buffalo Pottery Company of New York. The …erglaze decorations usually depicted literary or historical events. Pastel …des were generally used in finishing, giving the jugs a particularly delicate …

DEDHAM POTTERY

…stinctively marked by a unique blue spider-web underglaze, Dedham pottery …s first created in New England in the late 19th century. Produced in more …n a dozen separate patterns, Dedham pottery was manufactured in quantity …il the late 1890's. Animal and floral patterns were the most common, with … Rabbit design being the most popular. From 1895 to 1942 when the fac-…y closed, a tiny rabbit on the base of each piece indicated its authenticity.

DELFT POTTERY

…ith a history dating back over three centuries, Delft ware originated among … guild craftsmen of western Holland. Later it was produced in Liverpool, …gland. Delft pottery may be recognized by its distinctive blue decorations … a polished, glazed background.

ALL ABOUT POTTERY

All Pottery depicted and priced on the following pages is herein describ

GREENAWAY

Skilfully drawn illustrations of children and animals appeared on some ty
of English Staffordshire pottery during the later 1800's. This was the worl
Kate Greenaway, whose illustrations also appeared in many children's bc
of the period. Her plates and mugs are becoming quite scarce and theref
command a respectably high price.

PARIAN WARE

Hard-baked in a hot oven, this unglazed pottery bears a strong resembla
to mottled marble. Its white finish is polished after baking, giving it an ove
smooth appearance. Among English potters, Parian was a favorite in the p
duction of statuettes and figurines. Many other items including pitchers, va
jewelry, tea sets and plaques were also produced in Parian.

MAJOLICA POTTERY

A richly-colored earthenware glazed with tin oxide in baking, Majolica is
bright-hued, glassy pottery. Deriving its name from the island of Major
this soft pottery was well known throughout Europe during Medieval tim
In the United States, Majolica was first produced in Maryland and later
Pennsylvania by Griffen, Smith & Hill Co. The latter pottery was cal
"Etruscan Majolica" and bore the initials of the company.

MOCHA WARE

A soft cream-colored pottery decorated with seaweed, trees or earthworms a
surrounded with multi-colored bands, Mocha was made in England in the la
1790's. Although many types of Mocha ware were produced, the most popul
forms were drinking mugs and water pitchers.

ROOKWOOD POTTERY

Smoothly-finished art pottery with subtle underglazings of brown and yello
was made in Ohio from the late 1800's onwards, by the Storer family of C
cinnati. It was given the name of Rookwood after the family estate. As t
only true form of American Art Pottery, Rookwood is eagerly sought after
both dealers and collectors.

SALT CONTAINER

Pottery (Common): All Prices are for Good Condition	*A.B.P.	Retail
1. ☐ Barrel Bank. Gilt hoops on sides.....................	7.50	15.00
2. ☐ Bowl. 10" diameter. Azure blue.....................	6.00	12.00
3. ☐ Camel Figurine. 12" H. Chalky white................	13.50	28.00
4. ☐ Cash Register. White with yellow glaze.............	7.50	15.00
5. ☐ Cat Figurine. Yellow eyes. Tapered neck............	10.00	20.00
6. ☐ Churn. Butter. Flight of wildfowl. Chip on base....	8.00	16.50
7. ☐ Crock. Floral and leaf decorations. Blue glaze.....	9.50	18.00
8. ☐ Crock. 3-gal. capacity. Gray with blue flowers & figure....	10.00	20.00
9. ☐ Crock. Floral and leaf decorations. Green glaze.....	9.50	18.00
10. ☐ Crock. 4-gallon capacity. Flying eagle on gray field. Signed "Reppert, Pa."...................	25.00	50.00
11. ☐ Cruet. Blue floral decorations.....................	10.00	20.00
12. ☐ Foot Warmer. Shaped like suitcase. Marked "England"	12.50	25.00
13. ☐ Jug. 16" H. Hand-painted flight of birds...........	26.00	52.00
14. ☐ Jug. 3-gallon capacity. Flying birds. Light glaze...	22.50	45.00
15. ☐ Mold. Shaped like fish. (Food Mold)...............	7.50	15.00
16. ☐ Mold. Turk's Head. Pennsylvania pottery...........	9.50	19.50
17. ☐ Pig. Hot water bed warmer........................	6.00	12.00
18. ☐ Pitcher. 6-1/2" H. Pennsylvania Tan ware. Rare......	37.50	75.00
19. ☐ Pitcher. New England mfg..........................	21.50	43.00
20. ☐ Salt Box. Hanging-type. Blue with "Salt" on front. Pine wood top......................	18.50	38.00
21. ☐ Tea Pot. Fluted sides. Applied handle and spout........	20.00	41.50

In the latter part of the century, the first Pottery designated Bennington-Rock
ingham was produced in Bennington, Vermont. Created originally from salt
glazed clay, Bennington Pottery was produced in Vermont and later in Maryland
until the mid-1850's. Articles included a complete line of kitchen utensils as
well as items for the rest of the household. Bennington is found in 2 general
types, Parian Pottery-dull white, and mottled brown with glaze.

*Bennington pottery is being reproduced. Mainly in mottled brown, and in
the most popular pieces.*

All Prices Shown are For Good Condition: ORIGINAL PIECES ONLY

Item & Description	*A.B.P.	Retail
☐ Basket. With shaped handle..	15.00	30.00
☐ Bed Pan..	10.00	20.00
☐ Bottle. Marked. Coachman. 1894...............................	135.00	270.00
☐ Bowl. Rockingham glaze. With curved spout................	28.00	55.00
☐ Bowl. Barber's. Signed "Norton 1841".......................	112.00	225.00
☐ Bucket. With curved wire grip.................................	25.00	50.00
☐ Cake Mold. 10" H. In shape of rabbit.......................	12.00	25.00
☐ Coffee Urn. Rockingham glaze. Applied handles..........	45.00	90.00
☐ Crock. 2-gal. capacity. Marked "Julius Norton"..........	25.00	50.00
☐ Cuspidor. Rockingham flint enamel...........................	40.00	80.00
☐ Cuspidor. Marked "Lyman Fenton & Co., Bennington, Vt."	45.00	90.00
☐ Door Knobs. Mottled pair with engravings..................	10.00	20.00
☐ Flask. With diving eagle.......................................	25.00	50.00
☐ Foot Warmer. Rockingham glaze. Owl head................	50.00	100.00
☐ Hound. Set on sculptured base................................	75.00	150.00
☐ Jug. 1-gal. capacity. Bluebird design.......................	16.00	32.00
☐ Jug. 3-gal. capacity. Rich floral decor. Signed "norton"	37.50	75.00
☐ † Pitcher. Hunting scene. Running stag. Hound Handle...	57.50	115.00
☐ Pitcher. Porcelain. Smear-glazed neck......................	17.50	34.00
☐ Salt Box. With sculptured shelf..............................	25.00	50.00
☐ Tobacco Jar. Man wearing skull cap.........................	24.00	48.00
☐ **Tea Pot. Rebekah at the Well †................................	35.00	70.00
☐ † Toby Jug. Rockingham glaze..................................	105.00	210.00
☐ Toby Jug. Man with mustache. Rockingham glaze	90.00	180.00
☐ Water Cooler. Marked "Norton". No lid......................	21.00	42.00

*A.B.P. – Average Buying Price †Reproduced Item **Questionable as to Authenticity

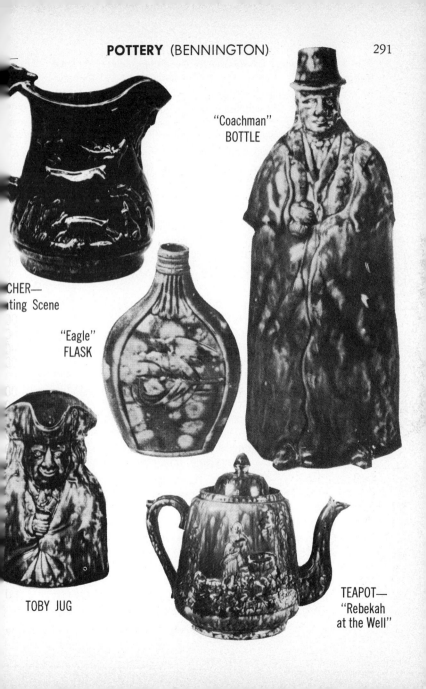

"Coachman"
BOTTLE

CHER—
ting Scene

"Eagle"
FLASK

TOBY JUG

TEAPOT—
"Rebekah
at the Well"

POTTERY (BUFFALO)

Item & Description	Prices are for Good Condition	*A.B.P.	R
Buffalo:			
Baby's Dish. Blue enamelled design		22.50	45
Butter Dish. Wide base with fluted sides. With cover ..		55.00	110
Cereal Bowl. 7-1/2" diameter. Playing children		15.00	30
Dish. With cover. Bands of gold		14.00	28
Dish. Deldare ware. Singing children		21.50	43
Dish. "Ye Lion Inn" 7-1/2" diameter. Deldare ware....		41.50	82
Fruit Bowl. 9" diameter. "Ye Village Tavern" Deldare ware		111.50	225
Humidor. 7" H. Hunting scene. With cover		85.00	160
Mug. 2" H. "Fallowfield Hunt". Chip on handle		20.00	42
Pitcher. 7" diameter. "Old Soldier"		65.00	130
Plate. 8" diameter. Scene of children playing		12.00	24

POTTERY (DEDHAM)

Item & Description		*A.B.P.	R
Dedham:			
Coaster. In shape of elephant		12.50	25
Creamer. With curved handle		37.50	75
Cup & Saucer. Prancing rabbit		41.25	82
Inkwell. Imperial British Lion with Crest		30.00	60
Plate. 6" diameter. Magnolia pattern		21.50	40
Plate. 6" diameter. Twisted grapes with leaves		25.00	42.
Plate. Swimming duck		15.00	30.
Plate. 7-1/2" diameter. Rabbit border		21.50	43.
Plate. 8-1/2" diameter. Leaping dolphin		43.50	87.
Salt & Pepper Shakers. The pair		24.00	48.
Vase. Erupting volcano. Signed and numbered		105.00	210.

POTTERY (DELFT)

Item & Description		*A.B.P.	R
Delft:			
Charger. 13-1/2" diameter. 18th Century polychrome		75.00	150.
Clock. 5-1/4". Scrolled edges		21.00	42.
Cracker Container. With cover		22.50	45.
Figurines. 13" H. Seated cats. Colorful grey animals..		68.00	137.
Lamp. Floral decorations. Sculptured base and bowl..		54.00	108.
Plate. 9" dia. Turning windmill with nautical designs Signed "Groot". Excellent condition		125.00	250.0
Plate. 8" diameter. Hand-painted sailing vessels		15.00	31.
Plate. 12" diameter. Hand-painted Chinese village. Rare		175.00	350.
Platter. 15" diameter. Blue and white Dutch design. Marked Delft. Excellent condition		22.50	45.0

POTTERY
BUFFALO

DEDHAM

DELFT

Item & Description	Prices are for Good Condition	*A.B.P.	Retail
Delft:			
Tray. 12" diameter. Dutch farmers.............................		17.50	35.00
Urn. Fluted neck. Rich blue and white glazing............		15.00	30.00
Vase. 10" H. Windmill with floral borders..................		25.00	50.00
Vase. 10" H. Scenes of barges on wide canal..............		16.00	32.00
Vase. 12" H. Water scene with fishermen..................		20.00	40.00

Average Buying Price.

Item & Description All Prices are for Good Condition	*A.B.P.	Re
Kate Greenaway:		
Book of Games. Intricately colored illustrations............	11.75	23
Book. Fairy Tale of Mother Goose. Engraved, illustrations by K. G.	15.00	30
Child's Tea Set. Included are plate, cup and saucer	17.25	34
Coffee Pot. With painted figures on sides......................	35.00	70
Hot Plate. Made in Germany..	20.00	40
Napkin Holder. Dancing children.................................	12.50	25.
Plate. 8-1/2" diameter. Children skating.......................	13.75	27.
Salt & Pepper Shakers. Hand-painted design.................	19.75	39.
Vase. 11" H. Floral and leaf decorations.......................	12.50	25.

(PARIAN WARE)

Item & Description	*A.B.P.	Re
Parian Ware:		
Bowl. Sculptured classical figures. Royal Wedgewood..	21.25	42.
Bowl. Fruit. Blue and white floral decorations..............	2.50	25.
Box. Heart-shaped with scrolled sides and covers........	18.00	36.
Bust of Lincoln. 7-1/2" H. Signed...............................	16.25	32.
Bust of Beethoven. 8" H. Sharply-chiselled features....	30.00	60.
Bust of Venus de Milo. 8" H. Signed...........................	30.00	60.
Candlesticks. Blue and white. Signed "Alcock 1842"....	37.50	75.
Cornucopia. Running dogs sculptured on sides.............	21.25	42.
Dish. Shaped as two hands. Signed.............................	27.50	55.C
Dish. With cover. Lily pads and floral decorations........	31.00	62.C
Figure. Madonna with Child. 16" H. Signed "Copeland" Rare..	65.00	160.C
Figurine. 4" H. Sitting dog..	12.50	25.C
Figurines. 10" H. Girls holding pitchers and wheat stalks	32.50	65.C
Figurine. Young girl at prayer with open book..............	45.00	90.C
Figurines. Grecian statues in white alabaster. Set of 3..	80.00	160.C
Figurine. Chimney sweep with broom...........................	21.00	42.0
Figurine. Three Graces..	20.00	40.C
Hen. Sculptured feathers...	40.00	80.0
Jug. 4-1/2" H. Blue and white. Mintoni.......................	11.50	22.C
Jug. White alabaster with hand-painted figures............	23.75	47.5
Match Holder. Gray and white mouse. Life size............	13.00	26.0
Pitcher. Lily and lilac floral decorations......................	38.00	76.0
Pitcher. Hunting scene. Wild bird and dog...................	57.50	105.0
Sugar Container. Floral decorations.............................	38.00	76.5
Vase. Floral design with leaves. Signed.......................	42.50	85.0

FIGURE

VASE

PITCHER

PITCHER

POTTERY (MOCHA WARE)

PITCHER

6.

11.

PITCHER

All Prices are for Good Condition unless otherwise noted.

Item & Description	*A.B.P.	Reta
Mocha Ware:		
1. ☐ Bowl. 10" diameter. Yellow ware with striped banding..	37.50	75.
2. ☐ Bowl. 11" diameter. Seaweed pattern............................	45.00	90.
3. ☐ Bowl. 13" diameter. Blue seaweed pattern..................	57.50	115.
4. ☐ Muffin Tray. 5" diameter. Applied handle.....................	20.00	40.
5. ☐ Mug. 3-3/4" H. Chipped handle...................................	19.50	38.
6. ☐ Mug. Beer. With scrolling and multi-colored bands......	37.50	76.
7. ☐ Mug. Tree pattern..	38.75	78.
8. ☐ Pot. Tan with Blue Seaweed pattern...........................	12.50	25.
9. ☐ Pitcher. 7-1/4" H. Banding on cream background. Earthworm design...	47.50	95.
10. ☐ Salt Container. Fluted edges......................................	15.00	30.
11. ☐ Urn. Banded ivory with tapered base. Matching ball cover. Excellent condition.......................................	60.00	120.

*Average Buying Price

A form of pottery that was originally glazed with a shiny opaque white tin oxide and then decorated in bright colors. The name is a derivative of the word Majorca, one of the islands off the Eastern coast of Spain where this type of pottery is said to have originated in the very early Renaissance Period. Later made in Italy, France (where it was called Faience), Germany and other variations in Holland (Delft) and England. Made continuously since the 12th or 13th century it reached the height of its popularity in the products of English and American potters in the 19th century. It is these products that are collected today as much of the earlier ware is now in private collections and museums. The 19th century versions used a transparent tin or lead glaze. Much of it has a lavender or pink interior with some part of the exterior having a mottled effect. Many pieces made in shape of animals, fish, vegetables and other forms. Many others have an impressed design like the cauliflower design by Wedgewood, or the Shell and Seaweed of the American Etruscan Majolica. The late 19th century American pieces were often acquired as premiums.

Many of the pieces are marked. The best known mark is the monogram made of the letters GHS representing the names Griffen, Smith and Hill the makers of Etruscan Majolica.

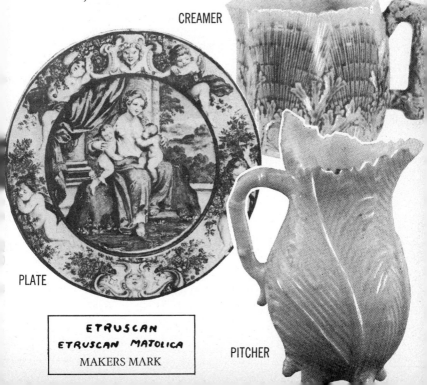

CREAMER

PLATE

ETRUSCAN
ETRUSCAN MATOLICA
MAKERS MARK

PITCHER

POTTERY (MAJOLICA)

All prices shown are for Good Condition

Item & Description	*A.B.P.	Retail
1. ☐ Basket, twisted handle, pink inside, basket weave exterior	22.00	45.00
2. ☐ Bowl, leaf shape with acorn and oak leaf design	15.00	30.00
3. ☐ Bowl, 8" diam., Etruscan shell and seaweed design	22.00	45.00
4. ☐ Bread Plate "Eat to Live, Not Live to Eat" with closed handles	15.00	30.00
5. ☐ Creamer, Etruscan Shell & Seaweed	30.00	70.00
6. ☐ Creamer, vegetable leaf design in green	15.00	30.00
7. ☐ Cup and Saucer, Cabbage design, light interior bright green exterior	7.00	15.00
8. ☐ Cup and Saucer, Etruscan Shell and Seaweed design, rose lavendar inside	28.00	60.00
9. ☐ Jar, Tobacco, Shape of owl, in white, green and brown	12.00	25.00
10. ☐ Jardiniere, in colored floral design on dark brown background 20" diam	35.00	75.00
11. ☐ Pitcher, dark brown in bark design and log handle and small flowers	17.00	35.00
12. ☐ Pitcher, Water, Shell and Seaweed 8" high	38.00	80.00
13. ☐ Plate, 8" dark Mottled brown with some green, marked "Wedgewood."	5.00	12.00
14. ☐ Plate 8", similar pattern impressed recesses for oysters	8.00	18.00
15. ☐ Stand, Umbrella 10" diam., by 28" high, brown, with large colored flowers	18.00	40.00
16. ☐ Sugar bowl in leaf design, marked Etruscan	12.00	25.00
17. ☐ Teapot, Bamboo design, light colors, marked Etruscan	18.00	40.00
18. ☐ Teapot, Shell and Seaweed pattern, pink inside, marked Etruscan	38.00	80.00
19. ☐ Vase, Fish shape and colored in gray, white and pink	8.00	18.00
20. ☐ Vase, corn design in green and yellow, 8" high	10.00	20.00
21. ☐ Vase, Sanded Majolica in light ecru, with band of pansies 6" high	15.00	30.00

*Average Buying Price

POTTERY (MAJOLICA)

All Prices are for Good Condition unless otherwise noted.

Item & Description	*A.B.P.	Retail
1. ☐ Basket. Green medallion with sculptured figures..........	25.00	50.00
2. ☐ Basket. Sanded ground glass. Applied floral decorations	23.25	47.50
3. ☐ Boat Dish. With scaled fish on lid................................	30.00	60.00
4. ☐ Cake Plate Set. Raised floral decorations. Signed. Three plates...	13.00	26.00
5. ☐ Cake Plate. Floral decorations. Applied handles............	19.25	38.50
6. ☐ Compote. 5" diameter. Turquoise ground with florals and leaves..	16.00	32.00
7. ☐ Creamer. Frog sitting on lily pad................................	15.00	30.00
8. ☐ Dish. In shape of boat. With fish on leaves. Covered. Signed	28.00	56.00
9. ☐ Fruit Container. Woven basketweave design...................	17.00	32.00
10. ☐ Jardiniere. 11" H. Ornately decorated. Minton. Signed..	45.00	90.00
11. ☐ Jug. Large four-footed acorn design. With stopper........	12.50	25.00
12. ☐ Mug. Bird in flight. With twig handle...........................	13.75	27.50
13. ☐ Mug. Barrel shaped with lavender blossoms. Blue green	10.00	21.50
14. ☐ Mug. Floral design in royal blue & canary yellow interior	11.50	23.00
15. ☐ Pitcher. Cream and light yellow with floral decorations..	10.00	20.00
16. ☐ Pitcher. 9" dia. Water. Green & beige shaded. Etruscan	26.25	52.50
17. ☐ Pitcher. 7" diameter. Shell and Seaweed pattern..........	9.00	18.00
18. ☐ Plate. 8" diameter. Marked "G.S.H.". Basketweave with figures..	10.50	21.00
19. ☐ Plate. 9" dia. Flowers with leaf design. Etruscan..........	9.50	18.00
20. ☐ Plate. 9" dia. Raspberries & floral arrangement.	19.00	38.00
21. ☐ Sauce Dish. 6" diameter. Flower and leaf decorations..	7.50	15.00
22. ☐ Tea Pot. Shell and Seaweed pattern. Applied handles. With cover..	55.00	110.00
23. ☐ Vases. Sanded finish. Bulbous bases. The pair in excellent condition..	65.00	130.00
24. ☐ Vase. Short foot. Basketweave pattern........................	9.00	18.00

*A.B.P.—**Average Buying Price see pg. 5**

POTTERY (ROOKWOOD-ART POTTERY)

The Rookwood Pottery company was founded in 1880 by Mrs. Maria Longworth Storer, in Cincinnati, Ohio.

Soft underglaze colors of brown and yellow, and naturalistic decorations are typical of Rookwood pottery. Individual pieces signed by the artist or designer exist. These are one of a kind and were not duplicated. The Marks, reversed "R" and letter "P" appear on the bottom of all pieces from 1886 to 1914. The most desired Rookwood was produced between 1880 and 1914.

All Prices Shown are for Rookwood in Perfect Condition:

Item, Description & Date	*A.B.P.	Retail
Ashtray. With match container. Bat spread wings. 1924.	37.50	75.00
Bowl. 8" diameter. Floral matte finish glaze. Marked "CST". 1915	22.00	44.00
Bookends. Brown rook on leaf. Floral background. Pr.	36.00	72.00
Bowl. 8" dia. On pedestal with 2 handles. Signed. 1924	40.00	80.00
Candlesticks Seahorse design. The pair, marked 1916..	21.50	43.00
Creamer and Sugar Bowl. Berries and cherries design. Marked 1901	46.50	92.75
Ewer. 10" H. Floral spray surrounded by leaves. 1898.	125.00	250.00
Ewer. Glaze floral decorations. Standard. 1901, 9" high	35.00	70.00
Inkwell. Blue matte finish. Royal British Lion. 1928.	12.00	24.00
Lamp. 10-1/2" H. Pine cone decor. Tapered base. Marked and signed. 1920	45.00	90.00
Mug. Portrait of Monk. Standard glaze. 1920	70.00	140.00
Paperweight. 5-1/2" H. Ivory seated cat. 1924	30.00	60.00
Paperweight. Dog. White-matte finish. 1927	22.50	45.00
VASES:		
Blue cherries on turquoise ground. 1952	30.00	60.00
White crocus on blue field. Signed "Rehm" 1904	75.00	150.00
Floral decoration. Standard glaze. 1893. 8-1/2" H	100.00	200.00
Floral decoration. Standard glaze. 6-1/2" H. 1896	80.00	160.00
Yellow Daisies. Signed by Leona Van Briggle. 1900	80.50	161.00
Green Holly Leaves. Van Briggle. No date	64.00	128.00
Bottle Shaped. Standard glaze. Signed Jeanette Swing 1902	50.00	100.00
Small Fluted. Handles on each side. Standard glaze Marked 1898	31.50	60.00
Caramel Leaves. Unsigned. Marked 1901.	67.50	135.00

*A.B.P.—Average Buying Price see pg. 5

Political Americana—One of the fastest growing hobbies today—the collecting of ephemera and relics from our past Presidential Campaigns. Banners — Buttons — Badges — Medals — Tokens — Handkerchiefs — Ribbons — Ballots — Songsters — Broadsides — Prints — Torches — Flags, all have value and are eagerly sought after. Brass Inaugural clothing buttons of George Washington — "Long Live The President" ($200 to $300), Third Party Candidates, Prohibition, Socialist (a Debs celluloid button depicting him in convicts clothing, while running for president sells for $85.00), Communist, Populist, Greenback, and Progressive, all these parties fielded presidential candidates and are usually rarer than items from the two major parties.

The forerunner of today's celluloid buttons were the small brass and white metal tokens of the last century. These had the nominees bust on one side with an appropriate slogan on the reverse. They usually are found with a small hole in the top — a ribbon went thru it and it was worn on the lapel or cravat of a party supporter. Some tokens from the famous 1840 Log Cabin - Hard Cider - Harrison Campaign bring less money than rare celluloid buttons of the 1920's. Mechanical items such as the movable Gold and Silver bugs, nosethumbers, look-thru miniature pigs with candidates pictures inside, mechanical coffins all are avidly collected.

Fakes — As in every hobby when pieces are in demand, fakes start to appear. Remember — there are no known celluloid pinback buttons before 1896. Thus a celluloid button with pictures of Cleveland and Hendricks on it is a fake and a fantasy. Large corporations have issued sets of buttons in the past few years as advertising and sales promotion gimmicks. Replicas of rare buttons are in these sets but they are usually lithographed (printed directly on the metal button) rather than on paper and under celluloid as the originals are. They are also the wrong size where the original is only ⅞″ dia. the replica may be 1½″ and vice versa.

Jugate refers to a political item that shows both pictures of the Presidential and Vice-Presidential candidate on it. Buttons of local candidates such as mayors, governors, congressmen etc. have very limited appeal and very little commercial value unless the candidate later became famous, thus a "Franklin D. Roosevelt For Governor" button, a "Harry Truman for Judge" or a "Honey Fitz" (JFK'S grandfather) would all be of value to the collector.

Courtesy: Charles McSorley, Political Americana, Box 21, Closter, New Jersey

PRESIDENTIAL CAMPAIGN CELLULOID BUTTONS

(Under 1½" Dia.)

All Prices Shown are for Very Fine Condition

	Candidate & Date		Retail Jugates	Retail Single Picture
1.	McKinley & Hobart	1896	8.00	5.00
2.	Bryan & Sewall	1896	15.00	8.00
3.	McKinley & TR	1900	7.00	5.00
4.	Bryan & Stevenson	1900	15.00	8.00
5.	TR & Fairbanks	1904	12.00	5.00
6.	Parker & Davis	1904	20.00	10.00
7.	Taft & Sherman	1908	12.00	6.50
8.	Bryan & Kern	1908	15.00	7.00
9.	Wilson & Marshall	1912	15.00	10.00
10.	Taft & Sherman	1912	12.00	5.00
11.	TR & Johnson	1912	Rare	5.00
12.	Wilson & Marshall	1916	15.00	10.00
13.	Hughes & Fairbanks	1916	35.00	12.00
14.	Harding & Coolidge	1920	Rare	5.00
15.	Cox & FDR	1920	Rare	75.00
16.	Coolidge & Dawes	1924	15.00	12.00
17.	Davis & Bryan (Charles)	1924	Rare	75.00
18.	LaFollette & Wheeler	1924	45.00	20.00
19.	Hoover & Curtis	1928	60.00	10.00
20.	Smith & Robinson	1928	60.00	8.00
21.	FDR & Garner	1932	25.00	2.00
22.	Hoover & Curtis	1932	60.00	10.00
23.	FDR & Garner	1936	25.00	2.00
24.	Landon & Knox	1936	35.00	6.00
25.	FDR & Wallace	1940	7.50	2.00
26.	Willkie & McNary	1940	30.00	3.00
27.	FDR & Truman	1944	30.00	2.00
28.	Dewey & Bricker	1944	20.00	3.00
29.	Truman & Barkley	1948	15.00	3.00
30.	Dewey & Warren	1948	5.00	3.00

Dealers would usually pay 40-60% of these Prices, Political items made after 1932 are usually Purchased in Lots rather than Singly.

PRESIDENTIAL CAMPAIGN CELLULOID BUTTONS 303

Courtesy: Charles McSorley, Political Americana, Box 21, Closter, New Jersey

PRESIDENTIAL CAMPAIGN TOKENS

Prices for the Commonest Pieces, Usually Brass

All Prices Shown are for Very Fine Condition

	Candidate & Date		Retail
31. ☐	Andrew Jackson	1828	20.00
32. ☐	John Quincy Adams	& 1832	Rare
33. ☐	Martin Van Buren	1836	15.00
34. ☐	Wm. Henry Harrison	& 1840	7.50
35. ☐	James K. Polk	1844	100.00
36. ☐	Henry Clay	1844	10.00
37. ☐	Zachary Taylor	1848	15.00
38. ☐	Lewis Cass	1848	65.00
39. ☐	Franklin Pierce	1852	15.00
40. ☐	Winfield Scott	1852	12.00
41. ☐	James Buchanan	1856	12.00
42. ☐	John C. Fremont	1856	12.00
43. ☐	Millard Fillmore	1856	15.00
44. ☐	Abraham Lincoln	1860	25.00
45. ☐	Stephen Douglas	1860	20.00
46. ☐	John Breckinridge	1860	60.00
47. ☐	John Bell	1860	20.00
48. ☐	Abraham Lincoln	1864	25.00
49. ☐	George McClellan	1864	15.00
50. ☐	John C. Fremont	1864	35.00
51. ☐	U. S. Grant	1868	15.00
52. ☐	Horatio Seymour	1868	15.00
53. ☐	U. S. Grant	1872	18.00
54. ☐	Horace Greeley	1872	18.00
55. ☐	R. B. Hayes	1876	35.00
56. ☐	S. J. Tilden	1876	35.00
57. ☐	James Garfield	1880	7.50
58. ☐	Winfield S. Hancock	1880	7.50
59. ☐	Grover Cleveland	1884	7.50
60. ☐	James G. Blaine	1884	10.00
61. ☐	Benjamin Harrison	1888	5.00
62. ☐	Grover Cleveland	1888	5.00
63. ☐	Grover Cleveland	1892	7.50
64. ☐	Benjamin Harrison	1892	7.50

Dealers would usually pay 40-60% of these Prices, Political items made after 1932 are usually Purchased in Lots rather than Singly.

GEORGE WASHINGTON
INAUGURAL BUTTON

33.

34.

35.

37.

39.

41.

42.

43.

44.

45.

48.

49.

52.

52.

51.

54.

54.

57.

58.

67.

59.

44.

45.

1860
FERROTYPES

46.

47.

48.

52.

53.

Courtesy: Charles McSorley, Political Americana, Box 21, Closter, New Jersey

Political Ribbons, used in America's early days were usually made of silk and range in size from lapel Ribbons to Wall Banners. Sizes shown are in proportion to original sizes. Prices quoted are for current Retail Prices.

A dealer's offer of 40% to 60% of stated value would be fair.

All Prices Shown are for Very Fine Condition

	Candidate & Date		Retail
1.	☐ Andrew Jackson	1828	$300.00
2.	☐ Clay & Frelinghuysen	1844	250.00
3.	☐ Pierce & King	1852	250.00
4.	☐ James Buchanan	1856	50.00
5.	☐ Stephen Douglas	1860	90.00
6.	☐ Stephen Douglas	1860	200.00
7.	☐ Abraham Lincoln	1860	250.00
8.	☐ Abraham Lincoln	1860	250.00
9.	☐ Abraham Lincoln	1864	150.00
10.	☐ Abraham Lincoln	1860	250.00
11.	☐ Jefferson Davis	1861	300.00
12.	☐ Seymour & Blair	1868	250.00

1.

2.

3.

FOR PRESIDENT
AMES BUCHANAN.

FOR VICE-PRESIDENT
JOHN C. BRECKINRIDGE.

We Po'ked 'em in '44.
We Pierced 'em in '52.
And we'll "Buck 'em" in '56.

6.

DOUGLAS
AND
JOHNSON.

THE UNION
NOW AND
FOREVER.

For President,
ABRAHAM LINCOLN.

For Vice President,
ANDREW JOHNSON.

9.

Our Ticket.
1860.
FOR PRESIDENT:

ABRAHAM LINCOLN.
FOR VICE PRESIDENT:
HANNIBAL HAMLIN.

THE SOUTH FOREVER!

SOUTHERN CONFEDERATION

JEF. DAVIS, Prest.

A. H. STEPHENS, Vice President.

OUR TICKET.

OUR MOTTO:
This is a White
Man's Country;
Let White Men
Rule.

10.   11.   12.

Courtesy: Charles McSorley, Political Americana, Box 21, Closter, New Jersey

SILVER (SOLID "STERLING" or "COIN")

Items cast of pure silver. The most refined are of "sterling" or "coin silver"
Pieces listed are the few most readily obtainable.

All Prices are for Very Good Condition:
Item and Description
FLATWARE

		A.B.P.	Ret
1. ☐	Forks. Berry or Oyster; long prongs, fancy chased or gilt prongs. Various patterns marked "STERLING" or "PURE COIN"	3.00	6.
2. ☐	Forks. Oyster or Pickle; short prongs, gilt or enameled prongs. Various patterns marked "STERLING" or "PURE COIN"	3.00	6.
3. ☐	Forks. Serving; cold meat or salad. Curved prong. Various patterns marked "STERLING" or "PURE COIN"	6.00	12.
4. ☐	Forks. Serving; cold meat or cake. Straight prong. Various patterns marked "STERLING" or "PURE COIN"	6.50	12.
5. ☐	Knives. Fish and Ice Cream. Various patterns Marked "STERLING" or "PURE COIN"	7.00	15.0
6. ☐	Spoons. BonBon. Various patterns marked "STERLING" or "PURE COIN"	7.00	15.0
7. ☐	Spoons. Berry or Salad Serving. Various patterns marked "STERLING" or "PURE COIN"	7.00	15.0

*VANITY ITEMS

8. ☐	Hairbrush. Long handle, beaded edge with scroll work marked "STERLING" or "PURE COIN" with matched comb	22.50	40.0
9. ☐	Hand Mirror. Floral pattern marked "STERLING" or "PURE COIN"	18.00	35.0
10. ☐	Hand Mirror. Beaded edge with scroll work marked "STERLING" or "PURE COIN"	14.00	30.0
11. ☐	Military Brush Set. Marked "STERLING" or "PURE COIN"	30.00	55.0
12. ☐	Velvet Brush or Clothes Brush. Marked "STERLING" or "PURE COIN"	9.50	17.5

*These items were usually made in pattern sets. Complete sets are almost impossible to find in shops, but pairs are fairly common.

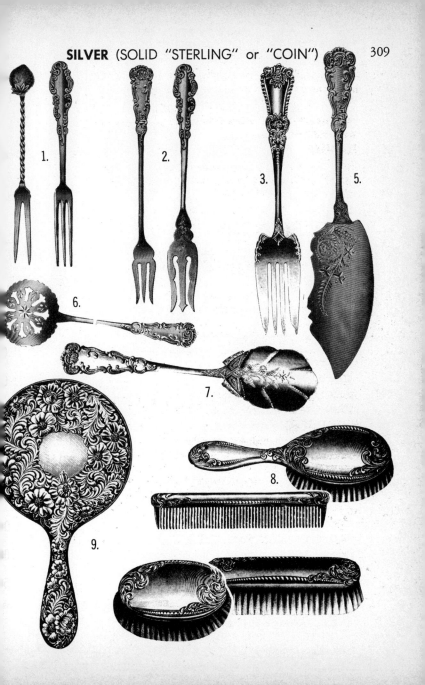

1.

2.

3.

5.

6.

7.

8.

9.

SILVER (SOLID "STERLING" or "COIN")

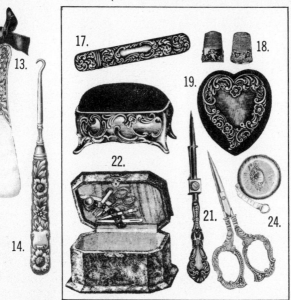

Item & Description	*A.B.P.	Ret
13. ☐ Shoe Horns	6.00	12.0
14. ☐ Button Hooks	3.00	6.0
MANICURE ITEMS		
15. ☐ Scissors, cuticle, and others	3.00	6.0
16. ☐ Files and cuticle pusher	2.50	5.0
SEWING ITEMS		
17. ☐ Needlecases	5.00	10.0
18. ☐ Thimbles	1.50	3.0
19. ☐ Pincushions	4.00	8.0
20. ☐ Pincushion Boxes	11.00	22.0
21. ☐ Bodkins and Ribbon Pulls	2.00	4.0
22. ☐ Chatelaines—complete set with 4 implements	35.00	75.0
23. ☐ Embroidery scissors with sheath	10.00	20.0
24. ☐ Tape Measures	5.00	10.0

Large size, unusual patterns, forms or designs—DOUBLE PRICE

***A.B.P.—Average Buying Price see pg. 5**

Courtesy: Old Horizons Antiques, 276 Bleecker St., N.Y.C. 10014

ly plating efforts resulted in "Sheffield" Silver. The base metal is copper.

1.

2.

5.

7.

Item, Description and Date	A.B.P.	Retail
☐ Basket. Cake or Bread. Ornate beaded rims. Early 1800's	65.00	120.00
☐ Candle Snuffer with rest. Shaped like hat	20.00	45.00
☐ Candlesticks. Telescopic. Circa 1800. Pair	85.00	150.00
☐ Coffeepot. 7 cup or 8 cup capacity, light scroll work. Circa 1800	150.00	230.00
☐ Cooler. For wine or champagne, with handles. Flat bottom or pedestal bottom. Circa 1830	75.00	150.00
☐ Entree Dish, with Cover. Flaired handles, wooden grips	65.00	125.00
☐ Goblets. Water or wine. Finely etched designs, flared rims. Late 1790's to 1800. Pair	95.00	175.00
☐ Meat Platter. 26 inches long. Beaded edge. scrolled handles. Circa 1820	90.00	160.00
☐ Salt and Pepper Holders. Blue glass linings with tray. Late 1790's	40.00	75.00
☐ Teapot. Pedestal Base. Seven sided, flaired neck, with scroll work, crested top. Classic handle About 1790	125.00	200.00
☐ Tray. 16" x 25". Ornate handles, fine scroll work in center. Four fluted legs	75.00	140.00
☐ Tray. 20" x 30". For tea service, very ornate floral patterns at center	140.00	250.00

Prices on Sheffield Silver, other than famous makers (Boulton, etc.), holding at past price levels.

SILVER (PLATED)

An electrolytic process of plating silver to various alloy bases was perfecte
the 1850's, making it possible for even the most modest household to po
decorative silver pieces.

**These prices may vary sho
depending on the locality.**

5.

12.

20.

All Prices are for Good Condition

	Item & Description	*A.B.P.	Ret
1. ☐	Basket. For candy. Round, squat shape with curved, reeded handle. Ornate scroll designs on sides. Silver plated	20.00	37
2. ☐	Basket. For fruit. Flat dish-shape with scrolled legs and handle. Fluted sides. Silver plated	22.50	42
3. ☐	Butter Dish. Large, ornately scrolled silver bulb. With dome-shaped cover and high curved handle. Silver plated	20.00	45.
4. ☐	Butter Dish. Dome shaped cover with bulb handle. Base is fluted with four balled feet. Silver plate	17.50	30.

*A.B.P. — Average Buying Price

Courtesy: OLD HORIZONS, 276 Bleecker Street, N.Y.C. 10014

SILVER (PLATED)

All Prices are for Good Condition

Item & Description	A.B.P.	Retail
☐ Butter Dish. Wide flat bowl with circular, drop-sided cover. Silver plated	14.00	25.00
☐ Candlestick. Deep bowl with curved, feather handle. Straight candle support. Silver plated	15.00	27.50
☐ Candlestick. Ornately cut, sculptured base and stem. Wide, cylindrical holder. Silver plated	16.00	30.00
☐ Candy Dish. Wide, flat plate with handsome leaf and scroll designs on outer edges. Silver plated	30.00	60.00
☐ Castor Set. Five bottle set. Matched, covered group in excellent condition. Silver plated	30.00	50.00
☐ Coffee Percolator. Large, double-handled urn shape with spigot and faucet. Flat base and scrolled sides. Silver plated	45.00	75.00
☐ Cup. Child's. "Tom The Piper's Son" nursery rhyme engraved. Reeded handle. Silver plated	12.50	20.00
☐ Cup. Squat with scrolled overlay. Silver plated	10.00	20.00
☐ Pickle Castor. Squat bowl with floral and leaf designs on side. Curled feet. Complete with tongs. Silver plated	12.50	25.00
☐ Service. Tea. 3-piece set, with creamer, sugar bowl and tea pot. Victorian design. Silver plated	55.00	85.00
☐ Sugar Bowl. Low bowl with domed cover. Long, curved handles	10.00	20.00
☐ Tea Pot. Floral and leaf design. Curled feet. Domed-cover with long curved handle and feet. Silver plated	25.00	40.00
☐ Tea Pot. High, bulbous neck. Curved feet and spout. Covered with sculptured top. Silver plated	27.50	47.50
☐ Water Set. High pitcher with floral decorations and reeded handle. Covered with sculptured goblet. Silver plated	35.00	65.00
☐ Water Set. Scrolled pitcher with stand. Curved feet. Mounted handle which swivels at center. Two goblets. Silver plated	40.00	75.00
☐ Water Pitcher. Curved, squat design with tiny floral decorations. Wide neck and flared mouth. Reinforced handle. Silver plated	27.50	50.00

SHAVING MUGS

In the latter part of the 19th century, shaving mugs of various sizes a shapes were quite popular. They were generally kept at the local barber sh and had the owner's name and occupation inscribed on the outside.

All prices are for Good Condition

Item & Description:	*A.B.P.	Ret
☐ Accordion	31.50	65
☐ Anchor. With owner's name inscribed	18.00	42.
☐ Anvil, Tongs and Hammer	22.50	57.
☐ Architect's insignia	19.00	40.
☐ Athlete. High Jumper	39.00	78.
☐ Athlete. Track star	45.00	85.
☐ Baggage Master with Truck and Car	35.00	67.
☐ Bakery Wagon. Driver and horse	35.00	67.
☐ Bartender	40.00	78.
☐ Baseball Player	58.00	100.
☐ Baseball with bats	52.00	84.0
☐ Beer Bottle & Glasses around barrel of Beer	32.50	60.0
☐ Beer Wagon with horse and driver	38.00	76.
☐ Bicycle	42.00	84.
☐ Bill Poster	48.50	97.
☐ Boiler Maker at work	39.00	78.
☐ Bookmaker at work	42.00	84.
☐ Brakeman operating brake	35.00	71.
☐ Bridge, Steel	36.00	73.
☐ Buggy, Horse & Driver	32.50	65.0
☐ Butcher killing steer	32.50	65.0
☐ Caboose	34.00	68.2
☐ Camera	55.00	110.2
☐ Carpenter at work	31.00	64.0

Fraternal Shaving Mugs (Masons, K. of C., Pythians,) ***A.B.P.— Average Buying Price** *range in price from $15.00 to $30.00.*

Item & Description	*A.B.P.	Retail
Clothing Store	35.00	71.50
Coal Miner at work	55.00	100.00
Cooper at work making barrels	38.00	77.50
Dentist and False Teeth	61.50	92.50
Doctor tending patient (pulling teeth)	98.00	130.00
Drug Store	34.00	68.25
Druggist at work	32.50	65.00
Engine in Station	29.00	58.50
Fire Steam Engine	75.00	130.00
Flour and General Store	38.00	77.50
Furniture Store	32.50	65.00
Guns. Crossed rifles and targets	42.00	80.00
Hatter at work	35.00	71.50
Hotel Register	39.00	78.00
Ice Wagon. Horse and driver	42.00	82.00
Jewelry Store	39.00	78.00
Jockey	42.00	80.00
Livery Stable	52.00	104.00
Locomotive	39.00	78.00
Marble Cutter at work	31.50	68.50
Milk Wagon. Horse and Driver	35.00	71.50
Minister in Pulpit	75.00	130.00
Painter at work	39.00	78.00
Piano Player	39.00	78.00
Policeman	58.00	117.00
Printer setting type	30.00	62.50
Prizefighter	160.00	260.00
Restaurant and Bar	35.00	71.50
Sawmill	37.00	70.00
Shoe Dealer	29.00	58.00
Steamship	36.00	73.50
Tailor. With assistant	30.00	60.00
Telegrapher	32.50	65.00
Tow Truck and driver	43.50	87.75
Tug Boat	75.00	126.00
Undertaker	160.00	260.00

A.B.P. — Average Buying Price — See Page 5

TOLE — (TINWARE)

The term Tole was generally used to refer to painted items made of sheet me
Popular usage came to mean all tinware. All Tole items are of a practical natu

NOTE: Reproductions are made.

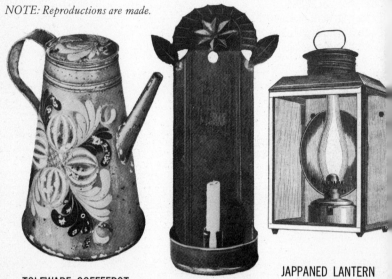

TOLEWARE COFFEEPOT

CANDLE HOLDER

JAPPANED LANTERN

All Prices Shown are for Good Condition:

Prices for Origin
Pieces Only

Item & Description	*A.B.P.	Re
☐ Bathtub. 16" deep, 30" around	16.00	40.
☐ Candle-Holder. Wall-type. 18th century (Revere)	27.00	55.
☐ Candle Molds. Makes 12 Candles	11.00	35.
☐ Canisters. Coffee or Tea (2)	6.00	12.
☐ Card-rack. For Postcards	11.00	22.
☐ Coffee Pot. Large, decorated with stencil flowers	12.00	24.
☐ Cookie Cutters. Various Animals, simple shapes	2.50	5.
☐ Dipper. Long-handled	3.50	9.
☐ Dispatch Case	3.50	7.
☐ Foot Warmer. Pierced pattern; round shape	6.50	13.
☐ Gun Powder Case	9.00	18.
☐ Jack-O-Lantern. Pair	6.50	13.
☐ Lantern. With Snuffer	12.00	24.

*A.B.P. — Average Buying Price

TOLE — (TINWARE)

COOKIE CUTTER

CANDLE MOLD

TEA POT

WATER PITCHER

All Prices Shown are for Good Condition:

Item & Description	*A.B.P.	Retail
Match Safe. Double	2.50	5.50
Mold. Full-sized Turkey with cover	18.00	26.00
Mustache Curling Set	7.50	15.00
Pint Measure. With handle and spout	2.00	4.50
Pitcher. Water, with floral decor	11.50	30.00
Rattle. Baby's, with whistle handle. Porcelain mouth	5.50	11.50
Scoop. General Store Type	3.50	7.50
Spice Box. 6 round tin boxes in handled container	6.00	12.50
Syrup Pitcher. Pint-size with lid	4.00	8.00
Tray. Chippendale-type, decorated w/flowers & scroll●	18.00	40.00
Wash Bowl and Pitcher	13.00	28.00

.B.P. — Average Buying Price — See Page 5
●le trays range from $7.00 to $65.00.

TIN CONTAINERS (CANS)

To retard food spoilage, early 19th century efforts produced the first
containers. Containers, with lids hinged or not, that could be reused, are
most desirable. Containers fashioned to resemble actual objects, or facsir
tins are the most valuable. Geometric tins less valuable. Condition, ra
and age effect the price. Location of sale effects price. "Hot" tins comm
the same price regardless of area. Huntley & Palmer tins are very desira

All Prices are for Good Condition unless otherwise noted.

	Item & Description	Re
1. ☐	Baker's Breakfast Cocoa.....................................	1
2. ☐	Blue Label Soup. 1850......................................	8
3. ☐	Bimbo English Cleanser. 1850............................	1
4. ☐	Colgan's Taffy Tolu. Square Can. 1887..................	28
5. ☐	Dedham's Licorice. 1888. With open window........	22
6. ☐	Fry's Concentrated Cocoa. High oval can.............	25
7. ☐	FFFG Gunpowder. Tin box (Dead-Shot).................	28
8. ☐	Great Books Cookie Tin. In shape of two shelves of books. Huntley Palmer mfg. Co. ca. 1890..............	40.00-90
9. ☐	Highland Brand Evaporated Cream. British. Large squat can..	20
10. ☐	Huntley & Palmers Biscuit Tin, Hinged lid. Made in form of old coach light, pix on sides......................	25.00-35
11. ☐	Huntley & Palmers Breakfast Biscuits (pull off lid). Large size, paper label—top, bottom, sides. ca. 1900	10.00-15
12. ☐	Lucky Strike Club Plug Tobacco (hinged lid)..........	2.00-5
13. ☐	Kensett & Co. Canned fish. 1842. Original American canning company..	25
14. ☐	Mayo's Brownie Tin (pull off lid). Humpty-Dumpty type 7" x 9" cir...	40.00-60.
15. ☐	New Mikado Oil & Gasoline Can. Complete with filler top and top-mounted pump for filling gas lamps....	35.
16. ☐	Parke-Davis Aspirin Box. Ca. 1890. Fluted top on square can...	15.
17. ☐	Superior Toothpowder. Colorfully illustrated container..	10.
18. ☐	Windsor Coffee. Tall can with angled cap. 1895......	15.
19. ☐	Windsor Coconut (pull off lid) paper label.............	5.00-8.
20. ☐	Woodman Bros. Canned tuna. Late 1850's. Maryland mfg...	30.

7.

14.

10.

12.

8.

Coffee (6" x 13" in cir.)—
w top lid...............3.00-5.00

ad Cigarettes (5-1/2"x4-1/4" x
/2"—hinged lid......2.00-4.00

19.

3.

ourtesy: Ernest L. Pettit, Book of Collectible Tin Containers (Book I—$3.95, Book II—$4.95)
Wynantsville, N.Y. 12198.

One More Shot

Taking the Oath
and
Drawing Rations

The Council
of War

Lincoln,
Stanton,
Grant

The Wounded Scout

the 1860's, American artist John Rogers created a new kind of sculpture, sisting of large, life-like figure groups. His first work, "The Checker yers" met with such success that fifty such groups followed. Pressed into lds and produced by the thousands, Rogers Statuary has become increasingly ular among collectors during the past decade.

All Prices are for Good Condition Unless Otherwise Noted.

Item & Description	Retail
Checker Players. 1860	80.00
Coming to the Parson	78.00
Fairy Whispers. Ca. 1861	75.00
Fetching The Doctor	85.00
First Love	70.00
Football	110.00
Going For The Cows	110.00
John Alden and Priscilla	92.00
King Lear and Cordelia	72.00
Legend of Sleepy Hollow. Three studies	110.00
Miles Standish	75.00
One More Shot	115.00
Othello. Large group scene	85.00
Rip Van Winkle	95.00
Romeo and Juliet. Love scene	72.00
Taking The Oath and Drawing Rations	110.00
The Bath. 1890	80.00
The Charity Patient	105.00
The Council of War. President Lincoln, Secretary Stanton and General Grant	185.00
The Country Post Office	110.00
The Fugitive Story	80.00
The Picket Guard. Union soldier	90.00
The Slave Auction	82.00
The Slave Market	90.00
The Town Pump	92.00
The Watch on the Santa Maria	75.00
The Wounded Scout	85.00
Union Refugees	92.00
Weighing The Baby. Family scene	95.00

SHAVING SETS

Most shaving mugs were made of china, glass, or stoneware, especially th[...]
found in 19th century barber shops. Silver and silver plate were also used
sets with brush and soap cup. Being unbreakable these sets were popular v[...]
travelling men. The soap cups were made with handles and without hand[...]
Silver handle brushes could be purchased separately to be used with ch[...]
shaving cups. Both the handle of the brush, and the cup, were often engra[...]
with the owner's name.

1.

*See pages 314-315, for
Chinaware Shaving Mugs*

2.

3.

All prices are for Good Condition.

Item & Description:	*A.B.P.	Reta[...]
1. ☐ Shaving Brush, Solid Silver Handle, Plain	10.00	20.[...]
2. ☐ Shaving Set, Brush & Soap Cup, Solid Silver	22.50	45.[...]
3. ☐ Shaving Set, Brush & Soap Cup with Handle, Solid Silver Heavily Engraved, Floral Design	48.00	95.[...]

*A.B.P. — Average Buying Price

NOTE: Silver Plated items are 50% of quoted Retail Price.

and 20th century publications are the most sought after. Catalogues from
s and Montgomery Ward are the most valuable. Specialty catalogues,
as Lamps, Guns, Arms, Silverware, Photo Equipment, Clocks are also
e valuable.

BUFFALO BILL WEEKLY   1904 SEARS, ROEBUCK CATALOG

Item & Description Prices are for Good Condition	*A.B.P.	Retail
Art Journal. (1876)...	6.00	12.50
Buffalo Bill Weekly (1916), Street & Smith, ea. issue....	2.00	4.00
Country Life & Times in America (1908)......................	1.00	2.50
Catalogue, Cray Brothers. (1916)...............................	4.50	9.75
Firearms. Pistols, rifles & shotguns. (1884) Catalogue..	6.50	20.00
Godey's Lady's Book. (1865) w/color plates................	10.00	25.00
Godey's Lady's Book. (1859) w/color plates................	12.00	30.00
Harper's Magazines. 6-mo. ser., 1866, hard bound......	6.00	12.00
Ladies Home Journal. 10 years to 1918. Each yr.........	1.00	2.00
Macy's Catalogues. 1907-1909. Each yr......................	8.00	20.00
Montgomery Ward & Co. 1912, 874 pgs. General Cat...	25.00	65.00
National Geographics, 1920 thru 1930**....................	1.00	2.50
Peterson's Magazine. Mid 19-century. Ea. book, w/color	12.00	25.00
Sears Catalogues. 1931-32. Each................................	10.00	22.00
Sears Catalogue. 1904, 1240 pgs. General Cat.............	30.00	75.00
Saturday Evening Post. 1900-1920, each issue............	.50	1.50

*A.B.P. — Average Buying Price   **1930—1960 $1.00 ea.

TOBACCO JARS & HUMIDORS

Made of wood, china, pottery, iron or other metals, the Tobacco Jar
generally a combination humidor and pipe holder. Frequently, it was not o
functional but also quite ornately decorated. Sculptured heads, figures,
animals were quite common.

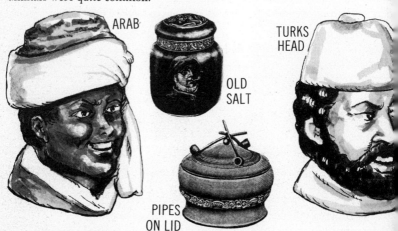

ARAB

OLD
SALT

TURKS
HEAD

PIPES
ON LID

Item & Description — Prices are for Good Condition:	*A.B.P.	Re
☐ Arab. Wearing headdress...	20.00	42
☐ Buffalo, Pottery. Deldare Ware....................................	35.00	70
☐ Bulldog. Bristol Ware...	15.00	38.
☐ Devils Head. Color Red, Bee on side of head................	11.00	28.
☐ Egyptian Queen. Exotic Face.....................................	16.00	38.
☐ Girl's Face. With light hair. Hat functions as cover........	20.00	40.
☐ Indian Chief. Majolica. Feathered headdress................	16.00	40.
☐ Jockey. Colored boy with cap. Majolica pottery............	16.00	40.
☐ Lion's Head...	15.00	30.
☐ Man. Seated on chair. Staffordshire China...................	28.00	56.
☐ Man. With Skull Cap. English pottery..........................	21.00	43.
☐ Monk. Fat, with laughing face, bisque chinaware..........	16.50	38.
☐ Monkey Head. Sports cap and pipe............................	25.00	50.
☐ Old Salt. Sea Captain, with cap and pipe (Illus.)...........	16.00	32.
☐ Pipes on Cover. Pink and green pottery (Illus.).............	17.50	42.
☐ Ram's Head. Majolica Ware..	15.00	30.
☐ Royal Bayreuth. Tapestry ware. Cows in field..............	32.50	70.0

*A.B.P. — Average Buying Price

r the newer toy collectors the field of Comic and Cartoon Character Toys
becoming quite popular. There are thousands of toys in this category, and
e have listed a representative cross-section of the most popular and desirable
ys. Toys priced here are complete, and if mechanical must be in good working
der. Paint condition must be good to fine. Toys in original box—slightly
gher value.

A fair offer to purchaxe by a dealer would be 35% to 50% of the prices
dicated below.

*e Pages 208-209
r Color Pictures*

Approximate Price (or Market Value) in Average Condition	Retail From	To
1. ☐ Popeye on Roof. Tin Mech. Marx..........................	25.00-50.00	
2. ☐ Popeye & Olive Oyl on Roof. Tin Mech. Marx........	25.00-50.00	
3. ☐ Popeye with Parrot & Cages. Tin Mech. Marx........	25.00-50.00	
4. ☐ Popeye in Air Plane. Tin Mech. Marx....................	25.00-50.00	
5. ☐ Popeye & Cart with Parrot. Tin Mech. Marx..........	25.00-50.00	
6. ☐ Popeye & Punching Bag. Tin Mech. Chein............	25.00-50.00	
7. ☐ Popeye in Barrel. Tin Mech. Chein......................	25.00-50.00	
8. ☐ Popeye Band. Tin Mech. Chein...........................	10.00-25.00	
9. ☐ Popeye Rollover Tin Figure..................................		
0. ☐ Tootsietoy "Funnies" Series, Set of 6, Cast Metal	over 100.00	
1. ☐ Amos & Andy "Fresh Air Taxi". Tin Mech. Marx....	75.00-100.00	
2. ☐ Charlie McCarthy, Mortimer Snerd Car. Tin Mech. Marx..	25.00-50.00	
3. ☐ Charlie McCarthy Car. Tin Mech. Marx..................	25.00-50.00	
4. ☐ Charlie McCarthy. Tin Mech. Figure. Marx............	25.00-50.00	
5. ☐ Joe Penner & Goo Goo the Duck. Tin Mech. Marx	50.00-75.00	

See Pages 208-209 for Color Pictures

Approximate Price (or Market Value) in Average Condition

Item, Description, and Manufacturer	Retail From	To
16. ☐ Spark Plug. Tin Mech.	50.00-75.0	
17. ☐ Maggie & Jiggs. Tin Mech.	50.00-75.0	
18. ☐ Li'l Abner Band. Tin Mech. Unique Art	50.00-75.0	
19. ☐ Howdy Doody Band. Tin Mech.	50.00-75.0	
20. ☐ Powerful Katrinka & Jimmy. Tin Mech.	75.00-100.0	
21. ☐ Powerful Katrinka & Jimmy in Wheel Barrel	75.00-100.0	
22. ☐ Toonerville Trolley. Tin Mech. German	75.00-100.0	
23. ☐ Toonerville Trolley. Tin Miniature, Non-Mech.	25.00-50.0	
24. ☐ Toonerville Trolley. Cast Iron Pull Toy	over 100.0	
25. ☐ Orphan Annie, Skipping Rope. Tin Mech.	25.00-50.0	
26. ☐ Sandy. Tin Mech.	10.00-25.0	
27. ☐ Mortimer Snerd. Tin Mech. Figure. Marx	25.00-50.0	
28. ☐ B. O. Plenty & Sparkle. Tin Mech. Marx	10.00-25.0	
29. ☐ Superman Rollover Tank, 4". Tin Mech. Marx	25.00-50.0	
30. ☐ Superman Rollover Air Plane, 6". Tin Mech.	25.00-50.0	
31. ☐ Buck Rogers Rocket Police Patrol. Tin Mech.	75.00-100.0	
31. ☐ Felix. Wooden Pull Toy with 2 Mice. Nifty Toys	25.00-50.0	
33. ☐ Felix "Speedy Felix" Wooden Roadster w/bellows Nifty Toys	50.00-75.0	
34. ☐ Felix Bowler, Bowling Game. Nifty Toys	25.00-50.0	
35. ☐ Felix on 3 Wheeled Scooter. Mech. 7". Nifty Toys	25.00-50.0	
36. ☐ Felix. Sparkler, Squeeze Mech. Felix's Head. Nifty	10.00-25.0	
37. ☐ Felix Wagon, Wooden Pull Toy. Nifty Toys	10.00-25.0	
38. ☐ Mickey Mouse Drummer. Tin Mech. Nifty Toy	75.00-100.00	
39. ☐ Mickey Mouse Circus, Wooden Pull Toy. Tumbling Mickey & Minnie. Nifty Toys	10.00-25.00	
40. ☐ Mickey Mouse Sparkler, Squeeze Mech. Mickey's Head. Nifty Toys	10.00-25.00	
41. ☐ Mickey Mouse Acrobat. Wooden Squeeze, 12". Nifty Toys	10.00-25.00	
42. ☐ Harold Lloyd. Tin Mech. Figure, 11"	over 100.00	
43. ☐ Amos & Andy. Tin Mech. Figure, 12"	25.00-50.00	
44. ☐ Happy Hooligan. Tin Mech. Figure, 5". Chein	over 100.00	
45. ☐ Charlie Chaplin. Tin Mech. Figure, 9". German		
46. ☐ Porky Pig. Tin Mech. Figure with Lasso. Marx	10.00-25.00	
47. ☐ Lone Ranger. Tin Mech. with Lasso, with Horse	10.00-25.00	
48. ☐ Uncle Wiggily Car. Tin Mech.	25.00-50.00	

See Pages 210-213 for all Toy Color Photos

e collecting of Toys ranks today in popularity with the collecting of Mechan-
and Still Banks. A few toys, particularly some of the earlier Tin and Iron
ces are approaching prices comparable to many mechanical banks. In
st cases Toys are not as scarce, therefore they are far less expensive. To
e "COLLECTOR VALUE", Toys must be complete, with no missing parts,
mechanical they should be in good working order. Paint condition should
"Good" to "Fine". Toys in original boxes have a slightly higher value.
ces quoted here are current RETAIL PRICES for ORIGINAL TOYS in
ood" to "Fine" condition. **A fair offer for purchase by a dealer would be
% to 50% of the stated Retail Value indicated below for a Toy in
ood" condition.**

ices quoted are for
RIGINAL TOYS ONLY.
productions are made, particularly
cast iron.

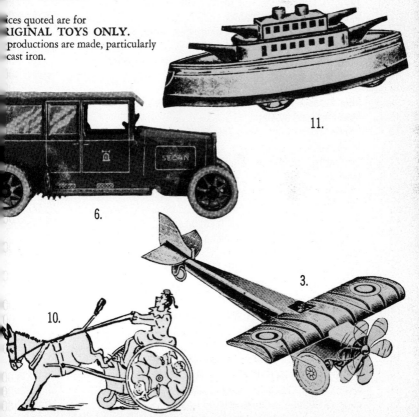

11.

6.

10.

3.

TOYS—TIN, IRON and WOOD

See Pages 210-213 for all Toy Color Photos

Item, Description, Manufacturer	Retail From
1. ☐ Airplane—"Dare-Devil Flyer", with hangar, with plane, with Blimp. 10" tall, Manufactured by Marx	25.00-50.0
2. ☐ Airplane—"Cross-Country Flyer", plane/airship/tower. 19" long, Manufactured by Marx	25.00-50.0
3. ☐ Airplane—U.S. Marines, single wing airplane, tin, mech. 17" x 17", circa 1930	25.00-50.0
4. ☐ Airplane—Ford Tri-Motor plane, pressed steel, 25"x24"	50.00-75.0
5. ☐ Airplane—Cast iron, single wing plane, 4" long	10.00-25.0
6. ☐ Auto, 4 door sedan, tin mech. with driver, 7" long. Manufactured by Lehmann	25.00-50.0
7. ☐ Auto, "Model T" Ford, 7" long, cast iron. Manufactured by Arcade	25.00-50.0
8. ☐ Auto, "Service Car", cast iron, nickeled wheels, 5" long. Manufactured by Hubley	10.00-25.0
9. ☐ "Big Parade", soldiers, trucks, ambulances, 24" long. Manufactured by Marx	50.00-75.0
10. ☐ "Balky Mule", tin, mech./clown driver, 7-1/4" long. Manufactured by Lehmann	25.00-50.0
11. ☐ Battleship, friction motor, 16" long. Manufactured by Dayton	25.00-50.0
12. ☐ "Bucking Bronco" with rider, tin, mech. 7" long. Manufactured by Lehmann	25.00-50.0
13. ☐ Buggy with driver, cast iron, medium size	25.00-50.0
14. ☐ Bus, Double Decker, tin, mech., 8-1/2" long. Manufactured by Lehmann	100.00-150.0
15. ☐ Cap Pistol, small, non mech. Patent 1887	10.00-25.0
16. ☐ Circus Wagon, 2 Horses, one Lion. Manufactured by Hubley 1906	50.00-75.0
17. ☐ Circus Wagon, 2 Horses, two Lions, 9-1/2" long. Manufactured by Hubley	50.00-75.0
18. ☐ "Corn Shooter" pistol, Cast iron	10.00-25.0
19. ☐ Cow, Calfskin, on platform, moos when pulled, 10" long..	25.00-50.0
20. ☐ Dump Truck, cast iron & tin, donkey, Harris, 1906	25.00-50.00
21. ☐ Dump Truck, cast iron, medium size	50.00-75.00
22. ☐ Elephant Jumbo, wooden with tin legs	10.00-25.00

10.

13.

14.

16.

17.

18.

19.

23.

Prices Quoted are for ORIGINAL Toys Only

Item, Description, Manufacturer	Retail From	T·
23. ☐ Fire Engine Hook & Ladder, 3 horses. Manufactured by Harris	50.00-75.0	
24. ☐ Fire Engine, Pumper, with Boiler, 3 horses. Manufactured by Hubley	75.00-100.0	
25. ☐ Fire Truck, pressed steel, medium size. Manufactured by Buddy "L"	25.00-50.0	
26. ☐ Fire Hose Wagon, cast iron, 2 horse & driver, 14" long. Manufactured by Hubley	50.00-75.00	
27. ☐ Frog, Tin mechanical, Jumps	10.00-25.00	
28. ☐ Hay Wagon, wooden with 2 horses, 14" long	25.00-50.00	
29. ☐ Ice Wagon & horse, wooden, "Silver Moon." Circa 1920, 22" long	25.00-50.00	
30. ☐ Ice Wagon with 2 horses, 10" long	25.00-50.00	
31. ☐ Light House, water basin with man & boat, tin mech., 12" long	50.00-75.00	
32. ☐ "Leapin' Lena", tin mech. car, 5-1/2" long	10.00-25.00	
33. ☐ Man sawing wood, tin mech., 5" long	10.00-25.00	
34. ☐ Monkey on Tricycle, tin mech	10.00-25.00	
35. ☐ Monkey "Tippo" climbing. Tin mech. Manufactured by Marx 1930	10.00-25.00	
36. ☐ "Pacer" with driver, cast iron, 1 horse 8" long. Manufactured by Hubley	50.00-75.00	
37. ☐ Patrol Wagon, cast iron, 2 horses, 10" long. Manufactured by Hubley	25.00-50.00	
38. ☐ "Pinched", cars in circle/cop/station, 10" x 10". Manufactured by Marx	25.00-50.00	
39. ☐ Sewing machine, nickel plated, 10" long	10.00-25.00	
40. ☐ Steam Engine, Horizontal, alcohol burner, mech., med...	25.00-50.00	
41. ☐ Steam Engine, V. or H., electrical Heater	10.00-25.00	
42. ☐ Steam Engine, vertical, alcohol burner, brass-iron	50.00-75.00	
43. ☐ Speed boat, with driver, cast iron, nickel wheels, 6" L...	10.00-25.00	
44. ☐ Stove "Royal" with utensils, cast iron, nickel plated	25.00-50.00	
45. ☐ Train Engine with tender, wood & tin, friction, 19" long Circa 1900	50.00-75.00	
46. ☐ Train set, miniature, 3 pieces 12" long. Manufactured by Harris	10.00-25.00	

Prices Quoted are for ORIGINAL Toys Only

30.

21.

HYGEIA ICE

42.

LENA 32.

41.

43.

44.

ROYAL

35.

Prices quoted are for
ORIGINAL TOYS ONLY.
Reproductions are made, particularly
in cast iron.

TOYS — TIN, IRON and WOOD
Prices Quoted are for ORIGINAL Toys Only

Item, Description & Date	Retail	
	From	To
47. ☐ Train engine, with tender, 2 cars manufactured by Hubley 1880....................	75.00	100.00
48. ☐ Tow Truck with driver, Black rubber wheels, 9" long...... Manufactured by Kingsbury............................	25.00	50.00
49. ☐ Touring car, 4 door, tin mech., manufactured by Bing....	75.00	100.00
50. ☐ Truck, "Pick-up", white rubber wheels, 5" long..............	10.00	25.00
51. ☐ Trolley, "Hill Climber"—tin, friction motor, 15" long Manufactured by Dayton....................	50.00	75.00
52. ☐ Zeppelin, "Akron", pressed steel, 28" long. Manufactured by Marx. Circa 1930............................	50.00	75.00
53. ☐ "Zig Zag", tin, mech., 2 wheels, 2 drivers. Manufactured by Lehmann.............................	75.00	100.00

47.

39.

49.

53.

51.

Item, Description & Date	Retail From	To
54. ☐ Hose Reel wagon, cast iron, 1 horse, 2 firemen, made by Carpenter-circa 1880, 14".long	100.00	150.00
55. ☐ Fire patrol wagon, cast iron, 3 horses, 4 firemen, made by Wilkens-circa 1900, 15" long	100.00	150.00
56. ☐ Train set, cast iron, locomotive, tender, 2 cars, made by Carpenter-circa 1900, 25" long	75.00	100.00
57. ☐ Fire patrol wagon, cast iron, 3 horses, driver & 4 firemen, made by Dent-circa 1910, 15" long	150.00	200.00
58. ☐ Reindeer & Santa sled, cast iron, 2 reindeer with original Santa figure, made by Hubley-circa 1926, 16½" long	150.00	200.00

Prices Quoted are for ORIGINAL Toys Only

Item, Description & Date	Retail From to
59. ☐ Hose reel, wagon, cast iron, 2 horses, 2 firemen, made by Wilkens-circa 1880, 15" long	150.00-200.00
60. ☐ Steam fire engine, tin and cast iron, steam boiler with fireman, made by Stevens & Brown Manufacturing-circa 1880, 15" long	150.00-200.00
61. ☐ Steam fire engine, cast iron, 2 horses with driver, made by Carpenter-circa 1880, 15" long	100.00-150.00
62. ☐ Steamer locomotive, tin, driven by live steam. English manufacture-circa 1910, 9" long	50.00-75.00
63. ☐ 5th wheel steamer, tin, bright yellow body. English manufacture-circa 1910, 8½" long	50.00-75.00

ORIGINS

Utensils and implements made of wood. Some of the following items isted may have been brought from the old country, but most were conceived and made of wood native to early America. The earliest American pieces differ according to the colonial settlements in which they originated, and exhibit the characteristics indigenous to New England, the Pennsylvania Dutch country, and the Virginia colonies. Later pieces can be attributed to the fast moving western frontier.

"EARMARKS" and WOODS

The key to judging the age, authenticity, and purpose of an item of woodenware is the "earmarks". The word, earmark, derived from the practice of branding a cow's ear for purposes of identification. The use of earmarks in identifying woodenware is slightly more complicated, and requires judicious use of the imagination. Most commonly sought are usage marks from wear, stains and odors. Woods used depended upon availability and durability. Maple is the most common wood found in household ware, due to its hardness, smooth finish, and attractive color. Pine ranks next as this tree grew in great profusion in the eastern United States; with birch, hickory, beech, chestnut, and the venerable oak following close behind.

USES

Woodenware can be classed on the basis of usage, of which the most plentiful are kitchen ware, eating and drinking utensils, and other household and farming tools.

LISTING

Items of woodenware exist in countless varieties and in such profusion that a complete listing would take volumes. We present the following as a representation of a cross-section of the items most readily available at most dealers and of greatest interest to the collector and novice alike. **A fair buying price by a dealer would be 50% off the quoted retail price.**

336

WOODENWARE

BOWLS · TANKARD · NOGGIN · BROOM · SLAT WASHBOARD

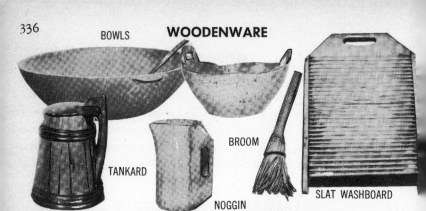

Item & Condition	Retail
EATING UTENSILS	
Bowls:	
14" x 23" (orig. paint)	31.00
15" diam. Burl (refinished)	72.00
16" diam. Maple (old)	23.00
22" long, 8" deep (turned)	37.00
Drinking Cup	9.00
Eating Spoons:	
Refinished	6.50
Rough	5.50
Noggins	6.50
Plates	8.75
Platters	13.00
Spoon Holder	12.00
Tankards with cover	12.00
Tankards with Toddy Hole	16.00
FARMING IMPLEMENTS	
Ox Yokes:	
With bows	45.00
Without bows	41.00
Pitch Forks:	
Four Tine	21.00
Two Tine	14.00
Shovels:	
Grain, all wood. Large	37.00
Wagon Parts:	
Wagon Jack	16.00
Wagon Seat	62.00
Wagon Wheel (different sizes)	30-80

Item & Condition	Retail
HOUSEHOLD ITEMS (Misc.)	
Brooms:	
Birch	15.00
Fireplace	10.00
Long handle, kitchen	15.00
Carrying Yolk	22.00
Cider Press	34.00
Clothes Mangler	28.00
Clothes Pins	2.50
Clothesline winder	8.00
Darning Egg, with handle	5.00
Foot Warmer for charcoal (as had)	9.50
Letter Writing box (refinished)	28.00
Sieves:	
Wooden Mesh (as had)	9.50
Horse Hair Mesh	14.00
Washboards:	
Slat	15.50
Spool	18.00
Washtub, Scrubbing Stick	4.00
Water Pump	16.50
Wall Bucket	13.50
Whetstone:	
Foot operated	56.00

Pictures Courtesy Charles E. Tuttle Co. "EARLY AMERICAN WOODENWARE" — Gould

SAP BUCKET & SPILES

KITCHEN & PANTRYWARE

Item & Condition	Approx. Retail
Baskets:	
Peck measure	13.00
Bowls:	
Chopping Bowl	20.00
Mixing Bowl	26.50
Boxes:	
Pill Box	11.50
Salt Box, Hanging pine, Dutch type (refinished)	47.50
Salt Box, 5½" x 6¼" x 6" high, covered pine (refinished)	23.00
Spice Box, Oval	20.50
Spice Box, Round	24.00
Sugar Box	15.00
Bread Peels (paddle for taking loaves out of oven)	20.00
Bread Trough	26.00

BUTTER MOLDS

SPICE BOX, ROUND

BREAD TROUGH

Item & Condition	Approx. Retail
KITCHEN & PANTRYWARE (cont.)	
Buckets:	
Sap Bucket	15.00
Sap Bucket. 11½" diam. Handle added (refinished)	21.00
Sugar, with cover	10.50
Sugar, without cover	9.00
Water Bucket	15.00
Butter Churn (as had)	28.00
Butter Molds:	
Cow (as had)	12.50
Flowers & Leaves (as had)	10.00
Round, lg. with leaf design (as had)	9.50
Round, Med. (as had)	8.00
Sheaf of Wheat (as had)	9.50
Butter Paddle (as had)	6.25
Butter Prints	12.50
Cheese Drainer	16.00
Cheese Press	42.50
Cookie Roller	6.25
Cooking Spoon	4.75
Dippers	8.50
Funnel	7.00
Hasty Pudding Stick	5.25

WEATHERVANES AND WHIRLIGIGS

A fair offer for purchase by a dealer would be 35% to 50% of stated Retail value, for a weathervane in "Good" condition.

All Prices are for Good Condition Unless Otherwise Noted.

	Item & Description	Retail
1. ☐	Archer. 30″ long. Minotaur-like figure holding drawn bow and wearing feathers. Copper	160.00
2. ☐	Automobile. Open roadster. Intricate detail. Heavy copper gilded with gold leaf. 26″ long	360.00
3. ☐	Automobile. Open top. Complete with goggled navigator and driver. Heavy copper	190.00
4. ☐	Banneret and Scroll. 3′ long. Ornately gilded copper.	250.00
5. ☐	Cannon. Mounted on spoked gun carriage. Reinforced barrel and stand. Copper	180.00
6. ☐	Cow. 42″ long. Short-horned Jersey. Scrolled direction indicators	230.00
7. ☐	Deer. 50″ long. Running buck with curved antlers. Full-bodied. Heavy copper	285.00
8. ☐	Dragon. 54″ long. Winged beast with snake-like tail. Crouching on stand above scrolled direction indicators	305.00
9. ☐	Eagle. 5′ scroll. Clawed feet resting on polished ball	385.00
10. ☐	Flag. Unfurled 48-star banner. With pointed standard	157.00
11. ☐	Fox. 30″ long. Running. Scrolled pointers. Copper	205.00
12. ☐	Greyhound. 30″ long. Long-legged animal standing on reinforced pedestal	230.00
13. ☐	Locomotive with Tender. 5′ long. Large model of late 19th century railroad machine	420.00
14. ☐	Lion. 4′ long. Large head with carved mane. Copper, mounted to reinforced base	430.00
15. ☐	Race Horse with Jockey. 32″ long Kentucky thoroughbred	170.00
16. ☐	Standing Indian. Original zinc finish. Single direction indicator. Rare	530.00
17. ☐	Trotting Horse. Sculptured, polished sides. Copper. Mounted.	380.00
18. ☐	Whirligig. 19th Century policeman. Single directional indicator	355.00
19. ☐	Whirligig. Man walking atop large umbrella. Carries walking stick	455.00
20. ☐	Whirligig. Flying Duck. Movable wings	430.00

CURRIER AND IVES PRINTS

A MIDNIGHT RACE ON THE MISSISSIPPI .... Large $875.00

Pictures Courtesy The Old Print Shop & New York Historical Society

The importance of Currier and Ives prints stems from the fact that the firm became the chronicler of the age through the production of thousands of prints depicting graphically that period in American history (1840 - 1890), known as the Industrial Revolution. In many cases the prints have recorded scenes of Americana as effectively as the eye of a camera. Exhibiting precise detail C & I prints were colored by hand by many artists. The firm was founded by Nathaniel Currier in 1835 and its existence spanned some 72 years.

Listing of all Currier & Ives prints is impossible, due to space limitations. The editors have compiled a listing of what they consider to be the most important prints, based upon historical significance and past and potential value appreciation. *Scenic prints, ships, disasters, political events and personages, wildlife, horses, sporting scenes,* and finally *fruit and flower* treatments are categories currently most popular. Other subjects, such as *portraits* and *biblical* scenes are available in greater number and are of less interest.

SIZE SPECIFICATIONS (EXCLUDING MARGINS):-

Small Folio	7-3/4″ —	13″
Medium Folio	13″ —	20″
Large Folio	20″ —	27″

CONDITION AND PRICING:-

Prices shown are for prints in fine condition, usually framed. Torn, faded, or stained prints command much lower values.

	Size	Retail
AARON CLARK, Mayor of New York City N. Currier; 1838	Small	50.00
ACCOMMODATION TRAIN, THE; 1875	Small	65.00
ACROSS THE CONTINENT; "Westward the Course of Empire Takes Its Way"	Large	44.00
ADMIRAL FARRAGUT'S FLEET ENGAGING THE REBEL BATTERIES AT PORT HUDSON, March 14, 1863	Small	65.00
ADMIRAL PORTER'S FLEET RUNNING THE REBEL BLOCKADE, April 16th, 1863	Small	48.00
AFFAIR OF HONOR, AN; "The Critical Moment"	Small	20.00
AFFAIR OF HONOR, AN; "Stray Shot" 1884	Small	20.00
AGE OF BRASS, THE; 1869	Small	52.50
AGE OF IRON, THE; 1869	Small	52.50
AGRICULTURAL HALL; 1876	Small	35.00
ALARM, THE; 1861	Small	65.00
ALL NICE AND HOT; N. Currier	Small	35.00
ALL RIGHT	Small	30.00
ALL WRONG; N. Currier	Small	40.00
AMATEUR MUSCLE IN THE SHELL; 1879	Medium	50.00
AMATEUR MUSCLE IN THE SHELL; 1879	Small	28.00
AMBUSCADE: THE	Medium	425.00
AMERICA; 1870	Small	30.00
AMERICAN AUTUMN FRUITS	Small	42.50
AMERICAN BROOK TROUT; 1872	Small	65.00
AMERICAN BUFFALOES	Small	75.00
AMERICAN CHAMPION YACHT "PURITAN", THE; 1885	Small	90.00
AMERICAN CHOICE FRUITS; 1869	Large	130.00
AMERICAN CLIPPER SHIP OFF SANDY HOOK LIGHT IN A BLIZZARD	Small	250.00
AMERICAN CLIPPER SHIP "WITCH OF THE WAVE"	Small	375.00
AMERICAN CLUB HUNT; "Halt On The Scent"; 1884	Small	50.00
AMERICAN CLUB HUNT; "Taking A Header"; 1884	Small	50.00
AMERICAN COAST SCENE, DESERT ROCK LIGHT HOUSE, MAINE	Medium	850.00
AMERICAN COTTAGE NO. 1; N. Currier	Small	40.00
AMERICAN COUNTRY LIFE; "May Morning"; 1855	Large	275.00
AMERICAN COUNTRY LIFE; "October Afternoon"; 1855	Large	275.00
AMERICAN COUNTRY LIFE; "Pleasures of Winter"; 1855	Large	300.00
AMERICAN COUNTRY LIFE; "Summer's Evening"; 1855	Large	200.00
AMERICAN DEAD GAME; 1866	Large	42.50
AMERICAN ECLIPSE; 1879	Small	75.00
AMERICAN EXPRESS TRAIN; N. Currier; 1853	Small	375.00
AMERICAN EXPRESS TRAIN; (Parsons); 1855	Large	2150.00
AMERICAN EXPRESS TRAIN; (Palmer); 1864	Large	1825.00
AMERICAN FARM LIFE; 1868	Medium	125.00
AMERICAN FARM SCENE; "In The Olden Time"	Small	60.00

	Size	Ret
☐ AMERICAN FARM SCENES, NO. 1; (Spring)	Large	400.
☐ AMERICAN FARM SCENES, NO. 2; (Summer)	Large	400.
☐ AMERICAN FARM SCENES, NO. 3; (Autumn)	Large	400.
☐ AMERICAN FARM SCENES, NO. 4; (Winter)	Large	900.
☐ AMERICAN FARMYARD — EVENING; 1857	Large	200.
☐ AMERICAN FARMYARD — MORNING; 1857	Large	200.
☐ AMERICAN FEATHERED GAME — MALLARD AND DUCKS; N. Currier 1854; (Oval)	Medium	165.
☐ AMERICAN FEATHERED GAME — PARTRIDGES; (Oval)	Medium	135.
☐ AMERICAN FEATHERED GAME — WOODCOCK AND GOLDEN EYE; N. Currier	Medium	145.
☐ AMERICAN FEATHERED GAME — WOODCOCK AND SNIPE; N. Currier; 1854; (Oval)	Medium	145.
☐ AMERICAN FEATHERED GAME — WOODCOCK AND SNIPE; N. Currier	Medium	145.
☐ AMERICAN FIELD SPORTS: "A Chance for Both Barrels"; 1857	Large	440.
☐ AMERICAN FIELD SPORTS: "Flush'd"; 1857	Large	440.
☐ AMERICAN FIELD SPORTS; "On A Point"; 1857	Large	440.
☐ AMERICAN FIELD SPORTS; "Retrieving"; 1857	Large	440.
☐ AMERICAN FIREMAN, THE; "Always Ready"; 1858	Medium	150.
☐ AMERICAN FIREMAN, THE; "Facing the Enemy"; 1858	Medium	150.
☐ AMERICAN FIREMAN, THE; "Prompt to the Rescue"; 1858	Medium	125.
☐ AMERICAN FIREMAN, THE; "Rushing to the Conflict"; 1858	Medium	150.
☐ AMERICAN FOREST GAME; 1866	Large	190.
☐ AMERICAN FOREST SCENE; "Maple Sugaring"; 1855	Large	1425.
☐ AMERICAN FRONTIER LIFE; "The Hunter's Stratagem"; 1862	Large	1325.0
☐ AMERICAN FRONTIER LIFE; "On the Warpath"; 1863	Large	1550.0
☐ AMERICAN FRUIT PIECE; 1859	Large	135.0
☐ AMERICAN FRUIT PIECE	Small	80.0
☐ AMERICAN FRUITS; 1861	Small	50.0
☐ AMERICAN GAME: 1866	Large	90.0
☐ AMERICAN GAME FISH; 1866	Large	145.0
☐ AMERICAN GIRL; 1871	Small	115.0
☐ "AMERICAN GIRL" and "LADY THORN" In Their Great Match for $2,000; 1869	Large	280.0
☐ AMERICAN HOMESTEAD (AUTUMN); 1869	Small	110.0
☐ AMERICAN HOMESTEAD (SPRING); 1869	Small	110.0
☐ AMERICAN HOMESTEAD (SUMMER); 1868	Small	110.0
☐ AMERICAN HOMESTEAD (WINTER); 1868	Small	225.0
☐ AMERICAN HUNTING SCENES; "An Early Start"; 1863	Large	640.0
☐ AMERICAN HUNTING SCENES; "A Good Chance"; 1863	Large	640.0
☐ AMERICAN JOCKEY CLUB RACES, JEROME PARK	Large	695.0
☐ AMERICAN LANDSCAPE; "Early Morning"	Large	275.0

	Size	Retail
AMERICAN LANDSCAPES (Four prints on one page)	Small	50.00
AMERICAN MOUNTAIN SCENERY; 1868	Medium	100.00
AMERICAN NATIONAL GAME OF BASE BALL, THE; "Grand Match For the Championship, etc." 1862	Large	3200.00
AMERICAN PRIVATEER, "GENERAL ARMSTRONG"	Small	195.00
AMERICAN PRIZE FRUIT; 1862	Large	150.00
AMERICAN PRIZE FRUIT	Small	50.00
AMERICAN RAILROAD SCENE; 1872	Small	375.00
AMERICAN RAILROAD SCENE; 1874	Small	250.00
AMERICAN RAILROAD SCENE; 1871; "Snowbound"	Small	450.00
AMERICAN RAILWAY SCENE AT HORNELLSVILLE; 1876	Large	2200.00
AMERICAN RIVER SCENERY; "View On The Androscoggin, Maine"	Medium	300.00
AMERICAN SHIP RESCUING THE CREW OF A BRITISH WARSHIP; 1863	Medium	200.00
AMERICAN SLOOP YACHT MAYFLOWER; 1886	Large	145.00
AMERICAN SLOOP YACHT VOLUNTEER; 1888	Large	155.00
AMERICAN SPECKLED BROOK TROUT; 1864	Large	250.00
AMERICAN STEAMBOATS ON THE HUDSON; 1874	Large	350.00
AMERICAN SUMMER FRUITS; 1875	Small	35.00
AMERICAN TAR, THE; "Don't Give Up The Ship"; N. Currier; 1845	Small	75.00
AMERICAN THOROUGHBREDS	Small	95.00
AMERICAN TROTTING STUD, ETHAN ALLEN, POCAHONTAS; 1866	Large	625.00
AMERICAN TROTTING STUD, MAMBRINO PILOT, FLORA TEMPLE; 1866	Large	620.00
AMERICAN WHALER; N. Currier	Small	350.00
AMERICAN WHALERS CRUSHED IN THE ICE; "Burning the Wreck to Avoid Danger to other Vessels	Small	400.00
AMERICAN WINTER SCENE: "The Falls" (Oval)	Small	75.00
AMERICAN WINTER SCENES; "Evening"; 1854	Large	975.00
AMERICAN WINTER SCENES: "Morning"; 1854	Large	1175.00
AMERICAN WINTER SPORTS; "Deer Shooting on the Shattagee"; N. Currier; 1855	Large	875.00
AMERICAN WINTER SPORTS; "Trout Fishing on Chateaugay Lake"; N. Currier; 1856	Large	1000.00
ANTELOPE SHOOTING; "Fatal Curiosity"	Medium	195.00
ANXIOUS MOMENT; "A Three Pounder Sure"; 1874	Medium	195.00
ANY PORT IN A STORM: 1884	Small	25.00
APPLES AND PLUMS; 1870	Small	30.00
APRIL SHOWER, THE	Small	45.00
ARABIAN; N. Currier; 1846	Small	50.00
ARGUING THE POINT; N. Currier; 1855	Large	420.00

AMERICAN HOMESTEAD (WINTER)   Small $225.00

	Size	Re
☐ ARKANSAS TRAVELLER, THE; 1870	Small	50
☐ ARMOURED STEEL CRUISER "NEW YORK"; 1893	Small	55
☐ ARTISTS' CREEK, NORTH CONWAY	Small	80
☐ ASSASSINATION OF PRESIDENT LINCOLN, THE; 1865	Small	50
☐ AT THE FAIR GROUNDS; 1890	Large	325
☐ AT THE FAIR GROUNDS; 1894	Large	300
☐ ATLANTIC MISSISSIPPI AND OHIO R.R. 1864	Large	1650
☐ ATTACKING THE BADGER; N. Currier	Small	60
☐ AUBURN HORSE, THE; 1866	Large	185
☐ AUTUMN; N. Currier (From an English print)	Small	27
☐ AUTUMN; C. & I.; 1871; (Girl's Head)	Small	17
☐ AUTUMN FOLIAGE	Small	25
☐ AUTUMN FRUITS	Medium	95
☐ AUTUMN FRUITS	Small	42
☐ AUTUMN FRUITS AND FLOWERS	Small	25
☐ AUTUMN IN NEW ENGLAND; "Cider Making"; 1866	Large	375
☐ AUTUMN IN THE ADIRONDACKS, LAKE HARRISON	Small	80
☐ AUTUMN ON LAKE GEORGE	Small	65
☐ AVAILABLE CANDIDATE, AN	Small	45
☐ AWFUL CONFLAGRATION OF THE STEAMBOAT "LEXINGTON"	Small	135
☐ AWFUL EXPLOSION OF THE "PEACEMAKER"; N. Currier; 1844	Small	100
☐ AWFUL WRECK OF THE MAGNIFICENT STEAMER "ATLANTIC" N. Currier 1846	Small	110

CURRIER & IVES PRINTS

HAYING-TIME "THE FIRST LOAD" (1868) . . . Large . . . $350.00

ROUNDING A BEND IN THE MISSISSIPPI (1866) . . . $1500.00

THE SLEIGH RACE (1859) . . . Large . . . $350.00

THE LIFE OF A FIREMAN—"THE FIRE" . . . Large . . . $400.00

CURRIER & IVES PRINTS

AMERICAN EXPRESS TRAIN (Palmer) 1864 . . . Large . . . $2000.00

THE LIFE OF A FIREMAN—METROPOLITAN SYSTEM (1866) . . . . Large $600.00

THE LIFE OF A HUNTER—"A TIGHT FIX" (1861) . . . Large . . . $7500.00*

THE ROAD—WINTER (1853) . . . Large . . . $2000.00

*World Auction Re

CURRIER AND IVES PRINTS

AUTUMN IN NEW ENGLAND—"CIDER MAKING" (1866) . . . Large . . . $1500.00

AMERICAN HUNTING SCENES—"A GOOD CHANCE" (1863) . . . Large . . . $750.00

CURRIER AND IVES PRINTS

THE FOUR SEASONS OF LIFE—"MIDDLE AGE" (1868) . . . Large . . . $250.00

THE PIONEER'S HOME (1867) . . . Large . . . $500.00

CURRIER AND IVES PRINTS

CLIPPER SHIP DREADNOUGHT OFF TUSKAR LIGHT (1856) . . . Large . . . $1600.00

SPEEDING ON THE AVENUE (1870) . . . Large . . . $1000.00

CURRIER AND IVES PRINTS

THE LIFE OF A FIREMAN — "THE RACE" (1854) . . . Large . . . $400.00

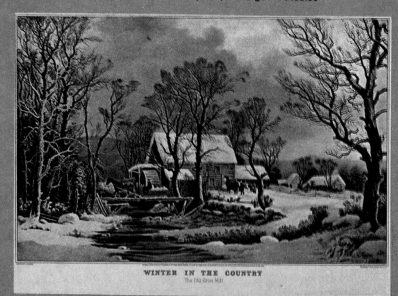

WINTER IN THE COUNTRY—"THE OLD GRIST MILL" (1864) . . . Large . . . $2000.00

CURRIER & IVES PRINTS (B)

	Size	Retail
BABES IN THE WOODS; "Young Partridges" 1868	Small	95.00
BACKED TO WIN; 1880	Small	40.00
BAD CASE OF HEAVES, A; 1875	Small	35.00
BAD HUSBAND, THE; 1870	Small	50.00
BAD POINT ON A GOOD POINTER, A; 1879	Small	50.00
BALK ON A SWEEPSTAKE; 1881	Small	40.00
BALLS ARE ROLLING — CLEAR THE TRACK	Small	75.00
BALTIMORE CLIPPER; (Rare)	Small	500.00
BALTIMORE IN 1880; 1880	Small	90.00
BAPTISM OF POCAHONTAS, THE	Small	25.00
BARE CHANCE, A; 1879	Small	30.00
BAREFACED CHEEK; 1881	Small	30.00
BARN FLOOR, THE	Large	300.00
BASE HIT, A; 1882	Small	65.00
BASS FISHING AT MACOMB'S DAM, HARLEM RIVER, N. Y.; N. Currier; 1852	Large	500.00
BATTERY, NEW YORK BY MOONLIGHT; N. Currier	Small	185.00
BATTLE SERIES; Revolutionary, War of 1812, Mexican, and Civil Wars (Battle Scenes)	Small	35.00-50.00
BATTLE OF FAIR OAKS, VA.; 1862	Large	80.00
BATTLE OF GETTYSBURG, PA., THE; 1863	Large	125.00
BATTLE OF MURFREESBORO, TENN.; 1862	Large	110.00
BATTLE OF THE GIANTS; "Buffalo Bulls on the American Prairies."	Small	425.00
BATTLE OF THE KINGS, THE; 1884	Large	140.00
BATTLE OF THE WILDERNESS, VA. THE	Large	175.00
BAY GELDING "ALLEY" By Volunteer. Record 2:19; 1879	Small	60.00
BAY STALLION "MAMBRINO"	Small	60.00
BEACH SNIPE SHOOTING; 1869	Medium	495.00
BEAR HUNTING (A Winter Scene)	Small	525.00
BEAR HUNTING; "Close Quarters" "Little Tight Fix"	Small	420.00
BEAUTIES OF BILLIARDS; "A Carom On the Dark Red"; 1869	Large	120.00
BEAUTIFUL PAIR; 1872; (Comic)	Small	30.00
"BEAUTY OF . . ." Scenic Series of Different Sections of the Nation	Small	25.00-35.00ea.
BEFORE MARRIAGE; "Anticipation"	Small	40.00
BELL RINGERS, THE; N. Currier	Small	30.00
"BELLE OF . . ." Steamship Series	Small-Med.	15.00-25.00
BELLE OF THE WINTER, THE	Medium	165.00
BENJAMIN FRANKLIN; "The Statesman and Philosopher" N. Currier; 1847	Small	100.00
BENJAMIN FRANKLIN; Bust Portrait	Medium	95.00
BEST HORSE, THE	Small	35.00

	Size	Re
☐ BEST TIME ON RECORD, THREE HEATS; GOLDSMITH MAID AND JUDGE FULLERTON	Small	62
☐ BETWEEN TWO FIRES; 1879	Small	55
☐ BEWILDERED HUNTER, THE; "Puzzle Picture"	Small	55
☐ BIBLE AND INTEMPERANCE, THE; N. Currier	Small	60
☐ BIBLE AND TEMPERANCE, THE; N. Currier	Small	55
☐ BIG THING ON ICE, A; 1862	Small	100
☐ BILLIARD SERIES; Different Shots	Small	45
☐ BILLY BOYCE — PACER	Small	47
☐ BIRD'S EYE VIEW: COLUMBIAN EXPOSITION AT CHICAGO; 1892	Large	95
☐ BIRD'S EYE VIEW OF GREAT SUSPENSION BRIDGE	Large	135.
☐ BIRD'S EYE VIEW OF THE HOME OF WASHINGTON	Small	100.
☐ BIRTHPLACE OF HENRY CLAY, THE; N. Currier	Small	65.
☐ BIRTHPLACE OF SHAKESPEARE, THE; N. Currier	Medium	65.
☐ BIRTHPLACE OF WASHINGTON, THE	Small	100.
☐ BITE ALL AROUND; 1879	Small	32.
☐ BITING LIVELY; 1882	Small	32.
☐ BLACK BASS SPEARING; "On the Restigouche, New Brunswick"	Medium	650.
☐ BLACK DUCK SHOOTING; 1879	Small	45.
☐ "BLACK HAWK"; N. Currier; 1850	Medium	225.
☐ "BLACK HAWK" AND "JENNY LIND"; 1850; N. Currier	Large	300.
☐ BLACK SQUALL, A; 1879	Small	30.
☐ BLACKFISH NIBBLE, A; 1880	Small	52.
☐ BLACKWELL'S ISLAND, EAST RIVER FROM 82nd STREET, N. Y.; 1880	Medium	225.0
☐ BLESSING OF A WIFE	Small	27.5
☐ BLESSING OF LIBERTY, THE; N. Currier	Small	35.0
☐ BLOOD WILL TELL; 1879	Small	47.5
☐ BLOOMER COSTUME, THE; N. Currier; 1851	Small	75.0
☐ BLOWER; "The King of the Road"; N. Currier	Small	55.0
☐ BLUE FISHING	Small	105.0
☐ BOATSWAIN, THE; N. Currier	Small	50.0
☐ BODINE; "Trotting Whirlwind of the West"; 1876	Small	57.5
☐ BODY OF THE MARTYR PRESIDENT, ABRAHAM LINCOLN; 1865	Small	50.0
☐ BOMBARDMENT AND CAPTURE OF FORT FISHER, N. C.	Small	75.0
☐ BOMBARDMENT AND CAPTURE OF FORT HENRY, TENN.	Small	75.0
☐ BOMBARDMENT AND CAPTURE OF FORT HINDMAN, ARK.	Small	47.5
☐ BOMBARDMENT AND CAPTURE OF FREDERICKSBURG	Small	42.5
☐ BOMBARDMENT AND CAPTURE OF ISLAND "NUMBER TEN" ON THE MISSISSIPPI RIVER; 1862	Large	175.0
☐ BOMBARDMENT OF FORT PULASKI, GEORGIA; 1862	Small	42.5

	Size	Retail
BOMBARDMENT OF FORT SUMTER	Small	50.00
BOMBARDMENT OF THE FORTS AT HATTERAS INLET, N. C.	Small	60.00
BOMBARDMENT OF TRIPOLI; N. Currier; 1846	Small	135.00
BOMBARDMENT OF VERA CRUZ; N. Currier; 1847	Small	50.00
BOSS OF THE ROAD, THE; 1884	Large	120.00
BOSS OF THE TRACK, THE; 1881	Small	35.00
BOSS TEAM, THE; 1882	Small	32.50
BOUND DOWN THE RIVER; 1870	Small	130.00
"BOUQUET OF . . ." Still-life Series	Small	40.00
BOWER OF ROSES, THE	Medium	47.50
BOY AND DOG	Small	35.00
BRACE OF MEADOW LARKS; 1879	Small	37.50
BRANDING SLAVES; N. Currier; 1845	Small	95.00
BRAVE BOY OF THE WAXHAWS, THE; 1876	Small	95.00
BRAVE WIFE, THE	Small	32.50
BREAKING THAT "BACKBONE"	Small	90.00
BRIC-A-BRAC MANIA; 1882	Small	30.00
BRIDAL BOUQUET, THE	Small	45.00
"BRIDAL VEIL" FALL, YO-SEMITE VALLEY, CALIF.	Small	95.00
BRIDAL WREATH, THE	Small	25.00
BRIG; N. Currier	Small	95.00
BRIGADIER-GENERAL SERIES — Heroes of various wars	Small	25.00
BRIG. GEN. W. T. SHERMAN, U. S. A.	Small	28.00
BRIG. GEN. WM. SPRAGUE, U. S. A.	Medium	35.00
BRIGAND, THE; N. Currier	Small	45.00
BRIGHAM YOUNG	Medium	40.00
BRILLIANT NAVAL VICTORY; 1862	Small	62.50
BRING UP YOUR HORSES; 1886	Large	165.00
BROADWAY, NEW YORK, FROM THE WESTERN UNION TELEGRAPH BUILDING, LOOKING NORTH; 1875	Large	1250.00
BROADWAY, NEW YORK, SOUTH FROM THE PARK: N. Currier	Small	175.00
BROOK TROUT FISHING: "An Anxious Moment"; 1862	Large	700.00
BROOK TROUT FISHING; 1872	Small	175.00
BROOK TROUT — JUST CAUGHT; 1858	Medium	80.00
BRUSH FOR THE LEAD, A; 1867	Large	435.00
BRUSH ON THE HOMESTRETCH, THE; 1869	Large	150.00
BRUSH ON THE ROAD; "Best Two in Three"; N. Currier; 1872	Small	65.00
BRUSH ON THE ROAD, A; MILE HEATS; "Best Two in Three"; N. Currier; 1853	Medium	150.00
BRUSH WITH WEBSTER CARTS, A; 1884	Small	175.00
BUFFALO AND CHICAGO STEAM PACKET "EMPIRE STATE"; N. Currier	Small	95.00
BUFFALO BULL, CHASING BACK	Large	300.00

CURRIER & IVES PRINTS (B)

BROOK
TROUT
FISHING

Small
$175.00

☐	BUFFALO CHASE, THE	Large	250.
☐	BUFFALO DANCE — TO MAKE THE BUFFALOES COME	Medium	150.
☐	BUFFALO HUNT ON SNOW SHOES; "Winter on the Northern Prairies"	Medium	230.
☐	BUFFALO HUNT; "Surrounding the Herd"	Medium	210.0
☐	BUFFALO HUNT — THE SURPRISE	Medium	200.
☐	BUFFALO HUNT UNDER THE WHITE WOLF SKIN	Medium	210.0
☐	BURNING OF CHICAGO, THE; 1871	Small	110.0
☐	BURNING OF THE CITY HALL, N. Y.	Small	140.0
☐	BURNING OF THE CLIPPER SHIP "GOLDEN LIGHT"	Small	100.0
☐	BURNING OF THE "HENRY CLAY" NEAR YONKERS; N. Currier; 1852	Small	75.0
☐	BURNING OF THE NEW YORK CRYSTAL PALACE	Large	425.0
☐	BURNING OF THE NEW YORK CRYSTAL PALACE	Small	100.0
☐	BURNING OF THE "OCEAN MONARCH"; N. Currier; 1848	Small	75.0
☐	BURNING OF THE PALACE STEAMER "ROBERT E. LEE"; 1882	Small	75.0
☐	BURNING OF STEAMSHIP "ERIE" OFF SILVER CREEK, LAKE ERIE; N. Currier	Small	75.0
☐	BURNING OF THE STEAMSHIP "AUSTRIA"	Small	55.0
☐	BURNING OF THE STEAMSHIP "GOLDEN GATE"	Small	75.0
☐	BURNING OF THE STEAMSHIP "NARRAGANSETT"	Small	60.0
☐	BURNING OF THE U. S. SHIP OF THE LINE "PENNSYLVANIA" 1861	Small	90.0
☐	BUSTIN' A PICNIC	Small	19.5
☐	BUSTIN' THE POOL; 1889	Small	22.5
☐	BUSTIN' THE RECORD	Small	50.0
☐	BUTT OF THE JOKERS, THE; 1879	Small	30.0
☐	BY THE SEASHORE; 1868	Medium	47.50

	Size	Retail
CALIFORNIA GOLD; N. Currier	Small	175.00
CALIFORNIA SCENERY; "Seal Rocks — Point Lobos"	Small	65.00
CALIFORNIA YO-SEMITE FALLS	Small	55.00
CAMPING IN THE WOODS; "A Good Time Coming"; 1863	Large	350.00
CAMPING IN THE WOODS; "Laying Off"; 1863	Large	350.00
CAMPING OUT; "Life in the Woods"; 1879	Medium	150.00
CAMPING OUT; "Some of the Right Sort"; N. Currier; 1856	Large	375.00
CANADIAN VOYAGEURS WALKING A CANOE UP THE RAPID	Small	85.00
CANADIAN WINTER SCENE	Medium	400.00
CANAL SCENE, MOONLIGHT; (ERIE)	Small	75.00
CAN'T BE BEAT; 1880	Small	25.00
CANVAS-BACKS	Small	80.00
CAPABILITY AND AVAILABILITY; N. Currier	Small	60.00
CAPITOL AT WASHINGTON; N. Currier	Small	50.00
CAPITULATION OF VERA CRUZ; N. Currier; 1847	Small	35.00
CELEBRATED TROTTING TEAM "EDWARD" AND "SWIVELLER"	Large	190.00
CELEBRATED WINNING HORSES AND JOCKEYS OF THE AMERICAN TURF; 1888	Large	195.00
CELEBRATED WINNING HORSES AND JOCKEYS OF THE AMERICAN TURF; 1889	Large	205.00
CELEBRATED WINNING HORSES AND JOCKEYS OF THE AMERICAN TURF; 1891	Large	225.00
CELEBRATED YACHT "AMERICA"	Small	150.00
CENTENNIAL EXHIBITION BUILDINGS, PHILA. 1875	Small	45.00
CENTRAL PARK IN WINTER	Small	400.00
CENTRAL PARK IN WINTER, SLEIGHING	Small	350.00
CENTRAL PARK — THE BRIDGE	Small	95.00
CENTRAL PARK — THE DRIVE; 1862	Medium	200.00
CENTRAL PARK — THE LAKE; 1862	Medium	200.00
CENTRAL PARK, WINTER — THE SKATING CARNIVAL	Small	250.00
CENTRAL PARK, WINTER — THE SKATING POND; 1862	Large	2000.00
CHAMPION IN DANGER, THE; 1882	Small	50.00
CHAMPION IN LUCK, THE; 1882	Small	50.00
CHAMPION IRISH SETTER "ROVER"	Small	125.00
CHAMPION PACER "JOHNSTON"	Large	175.00
CHAMPION PACER "MASCOT"	Small	50.00
CHAMPION PACER "MASCOT"	Large	165.00
CHAMPION RACE, A 1889	Small	75.00
CHAMPION ROWIST — THE PRIDE OF THE CLUB; 1876	Medium	75.00
CHAMPION SLUGGER — KNOCKING 'EM OUT; 1883	Small	30.00
CHAMPION STALLION "DIRECTUM"	Small	50.00

	Size	Re
☐ CHAMPION STALLION "GEORGE WILKES"; 1888	Large	12
☐ CHAMPION STALLION "MAXY COBB"	Large	12
☐ CHAMPION STEER OF THE WORLD; 1877	Small	6
☐ CHAMPION TROTTING QUEEN "ALIX"; 1893	Small	4
☐ CHAMPION TROTTING QUEEN "ALIX"; 1894	Large	13
☐ CHAMPION TROTTING STALLION "NELSON"; 1891	Large	14
☐ CHAMPION TROTTING STALLION "SMUGGLER"; 1875	Large	200
☐ CHAMPIONS AT CLOSE QUARTERS; 1892	Small	5
☐ CHAMPIONS OF BALL RACKET; "At the Close of the Season"; 1885	Small	4
☐ CHAMPIONS OF BALL RACKET; "On the Diamond Field"; 1886	Small	4
☐ CHAMPIONS OF THE BARN; 1876	Small	5C
☐ CHAMPIONS OF THE FIELD	Small	170
☐ CHAMPIONS OF THE MISSISSIPPI; "A Race for the Buckhorns"; 1866	Small	300
☐ CHAMPIONS OF THE UNION	Large	95
☐ CHANCES OF BILLIARDS, THE; "A Scratch All Around; 1869	Large	120
☐ "CHAN" AND "ENG"; (World Renowned Siamese Twins); 1860	Small	50
☐ CHANGE OF BASE, A; 1883	Small	25
☐ CHANGED MAN; 1879	Small	32
☐ CHASE (THE) — IN THE OLDEN TIME; N. Currier	Small	42
☐ CHATHAM SQUARE, NEW YORK: N. Currier	Small	175
☐ CHECK, A; "Keep Your Distance"; N. Currier	Medium	595
☐ CHICAGO AS IT WAS	Small	100
☐ CHICAGO IN FLAMES	Small	105
☐ CHIEF COOK AND BOTTLE WASHER; N. Currier	Small	25
☐ CHILDHOOD'S HAPPY DAYS; 1863	Medium	45
☐ CHILDHOOD'S HAPPY DAYS; 1863	Small	32
☐ CHILDREN AT PLAY	Small	27
☐ CHILDREN IN THE WOODS, THE	Small	27
☐ CHILDREN'S PIC-NIC, THE	Small	32
☐ CHIP OFF THE OLD BLOCK, A; N. Currier	Medium	75
☐ CHOICE APPLES	Small	35
☐ CHOICE FRUIT; 1865	Large	65
☐ CHRIST SERIES; Various Scenes Based on Biblical Episodes	Small	7.50-10.00 e
☐ CHRISTMAS SNOW	Min.	95
☐ CHRISTOPHER COLUMBUS; 1892	Small	47.
☐ CITY HALL AND COUNTY COURT HOUSE, NEWARK, N. J.	Small	175.0
☐ CITY HALL, NEW YORK; N. Currier	Small	120.
☐ CITY HALL AND VICINITY, NEW YORK	Small	130.
☐ CITY OF BOSTON, THE; 1873	Large	195.0

	Size	Retail
TY OF CHICAGO; (Steamshil); 1892	Large	165.00
TY OF NEW ORLEANS, THE; 1885	Large	225.00
TY OF NEW ORLEANS, THE	Small	95.00
TY OF NEW YORK; N. Currier; 1844	Small	165.00
TY OF NEW YORK; N. Currier; 1855	Large	425.00
TY OF NEW YORK AND ENVIRONS; 1875	Small	225.00
TY OF NEW YORK FROM GOVERNORS ISLAND; 1880	Large	350.00
TY OF NEW YORK FROM JERSEY CITY; N. Currier; 1849	Small	140.00
TY OF NEW YORK, THE; (Equitable Life Bldg.); 1876	Large	225.00
TY OF PHILADELPHIA, THE; 1875	Large	195.00
TY OF ST. LOUIS, THE; 1874	Large	225.00
TY OF SAN FRANCISCO, THE, 1877	Small	125.00
TY OF SAN FRANCISCO, BIRD'S-EYE VIEW FROM THE BAY, LOOK-ING SOUTHWEST; 1878	Large	250.00
TY OF WASHINGTON, LOOKING NORTH FROM THE POTOMAC 1891	Large	225.00
EARING, A; "On The American Frontier"	Small	100.00
LIPPER SHIP "ADELAIDE"; "Hove to for a Pilot"	Large	2200.00
LIPPER SHIP "COMET" OF N. Y.; N. Currier	Large	1100.00
LIPPER SHIP "CONTEST"; N. Currier; 1853	Large	1200.00
LIPPER SHIP "DREADNOUGHT"; N. Currier; 1854	Large	1210.00
LIPPER SHIP "DREADNOUGHT" OFF TUSKAR LIGHT; N. Currier; 1856	Large	1850.00
LIPPER SHIP "FLYING CLOUD"; N. Currier; 1853	Large	2100.00
LIPPER SHIP "GREAT REPUBLIC"; N. Currier; 1853	Large	1100.00
LIPPER SHIP "GREAT REPUBLIC"	Small	150.00
LIPPER SHIP "HURRICANE"; N. Currier; 1852	Large	3000.00
LIPPER SHIP IN A SNOW SQUALL, A.	Small	225.00
LIPPER SHIP "LIGHTNING"; N. Currier; 1854	Large	1925.00
LIPPER SHIP "NIGHTINGALE"; N. Currier; 1854	Large	2750.00
LIPPER SHIP "OCEAN EXPRESS"; N. Currier; 1856	Large	1100.00
LIPPER SHIP, OFF PORT	Small	200.00
LIPPER SHIP "QUEEN OF CLIPPERS"; N. Currier	Small	210.00
LIPPER SHIP "RACER"; N. Currier; 1854	Large	2500.00
LIPPER SHIP "RED JACKET"	Small	195.00
LIPPER SHIP "RED JACKET"; N. Currier; 1855	Large	1900.00
LIPPER SHIP "SOVEREIGN OF THE SEAS"; N. Currier; 1852	Large	2300.00
LIPPER SHIP "SWEEPSTAKES"; N. Currier; 1853	Large	1925.00
LIPPER SHIP "THREE BROTHERS"	Small	175.00
LIPPER SHIP "THREE BROTHERS"; 1875	Large	770.00
LIPPER SHIP "YOUNG AMERICA"; N. Currier; 1853	Large	2200.00
CLIPPER SHIPS HOMEWARD BOUND	Small	250.00

CURRIER & IVES PRINTS (C)

		Size	
☐	CLIPPER YACHT "AMERICA", THE; N. Currier	Medium	3
☐	CLIPPER YACHT "AMERICA", OF N. Y.; N. Currier	Small	2
☐	CLOSE FINISH, A; 1874	Small	
☐	CLOSE HEAT, A; 1873	Large	2
☐	CLOSE LAP ON THE RUN IN, A; 1886	Large	2
☐	CLOSE QUARTERS; 1866	Large	1
☐	COACHING SCENE	Large	2
☐	COCK-A-DOODLE-DO; (Rooster)	Small	
☐	COCK OF THE WALK; 1879	Small	
☐	COD FISHING — OFF NEWFOUNDLAND; 1872	Small	3
☐	COLORED INFANTRY	Large	

CURRIER & IVES PRINTS (D)

		Size	
☐	DAIRY FARM, THE	Small	4
☐	"DAN RICE"; 1868	Large	13
☐	DANGER SIGNAL, THE; 1884	Large	50
☐	"DANIEL D. TOMPKINS" AND "BLANC NEGRE"; N. Currier; 1851	Medium	17
☐	DANIEL WEBSTER; "New England's Choice for Twelfth President of the U. S.; N. Currier; 1848	Small	5
☐	DANIEL WEBSTER; "Defender of the Constitution"; N. Currier; 1851	Small	6
☐	DANIEL WEBSTER; N. Currier; 1852	Small	5
☐	DARK FORESHADING ON A FLASH PICTURE; 1890	Small	2
☐	DARKTOWN COMIC SERIES ("Darktown . . . .")	Small	25.00-3
☐	DARTMOUTH COLLEGE; (RARE)	Small	50
☐	DASH FOR THE POLE, A	Small	7.
☐	DAUGHTER OF THE REGIMENT, THE; N. Currier; 1849	Small	60
☐	DAUGHTER OF THE SOUTH, A	Small	25
☐	DAUGHTERS OF TEMPERANCE; N. Currier	Small	4
☐	DAY BEFORE MARRIAGE — THE BRIDE'S JEWELS	Small	27
☐	DEACON'S MARE GETTING THE WORD, 'GO', etc.; 1879	Small	4
☐	DEAD BROKE; 1873	Small	4
☐	DEAD GAME — QUAIL; 1872	Small	30
☐	DEAD GAME — WOODCOCK AND PARTRIDGE; 1872	Small	32
☐	DEAREST SPOT ON EARTH TO ME; 1878	Small	28
☐	DEATH BED OF THE MARTYR PRESIDENT, ABRAHAM LINCOLN; 1865	Small	60
☐	DEATH SCENE SERIES; (DEATH OF FAMOUS PERSONAGES)	Small	17.50-35
☐	DEATH OF MINNEHAHA, THE; 1867	Large	42
☐	DEATH OF TECUMSEH; N. Currier; 1841	Small	40
☐	DEATH SHOT, THE	Small	42

	Size	Retail
DECLARATION, THE; N. Currier; 1846	Small	25.00
DECLARATION COMMITTEE, THE; 1876	Small	75.00
DECLARATION OF INDEPENDENCE, THE; N. Currier	Small	65.00
DEER AND FAWN	Small	75.00
DEER HUNTING BY TORCHLIGHT	Medium	150.00
DEER HUNTING ON THE SUSQUEHANNA	Medium	125.00
DEER IN THE WOODS	Small	65.00
DEER SHOOTING IN THE NORTHERN WOODS	Small	135.00
DEER SHOOTING IN THE NORTH WOODS	Medium	120.00
DEFIANCE! (Stag and Deer)	Small	37.50
DELAYING A START; 1881	Small	55.00
DEMOCRACY IN SEARCH OF A CANDIDATE	Small	45.00
DEMOCRATIC PLATFORM, THE	Small	45.00
DEMOCRATIC REFORMERS; 1876	Small	45.00
DEPTHS OF DESPAIR, THE	Small	30.00
DESPERATE FINISH; 1885	Small	30.00
DESPERATE PEACE MAN	Small	25.00
DESSERT OF FRUIT, A; 1869	Small	45.00
DESTRUCTION OF JERUSALEM BY THE ROMANS; N. Currier	Large	50.00
DESTRUCTION OF TEA AT BOSTON HARBOR; 1846	Large	300.00
DESTRUCTION OF THE REBEL MONSTER "MERRIMAC"	Small	90.00
DESTRUCTION OF THE REBEL RAM "ARKANSAS"	Small	75.00
"DEWDROP"; 1886	Small	50.00
"DEXTER"; RECORD 2:17¼; 1871	Small	55.00
"DEXTER" AND "BUTLER"; 1874	Small	57.50
"DEXTER", "ETHAN ALLEN" AND "MATE"; 1874	Small	55.00
DEXTER'S TURF RECORD; 1867	Small	55.00
DEXTEROUS WHIP, A; 1876	Small	30.00
DICK SWIVELLER; 1878	Small	55.00
DIRECT; 1891	Small	50.00
DISCHARGING THE PILOT; N. Currier; 1856	Large	1350.00
DISCOVERY OF THE MISSISSIPPI, THE; 1876	Small	45.00
DISLOYAL BRITISH "SUBJECT", A	Small	40.00
DISPUTED HEAT — CLAIMING A FOUL!; 1878	Large	150.00
DISTANCED; 1878	Small	25.00
DISTANT RELATIONS	Small	35.00
DIS-UNITED STATES; The Southern Confederacy	Small	75.00
DO YOU LOVE BUTTER; 1878	Small	18.50
DOCTOR FRANKLIN; N. Currier	Small	100.00
DODGE THAT WON'T WORK, A; (Political)	Small	35.00
DOMESTIC BLOCKADE, THE	Large	115.00

	Size	Re
☐ DONE GONE BUSTED; 1883	Small	25
☐ DOREMUS, SUYDAMS AND NIXON	Medium	85
☐ DOUBLE-BARRELED BREECH LOADER; 1880	Small	35
☐ DOWN CHARGE	Small	125
☐ DRAW POKER — GETTING 'EM LIVELY; 1886	Small	32
☐ DRAW POKER — LAYING FOR 'EM SHARP; 1886	Small	32
☐ DRAWING CARDS FOR BEGINNERS	Small	40
☐ DREADFUL WRECK OF THE "MEXICO" ON HEMPSTEAD BEACH	Small	200
☐ DREAMS OF YOUTH; 1869	Small	50
☐ DREAMS OF YOUTH	Medium	95
☐ DRIVING FINISH, A; 1891	Large	100
☐ DRUNKARD'S PROGRESS, THE; N. Currier; 1846	Small	60
☐ DUSTED AND DISGUSTED; 1878 (Comic)	Small	30
☐ "DUTCHESS" OF ONEIDA	Small	60
☐ "DUTCHMAN"; N. Currier; 1850	Medium	250
☐ DUTCHMAN" AND "HIRAM WOODRUFF"; 1871	Small	200
☐ DYING BUFFALO BULL	Medium	175

THE DRUNKARD'S PROGRESS   Small $ 60.00

	Size	Retail
PLURIBUS UNUM; 1875	Medium	90.00
GER FOR THE RACE; 1893	Small	60.00
RLY AUTUMN IN THE CATSKILLS	Medium	110.00
RLY AUTUMN, SALMON BROOK, GRANBY, CONN.; 1859	Small	190.00
RLY SPRING	Medium	175.00
RLY WINTER; 1869	Medium	550.00
ST RIVER SUSPENSION BRIDGE; 1890	Small	85.00
TING CROW ON A WAGER — DE FUST BRACE; 1883; (Comic)	Small	27.50
TING CROW ON A WAGER — DE LAST LAP; 1883; (Comic)	Small	27.50
CHO LAKE, WHITE MOUNTAINS	Small	70.00
EDWARD", Record 2:19	Small	55.00
EDWARD", AND "SWIVELLER"; 1882	Small	57.50
EDWIN FORREST", Record 2:11¾; 1878	Small	55.00
EDWIN THORNE", Record 2:17½; 1882	Small	55.00
L CAPITAN — FROM MARIPOSA TRAIL	Small	70.00
LECTRIC LIGHT; 1879	Small	27.50
MPEROR OF NORFOLK; 1888	Small	62.50
NGLISH SNIPE; N. Currier	Small	80.00
NGLISH SNIPE; 1871; (C & I)	Small	80.00
NGLISH WINTER SCENE, AN	Small	120.00
NGLISH YACHT OFF SANDY HOOK, AN	Small	92.50
NTRANCE TO THE HIGHLANDS; 1864	Large	350.00
'ETHAN ALLEN" AND "MATE" AND "DEXTER"; 1867	Large	180.00
'ETHAN ALLEN" AND "MATE" AND "LANTERN" AND "MATE"; 1859	Large	190.00
EVACUATION OF RICHMOND, VA., THE; 1865	Small	50.00
EVENTIDE — OCTOBER; "The Village Inn"; 1867	Large	225.00
EVENTIDE — THE CURFEW	Small	40.00
EVERYBODY'S FRIEND; 1876	Medium	55.00
EXCITING FINISH; 1895	Small	57.50
EXCITING FINISH	Large	150.00
EXPRESS STEAMSHIP "AUGUSTA VICTORIA"	Small	45.00
EXPRESS STEAMSHIP "COLUMBIA"	Small	45.00
EXPRESS STEAMSHIP "FURST BISMARK", THE	Small	45.00
EXPRESS TRAIN, THE; N. Currier	Small	525.00
EXPRESS TRAIN, THE; 1859	Large	2200.00
EXPRESS TRAIN, THE; 1870	Small	450.00
EXPRESS TRAIN, THE; 1870*	Large	1500.00
EXTRAORDINARY EXPRESS ACROSS THE ATLANTIC; N. Currier; 1846	Small	150.00

ignette- 500)

CURRIER & IVES PRINTS (F)

	Size	R
☐ FAIR EQUESTRIAN, THE; 1857	Small	
☐ FAIR FIELD AND NO FAVOR, A; 1891	Large	1
☐ FAIR START, A	Small	
☐ FAIRMOUNT WATER WORKS	Medium	1
☐ FALL OF RICHMOND, VIRGINIA, THE; 1865	Large	1
☐ FALL OF RICHMOND, VIRGINIA, THE; 1865	Small	
☐ FALLS OF NIAGARA FROM THE CANADA SIDE	Large	3
☐ FALLS OF NIAGARA FROM CLIFTON HOUSE; N. Currier	Small	
☐ FAMOUS DOUBLE TROTTING TEAM "SIR MOHAWK" AND "NELLIE SONTAG"; 1889	Large	1
☐ FAMOUS TROTTER "MAJOLICA", THE; 1884	Large	1
☐ FAMOUS TROTTING GELDING "GUY"; Record 2:12½; 1888	Small	5
☐ FAMOUS TROTTING MARE "GOLDSMITH MAIN; Record 2-14; 1871	Small	5
☐ FARM AND FIRESIDE; 1878	Small	6
☐ FARM LIFE IN SUMMER — THE COOLING STREAM; 1867	Small	5
☐ FARM YARD NO. 1, THE; N. Currier	Small	4
☐ FARM YARD NO. 2, THE; N. Currier	Small	4
☐ FARM YARD IN WINTER, THE; 1861	Large	57
☐ FARM YARD PETS	Small	3
☐ FARM YARD — WINTER	Small	12
☐ FARMER'S HOME — AUTUMN, THE; 1864	Large	25
☐ FARMER'S HOME — HARVEST, THE; 1864	Large	25
☐ FARMER'S HOME — SUMMER, THE; 1864	Large	23
☐ FARMER'S HOME — WINTER, THE; 1863	Large	27
☐ FASHIONABLE TURN OUTS IN CENTRAL PARK; 1869	Large	80
☐ FAST HEAT, A; 1887	Large	12
☐ FAST HEAT, A; 1894	Small	6
☐ FAST TEAM AT A SMASHING GATE, A	Large	16
☐ FAST TEAM OUT ON THE LOOSE, A	Small	7
☐ FAST TEAM TAKING A SMASH, A	Small	7
☐ FAST TROTTERS ON A FAST TRACK; 1889	Large	15
☐ FAST TROTTERS ON HARLEM LANE, N. Y.; 1870	Large	35
☐ FAST TROTTING IN THE WEST; 1871	Large	19
☐ FAST TROTTING TO FAST WHEELS; 1893	Large	11
☐ FAVORITE HORSE, THE	Small	
☐ FAVORITE PONY, A; N. Currier	Small	27
☐ FAWN'S LEAP, CATSKILLS: (Oval)	Small	25
☐ FEAST OF FRUITS, A; (Oval)	Small	27
☐ FEAST OF ROSES; 1873	Small	42
☐ FEAST OF STRAWBERRIES, A	Small	50
		32

	Size	Retail
FEATHER WEIGHT MOUNTING A SCALPER, A; 1881	Small	35.00
FERRY BOAT, THE; N. Currier	Medium	110.00
FRIEND OF THE ROAD, THE; 1881	Large	120.00
FINEST IN THE WORLD: 1885	Small	50.00
FIRE DEPARTMENT - CERTIFICATE: 1877	Medium	25.00
FIRE ENGINE CO. "PACIFIC" BROOKLYN	Small	75.00
FIRST APPEARANCE OF JENNY LIND IN AMERICA; N. Currier; 1850	Medium	300.00
FIRST BIRD OF THE SEASON, THE; 1879	Small	42.00
FIRST COLORED SENATOR AND REPRESENTATIVES IN THE 41st-42nd CONGRESS; 1872	Medium	37.50
FIRST FIGHT BETWEEN IRON CLAD SHIPS OF WAR, THE; 1862	Small	100.00
FIRST GAME; N. Currier	Small	40.00
FIRST LANDING OF COLUMBUS, THE; 1892	Large	95.00
FIRST LESSON, THE; N. Currier	Medium	55.00
FIRST MEETING OF WASHINGTON AND LAFAYETTE; 1876	Small	90.00
FIRST PREMIUM GRAPES, 1865	Medium	100.00
FIRST PREMIUM POULTRY	Small	42.50
FIRST SMOKE — ALL RIGHT; 1870	Small	42.50
FIRST SMOKE — ALL WRONG; 1870	Small	42.50
FIRST SNOW, THE	Medium	150.00
FIRST TROT OF THE SEASON; 1870	Large	330.00
FIRST UNDER THE WIRE; 1878	Small	40.00
FISH OUT OF WATER; N. Currier	Small	32.50
FISHERMAN'S DOG, THE	Medium	27.50
FLAG OF THE UNION, THE	Small	27.50
FLIGHT OF THE MEXICAN ARMY AT THE BATTLE OF BUENA VISTA; N. Currier; 1847	Small	45.00
FLOATING DOWN TO MARKET; 1870	Small	95.00
"FLORA TEMPLE"; N. Currier; 1853	Large	225.00
"FLORA TEMPLE" AND "HIGHLAND MAIN"; 1853	Large	200.00
"FLORA TEMPLE" AND "LANCET" N. Currier	Large	180.00
"FLORA TEMPLE" AND "PRINCESS"; 1859	Large	180.00
"FLORIDA"	Large	130.00
FLOWER BASKET, A	Small	50.00
FLOWER VASE, THE; N. Currier; 1848	Small	65.00
FLOWER VASE, THE	Medium	75.00
FLOWERS; N. Currier	Small	50.00
FLOWERS — ROSES AND BLUEBELLS	Meduim	50.00
FLUSHING A WOODCOCK	Small	70.00
FLYING FISH; 1879	Small	60.00
"FLYING DUTCHMAN" AND "VOLTIGEUR"; N. Currier	Medium	200.00
FOLIAGE; (Four views on same sheet)	Small	37.50
FORDING THE RIVER; N. Currier	Medium	60.00

	Size	Re
☐ FOREST SCENE ON THE LEHIGH	Medium	12!
☐ FOREST SCENE, SUMMER	Small	6!
☐ FORT SUMTER— CHARLESTON HARBOR, S. C.	Small	7!
☐ "FOUR-IN-HAND"; 1861	Large	15C
☐ "FOUR-IN-HAND"; 1887	Small	6!
☐ FOUR MASTED STEAMSHIP "EGYPT" ON THE NATIONAL LINE; N. Currier	Small	65
☐ FOUR OARED SHELL RACE, A; 1884	Large	300
☐ FOUR SEASONS OF LIFE; 1868 — Four prints — Childhood, Youth, Middle Age, Old Age	Large	ea. 15C
☐ FOX CHASE; N. Currier; Four Prints — Gone Away, In Full Cry, Death, Throwing Off	Small	ea. 100
☐ FOX HUNTING; Four Prints — The Meet, The Find, Full Cry, The Death	Medium	ea. 225
☐ FOX'S OLD BOWERY THEATRE, THE LAST SCENE IN G. L. FOX'S PANTOMINE, "THE HOUSE THAT JACK BUILT"	Small	135
☐ FRAGRANT AND FAIR	Small	55
☐ FRAGRANT CUP; 1884	Small	37
☐ FRANKLIN PIERCE, "FOURTEENTH PRESIDENT OF THE U. S."; N. Currier; 1852	Small	40.
☐ FRANKLIN'S EXPERIMENT; 1876	Small	150.
☐ FREE TRADE AND PROTECTION; 1888	Small	30.
☐ FREEDMAN'S BUREAU, THE; 1868	Small	40.
☐ FREEDOM TO THE SLAVES	Small	80.•
☐ FRESH BOUQUET, A	Small	50.!
☐ FRONTIER LAKE, THE	Small	60.!
☐ FRONTIER SETTLEMENT, A	Medium	225.!
☐ FROZEN UP; 1872	Small	350.!
☐ FRUIT; 1861	Medium	50.C
☐ FRUIT, NO. 1, THE; N. Currier; 1848	Small	45.C
☐ FRUIT AND FLOWER PIECE; 1863	Medium	100.C
☐ FRUIT AND FLOWERS, No. 1; N. Currier; 1848	Small	50.C
☐ FRUIT AND FLOWERS, CHERRIES, STRAWBERRIES, etc.	Small	60.C
☐ FRUIT VASE; N. Currier; 1847	Small	45.C
☐ FRUITS, AUTUMN VARIETIES; 1871	Small	40.C
☐ FRUITS AND FLOWERS	Small	45.C
☐ FRUITS AND FLOWERS IN SUMMER	Small	45.C
☐ FRUITS AND FLOWERS OF AUTUMN	Medium	100.C
☐ FRUITS AND FLOWERS OF SUMMER	Medium	100.C
☐ FRUITS OF INTEMPERANCE, THE; N. Currier	Small	90.0
☐ FRUITS OF TEMPERANCE, THE; N. Currier; 1848	Small	100.0
☐ FUNERAL OF PRESIDENT LINCOLN; 1865	Small	110.0•

CURRIER & IVES PRINTS (F) 367

THE FOUR SEASONS OF LIFE: CHILDHOOD.

THE FOUR SEASONS OF LIFE: CHILDHOOD   Large $150.00

THE FOUR SEASONS OF LIFE: OLD AGE.

THE FOUR SEASONS OF LIFE: OLD AGE   Large $150.00

	Size	Retail
☐ FUST BLOOD, DE; 1882	Small	35.00
☐ FUST KNOCK-DOWN, DE; 1882	Small	35.00
☐ FUTURITY RACE AT SHEEPSHEAD BAY; 1889	Large	295.00

	Size	R
☐ GALLANT CHARGE SERIES (Civil War Scenes, Various Regiments)	Small	ea. 45.00-
☐ GAME COCK, THE; N. Currier	Small	
☐ GAME DOG, A; 1879	Small	
☐ GARDEN, ORCHARD AND VINE; 1867	Medium	1
☐ GARNET POOL, THE	Medium	1
☐ "GARRETT DAVIS; N. Currier; 1854	Large	4
☐ "GARRETT DAVIS"; N. Currier; 1854	Medium	1
☐ GEM OF THE ATLANTIC, THE; N. Currier; 1849	Small	1
☐ GEM OF THE PACIFIC, THE; N. Currier; 1849	Small	1
☐ GEMS OF AMERICAN SCENERY	Small	8
☐ GENERAL AND MRS. WASHINGTON; 1876	Small	5
☐ GENERAL ANDREW JACKSON; "The Hero"	Small	4
☐ GENERAL ANDREW JACKSON; "The Hero of New Orleans"	Small	4
☐ GENERAL ANDREW JACKSON AT NEW ORLEANS	Small	4
☐ GENERAL ANDREW JACKSON; "The Union Must and Shall Be Preserved"	Small	4
☐ "GENL. BUTLER" AND "DEXTER"; 1866	Large	22
☐ "GENL. BUTLER" AND "DEXTER"	Small	7
☐ GENERAL CHESTER A. ARTHUR; 1880	Medium	4
☐ GENL. FRANCIS MARION; 1876	Small	11
☐ GENL. FRANKLIN PIERCE; N. Currier; 1852	Small	3
☐ GENL. GEORGE WASHINGTON; (On horseback)	Medium	11
☐ GENERAL GRANT	Medium	6
☐ GENERAL GRANT	Large	8
☐ GENERAL GRANT AND FAMILY; 1867	Small	3
☐ GENERAL GRANT AT THE TOMB OF A. LINCOLN; 1868	Small	5
☐ GENERAL ISRAEL PUTNAM; C. Currier	Small	7
☐ GENERAL JAMES A. GARFIELD 20th PRESIDENT	Medium	5
☐ GENERAL LAFAYETTE; N. Currier	Small	5
☐ GENERAL ROBERT E. LEE	Small	5
☐ GENERAL SCOTT'S VICTORIOUS ENTRY INTO THE CITY OF MEXICO; N. Currier; 1847	Small	42
☐ GENERAL TAYLOR AND STAFF; N. Currier; 1847	Small	42
☐ GENL. TAYLOR AT THE BATTLE OF PALO ALTO; N. Currier; 1846	Small	42
☐ GENERAL TAYLOR AT THE BATTLE OF RESACA DE LA PALMA; N. Currier; 1846	Small	45
☐ GENERAL TOM THUMB; N. Currier	Small	45
☐ GENERAL TOM THUMB — Barnum's Gallery of Wonders, No. 1; N. Currier; 1849	Small	45
☐ GENERAL TOM THUMB & WIFE, COM. NUTT & MINNIE WARREN; "The Greatest Wonders in the World"; 1863	Small	50
☐ GENERAL TOM THUMB'S MARRIAGE; 1863	Small	52

	Size	Retail
GENERAL TRANSATLANTIC COMPANY'S STEAMER "NORMANDIE"	Small	75.00
GENERAL U. S. GRANT; 1884	Small	30.00
GEN. U. S. GRANT; "The Nation's Choice for President of the U. S."	Small	30.00
GEN. U. S. GRANT; "President of the U. S."	Small	30.00
GENERAL WILLIAM H. HARRISON; N. Currier	Small	32.50
GENERAL WILLIAM H. HARRISON AT THE BATTLE OF TIPPECANOE; N. Currier	Small	50.00
GENERAL Z. TAYLOR; "The Hero of the Rio Grande"; N. Currier; 1846	Small	45.00
GENERAL Z. TAYLOR; "Rough and Ready"; 1846	Small	35.00
GEORGE AND MARTHA WASHINGTON; (Pair)	Small	pr. 60.00
"GEORGE M. PATCHEN", "BROWN DICK" AND "MILLER'S DAMSEL"; 1859	Large	185.00
GEORGE WASHINGTON"; (Bust to left); N. Currier	Medium	65.00
GEORGE WASHINGTON; (Bust to right)	Medium	55.00
GEORGE WASHINGTON; (In uniform); N. Currier	Small	50.00
GEORGE WASHINGTON — First President; N. Currier	Small	55.00
GEORGE WASHINGTON AND HIS FAMILY	Large	125.00
"GIVE ME LIBERTY, OR GIVE ME DEATH!"	Small	85.00
GLEN AT NEWPORT, THE	Small	75.00
GLIMPSE OF THE HOMESTEAD, A; 1859	Medium	110.00
GLIMPSE OF THE HOMESTEAD, A; 1863	Medium	80.00
GLIMPSE OF THE HOMESTEAD, A; 1865	Small	50.00
GLORIOUS CHARGE OF HANCOCK'S DIVISION	Small	42.00
GOING AGAINST THE STREAM: N. Currier	Small	32.50
GOING IT BLIND: N. Currier	Small	40.00
GOING TO PASTURE — EARLY MORNING	Small	42.50
GOING TO THE FRONT; 1880	Small	42.50
GOING TO THE MILL; N. Currier	Small	40.00
GOING TO THE MILL; 1859	Medium	62.50
GOING TO THE TROT — A GOOD DAY AND GOOD TRACK	Large	320.00
GOING TO THE STREAM: N. Currier	Small	40.00
GOLD DUST; 1875	Small	42.50
GOLD MINING IN CALIFORNIA; 1871	Small	215.00
GOLD SEEKERS, THE; N. Currier; 1851	Small	175.00
GOLDEN FRUITS OF CALIFORNIA: 1869	Large	150.00
GOLDEN MORNING, A; N. Currier	Medium	70.00
GOLDEN MORNING, THE	Small	47.50
"GOLDSMITH MAID", Record 2:14; 1881	Small	35.00
"GOLDSMITH MAID" AND "AMERICAN GIRL"; 1868	Large	175.00

	Size	Retail
☐ GOLDSMITH MAID" AND "JUDGE FULLERTON"; 1874	Small	90.00
☐ "GOLDSMITH MAID" AND "LUCY"; 1874	Small	62.50
☐ GOOD CHANCE, A; 1863	Large	575.00
☐ GOOD DAY'S SPORT, A — HOMEWARD BOUND: 1869	Large	450.00
☐ GOOD HUSBAND, THE; 1870	Small	70.00
☐ GOOD MAN AT THE HOUR OF DEATH, THE; N. Currier	Small	30.00
☐ GOOD RACE, WELL WON, A; 1887	Large	150.00
☐ GOOD SEND OFF — GO!, A; 1872	Large	125.00
☐ GOOD SEND OFF — GO!, A; 1889	Small	50.00
☐ GOOD TIMES ON THE OLD PLANTATION	Small	95.00
☐ GOT 'EM BOTH; 1882	Small	50.00
☐ GOT THE DROP ON HIM; 1881	Small	32.00
☐ "GOVERNOR SPRAGUE" — BLACK TROTTING STALLION	Small	50.00
☐ GRAND BANNER OF THE RADICAL DEMOCRACY — FOR 1864	Small	50.00
☐ GRAND CALIFORNIA FILLY "SUNOL" — Record 2:10½	Small	60.00
☐ GRAND CALIFORNIA FILLY "WILDFLOWER"; 1883	Small	62.50
☐ GRAND CALIFORNIA TROTTING MARE "SUNOL"; 1890	Large	125.00
☐ GRAND CENTRAL SMOKE; 1876	Small	45.00
☐ GRAND CENTENNIAL WEDDING; 1876	Small	47.50
☐ GRAND DEMOCRATIC FREE SOIL BANNER; 1848	Small	75.00
☐ GRAND DISPLAY OF FIREWORKS; 1883	Small	75.00
☐ GRAND DISPLAY OF FIREWORKS AND ILLUMINATIONS	Medium	110.00
☐ GRAND DRIVE, CENTRAL PARK, N. Y., THE; 1869	Large	525.00
☐ GRAND FOOTBALL MATCH; Darktown against Blackville; "A Kick Off"; 1888	Small	35.00
☐ GRAND FUNERAL PROCESSION IN MEMORY OF GENERAL JACKSON; N. Currier	Small	125.00
☐ GRAND HORSE "ST. JULIEN," THE "KING OF TROTTERS" 1880	Small	55.00
☐ GRAND NATIONAL BANNER SERIES, Party Banners of Various Candidates	Small	ea. 30.00
☐ GRAND NEW STEAMBOAT "PILGRIM", THE LARGEST IN THE WORLD; 1883	Large	190.00
☐ GRAND PACER "FLYING JIB"; Record 2:05¾	Small	65.00

	Size	Retail
☐ GRAND PACER "RICHBALL"; Record 2:12½	Small	50.00
☐ GRAND PACER "KINGSTON"; 1891	Large	125.00
☐ GRAND RECEPTION OF KOSSUTH; N. Currier; 1851	Small	55.00
☐ GRAND SALOON OF THE PALACE STEAMER "DREW"; 1878	Small	110.00
☐ GRAND STALLION "MAXY COBB"; Record 2:13¼	Small	52.50
☐ GRAND THROUGH ROUTE BETWEEN NORTH AND SOUTH; 1878	Large	275.00
☐ GRAND TROTTER "CLINGSTONE"; Record 2:14; 1882	Small	42.50
☐ GRAND YOUNG TROTTER "JAY EYE SEE"; Record 2:10	Small	37.50
☐ GRAND YOUNG TROTTING MARE "NANCY HANKS"; 1890	Small	52.50
☐ GRAND YOUNG TROTTING STALLION "AXTEL"; 1899	Small	50.00
☐ GRAND YOUNG TROTTING STALLION "AXTEL"; 1899	Large	150.00
☐ GRANDEST PALACE DRAWING ROOM STEAMERS IN THE WORLD, "DREW" AND "ST. JOHN"; 1878	Large	195.00
☐ GRANT AND HIS GENERALS; 1865	Medium	90.00
☐ GRANT AND LEE MEETING NEAR APPOMATTOX COURTHOUSE, VA.; 1868	Small	45.00
☐ GRANT AT HOME; 1869	Small	30.00
☐ GRANT IN PEACE	Small	27.50
☐ GRAY GELDING "JACK" BY PILOT MEDIUM, Record 2:15; 1888	Small	50.00
☐ GRAY'S ELEGY — IN A COUNTRY CHURCHYARD; 1864	Large	90.00
☐ GRAZING FARM, THE; 1867	Large	235.00
☐ GREAT AMERICAN BUCK HUNT OF 1856, THE	Small	37.50
☐ GREAT BARTHOLDI STATUE; (Statue of Liberty)	Small	70.00
☐ GREAT BARTHOLDI STATUE; (Statue of Liberty)	Large	150.00
☐ GREAT BLACK SEA LION, THE MONARCH OF THE ARCTIC SEAS	Small	115.00
☐ GREAT CONFLAGRATION AT PITTSBURGH, PENNA.; N. Currier	Small	330.00
☐ GREAT DOUBLE TEAM TROT; 1891	Small	60.00
☐ GREAT DOUBLE TEAM TROT; 1870	Large	145.00
☐ GREAT EAST RIVER BRIDGE; 1872	Small	70.00
☐ GREAT EAST RIVER BRIDGE 1883 (Three Prints) #1, #2, #3	Small	ea. 35.00
☐ GREAT EAST RIVER SUSPENSION BRIDGE	Large	250.00
☐ GREAT EAST RIVER SUSPENSION BRIDGE; (Between New York and Brooklyn); 1881	Small	75.00
☐ GREAT EAST RIVER SUSPENSION BRIDGE (Between New York and Brooklyn); 1886	Large	320.00
☐ GREAT "EASTERN"; Record 2:19; 1877	Small	55.00
☐ "GREAT EASTERN", THE; (Ship)	Small	95.00
☐ GREAT EXHIBITION OF 1851; N. Currier	Medium	135.00
☐ GREAT EXHIBITION OF 1860	Small	55.00
☐ GREAT FAIR ON A GRAND SCALE, A; 1894	Small	90.00

CURRIER & IVES PRINTS (G)

	Size	Retail
☐ GREAT FIELD IN A GRAND RUSH, A; 1888	Large	145.00
☐ GREAT FIGHT AT CHARLESTON, S. C.; 1863	Small	90.00
☐ GREAT FIGHT BETWEEN THE "MERRIMAC" AND "MONITOR"; 1862	Small	125.00
☐ GREAT FIRE AT BOSTON; 1872	Small	85.00
☐ GREAT FIRE AT CHICAGO; 1871	Large	600.00
☐ GREAT FIRE AT ST. LOUIS, MO.; N. Currier; 1849	Small	175.00
☐ GREAT FIRE OF 1835; "The Ruins"	Large	225.00
☐ GREAT FIRE OF 1835	Large	250.00
☐ GREAT FIVE MILE ROWING MATCH FOR $4,000; 1867	Large	750.00
☐ GREAT HORSES IN A GREAT RACE — "SALVATOR" AND "TENNY" 1891	Large	145.00
☐ GREAT INTERNATIONAL BOAT RACE	Small	410.00
☐ GREAT INTERNATIONAL YACHT RACE, AUGUST 8, 1870	Large	800.00
☐ GREAT INTERNATIONAL YACHT RACE OF 1870	Small	150.00
☐ GREAT MATCH RACE: "A Dead Heat"; 1893	Small	85.00
☐ GREAT MISSISSIPPI STEAMBOAT RACE; 1870	Small	135.00
☐ GREAT NAVAL VICTORY IN MOBILE BAY	Small	55.00
☐ GREAT OCEAN YACHT RACE; 1867	Small	175.00
☐ GREAT OYSTER EATING MATCH; "The Start" 1886	Small	30.00
☐ GREAT OYSTER EATING MATCH; "The Finish"; 1886	Small	30.00
☐ GREAT PACER "JOHNSTON", Record 2:10; 1883	Small	60.00
☐ GREAT PACER "SORREL DAN", Record 2:14; 1880	Small	55.00
☐ GREAT POLE MARES, "BELLE HAMLIN" AND "JUSTINA"	Small	65.00
☐ GREAT PRESIDENTIAL SWEEPSTAKES OF 1856	Medium	100.00
☐ GREAT RACE AT BALTIMORE; 1877	Small	155.00
☐ GREAT RACE FOR THE WESTERN STAKES; 1870	Small	100.00
☐ GREAT RACE ON THE MISSISSIPPI; Between the "New Orleans" and the "St. Louis"; 1870	Large	400.00
☐ GREAT RACE ON THE MISSISSIPPI; "Robert E. Lee" defeating the "Natchez"; 1870	Large	400.00
☐ GREAT RACING CRACK "HINDOO"; 1881	Small	65.00
☐ GREAT REPUBLICAN REFORM PARTY	Small	60.00
☐ GREAT RIOT AT THE ASTOR PLACE OPERA HOUSE, N. Y.	Small	130.00
☐ GREAT ST. LOUIS BRIDGE ACROSS THE MISSISSIPPI	Small	165.00
☐ GREAT SALT LAKE, UTAH	Small	90.00
☐ GREAT SIRE OF TROTTERS "ELECTIONEER"; 1891	Small	55.00
☐ GREAT VICTORY IN THE SHENANDOAH VALLEY, VA.	Small	50.00
☐ GREAT WEST, THE; 1870	Small	175.00
☐ GREY EAGLE; N. Currier; 1850	Medium	145.00
☐ GREY MARE "EMMA B"; Record 2:22½	Small	45.00

THE GREAT FIRE AT CHICAGO   Large $600.00

THE GREAT WEST   Small $175.00

☐	GREY MARE "LUCY" — THE PACING QUEEN; 1879	Small	55.00
☐	GREY MARE "POLICE GAZETTE"; 1879	Small	55.00
☐	GREY TROTTING WONDER "HOPEFUL"; Record 2:14¾	Small	60.00
☐	GROUP OF LILIES	Small	50.00
☐	GROVER CLEVELAND — PRESIDENT OF THE U. S.	Small	32.50
☐	GUION LINE STEAMSHIP "ARIZONA"	Small	75.00
☐	GUNBOAT CANDIDATE, THE	Small	45.00

CURRIER & IVES PRINTS (H)

	Size	Retail
☐ HALT BY THE WAYSIDE, A	Small	55.00
☐ HAMBELTONIAN; 1871	Small	62.50
☐ HAMBURG-AMERICAN MAIL STEAMER "FRISIA"	Small	42.50
☐ HANNIS; 1881	Small	57.50
☐ HANOVER; 1887	Small	52.50
☐ HAPPY FAMILY — RUFFED GROUSE AND YOUNG; 1866	Large	3800.00
☐ HAPPY LITTLE CHICKS; 1868	Small	90.00
☐ HAPPY MOTHER, THE; (Deer)	Small	130.00
☐ HAPPY NEW YEAR; N. Currier	Small	67.50
☐ HARBOR FOR THE NIGHT, A	Small	67.50
☐ HARBOR OF NEW YORK, THE. From Brooklyn Bridge Tower	Small	210.00
☐ HARRISBURG AND THE SUSQUEHANNA; 1865	Medium	195.00
☐ HARRY WILKES; 1885	Large	135.00
☐ HARVARD COLLEGE, CAMBRIDGE, MASS.; N. Currier	Small	425.00
☐ HARVEST; N. Currier; 1849	Small	40.00
☐ HARVEST DANCE, THE; N. Currier; 1846	Small	25.00
☐ HARVEST FIELD, THE; N. Currier; (Oval)	Medium	95.00
☐ HARVEST MOON, THE	Medium	125.00
☐ HARVESTING	Small	65.00
☐ HARVESTING — THE LAST LOAD	Small	65.00
☐ HAUNTS OF THE WILD SWAN, THE; 1872	Small	100.00
☐ HAYING-TIME "The First Load"; 1868	Large	450.00
☐ HAYING-TIME; "The Last Load"; 1868	Large	450.00
☐ HEAD AND HEAD FINISH, A; (Poster)	Large	150.00
☐ HEART OF THE WILDERNESS, THE	Medium	125.00
☐ "HENRY"; Record 2:20½	Small	45.00
☐ HENRY CLAY; "The Farmer of Ashland"; N. Currier	Small	50.00
☐ HENRY CLAY OF KENTUCKY; N. Currier; 1842	Small	50.00
☐ HENRY CLAY — NOMINATED FOR 11th. PRES.; N. Currier	Small	50.00
☐ HERCULES OF THE NATION SLAYING THE DRAGON OF SECESSION (Political Cartoon)	Small	55.00
☐ "HERO" AND "FLORA TEMPLE"; N. Currier; 1856	Large	325.00
☐ HEROINE OF MONMOUTH; 1876 (Mollie Pitcher)	Small	100.00
☐ HIGH BRIDGE AT HARLEM, N. Y.; N. Currier	Small	115.00
☐ HIGH PRESSURE STEAMBOAT "MAYFLOWER"; N. Currier; 1855	Large	825.00
☐ HIGH-SPEED STEAM YACHT "STILETTO"	Small	125.00
☐ HIGH WATER IN THE MISSISSIPPI; 1868	Large	650.00
☐ HIGHLAND FLING; 1876	Medium	62.50
☐ HIGHLANDER; N. Currier; 1854	Large	385.00
☐ HILLSIDE PASTURE — SHEEP	Medium	62.50
☐ HILLSIDE PASTURES — CATTLE	Small	57.50

HOME FROM THE BROOK. (Under illustration)

HOME FROM THE BROOK

Large

$375.00

	Size	Retail
☐ HOLIDAYS IN THE COUNTRY — THE OLD BARN FLOOR	Large	275.00
☐ HOLIDAYS IN THE COUNTRY — TROUBLESOME FLIES; 1868	Large	200.00
☐ HOME FROM THE BROOK — THE LUCKY FISHERMAN: 1867	Large	375.00
☐ HOME FROM THE WOODS — THE SUCCESSFUL SPORTSMEN: 1867	Large	380.00
☐ HOME IN THE COUNTRY, A	Medium	125.00
☐ HOME IN THE WILDERNESS, A; 1870	Small	165.00
☐ HOME IN THE WILDERNESS, THE; 1875	Small	95.00
☐ HOME IN THE WOODS, A	Small	50.00
☐ HOME OF FLORENCE NIGHTINGALE, THE	Medium	55.00
☐ HOME OF THE DEER — MORNING IN THE ADIRONDACKS	Large	985.00
☐ HOME OF THE DEER; 1870	Small	65.00
☐ HOME OF THE DEER	Medium	125.00
☐ HOME OF THE SEAL, THE	Small	50.00
☐ HOME OF WASHINGTON, MT. VERNON; C. Currier; 1852	Medium	125.00
☐ HOME OF WASHINGTON, MT. VERNON	Small	65.00
☐ HOME OF WASHINGTON, MT. VERNON	Large	200.00
☐ HOME ON THE MISSISSIPPI, A; 1871	Small	110.00
☐ HOME, SWEET HOME; 1869	Large	135.00
☐ HOME, SWEET HOME	Medium	75.00
☐ HOME, SWEET HOME	Small	40.00
☐ HOME TO THANKSGIVING; 1867	Large	4200.00
☐ HOMEWARD BOUND; N. Currier	Small	130.00
☐ HONEST ABE TAKING THEM ON THE HALF SHELL (Political Cartoon)	Small	85.00
☐ HON. ABRAHAM LINCOLN; Portrait Without Beard	Medium	125.00
☐ HON. ABRAHAM LINCOLN; (Republican Candidate); 1860 (Oval)	Small	95.00

	Size	Retail
☐ HON. ABRAHAM LINCOLN— 16TH PRESIDENT; 1860	Medium	225.00
☐ HON. ABRAHAM LINCOLN: (Republican Candidate); 1860	Large	450.00
☐ HON. ABRAHAM LINCOLN — OUR NEXT PRES.; 1860	Small	95.00
☐ HON. JAMES G. BLAINE	Large	100.00
☐ HON. JEFFERSON DAVIS	Small	55.00
☐ HON. STEPHEN A. DOUGLAS	Large	85.00
☐ HONOUR! N. Currier	Small	37.50
☐ HOOKED! 1874	Small	100.00
☐ "HOPEFUL"; (Grey Horse)	Small	50.00
☐ "HOPEFUL"; 1876	Large	140.00
☐ "HOPEFUL" — Record 2:14¾	Small	45.00
☐ HORACE GREELEY	Medium	42.50
☐ HORSE FAIR, THE	Small	45.00
☐ HORSE FOR THE MONEY, THE	Small	60.00
☐ HORSE, KENNEL AND FIELD; 1893	Small	55.00
☐ HORSE THAT TOOK THE POLE, THE; 1875	Small	40.00
☐ HORSEMAN OF THE PERIOD; 1876	Small	65.00
☐ HORSES AT THE FORD; 1867	Small	62.50
☐ HORSES IN A THUNDERSTORM	Small	55.00
☐ HORTICULTURAL HALL	Small	45.00
☐ HOT RACE FROM THE START, A; 1893	Small	60.00
☐ HOT RACE TO THE WIRE, A; 1876	Small	60.00
☐ HOUR OF VICTORY, THE; 1861	Medium	50.00
☐ HOUSE IN ROXBURY, MASS., THE; N. Currier	Small	130.00
☐ "HOVE TO FOR A PILOT"; N. Currier; 1856	Large	2750.00
☐ HUDSON AT PEEKSKIL, THE	Small	95.00
☐ HUDSON, FROM WEST POINT, THE; 1862	Medium	250.00
☐ HUDSON HIGHLANDS, THE; 1867	Medium	330.00
☐ HUDSON HIGHLANDS, THE; 1871	Small	100.00
☐ HUDSON HIGHLANDS NEAR NEWBURG, N. Y.	Small	100.00
☐ HUDSON NEAR COLDSPRING, THE	Small	85.00
☐ HUDSON RIVER — CROW'S NEST	Small	80.00
☐ HUDSON RIVER STEAMBOAT "BRISTOL"	Small	125.00
☐ HUDSON RIVER STEAMBOAT "ST. JOHN"; 1864	Large	425.00
☐ HUES OF AUTUMN, THE; "On Racquette River"	Small	125.00
☐ HUMMING TROT, A; 1893	Small	50.00
☐ HUNDRED LEAF ROSE; N. Currier	Small	52.50
☐ HUNTER'S DOG, THE; N. Currier	Small	95.00
☐ HUNTER'S SHANTY, THE — IN THE ADIRONDACKS; 1861	Large	375.00
☐ HUNTER'S SHANTY, THE	Small	55.00

"HIGH WATER IN THE MISSISSIPPI."

**HIGH WATER
IN THE
MISSISSIPPI**

Large
$650.00

ICE-BOAT RACE ON THE HUDSON.

**ICE BOAT
RACE
ON THE
HUDSON**

Small
$400.00

☐ HUNTING CASUALTIES, NO. 575 — NO. 580	Small	ea.	90.00
☐ HUNTING, FISHING AND FOREST SCENES; 1867 — GOOD LUCK ALL AROUND	Large		300.00
☐ HUNTING, FISHING, AND FOREST SCENES — SHANTYING ON THE LAKE SHORE; 1867	Large		300.00
☐ HUNTING IN THE NORTHERN WOODS	Small		125.00
☐ HUNTING ON THE PLAINS; 1871	Small		175.00
☐ HUNTING ON THE SUSQUEHANNA	Medium		150.00
☐ HUSH! I FEEL HIM; 1880	Small		55.00
☐ HUSH! I'VE A NIBBLE	Small		55.00
☐ HUSKING; 1861	Large		1350.00
☐ HYDE PARK — ON THE HUDSON	Small		75.00

CURRIER & IVES PRINTS (I)

	Size	Retail
☐ I AM AS DRY AS A FISH	Small	52.50
☐ I TOLD YOU SO; 1860	Small	32.50
☐ ICE BOAT RACE ON THE HUDSON	Small	400.00
☐ IDLEWILD — ON THE HUDSON; "The Glen"	Small	60.00
☐ IMPENDING CATASTROPHE, AN	Small	35.00
☐ IMPENDING CRISIS, THE	Small	38.00
☐ IN A TIGHT PLACE — GETTING SQUEEZED; 1860	Medium	60.00
☐ IN THE HARBOR	Small	135.00
☐ IN THE MOUNTAINS	Small	62.50
☐ IN THE MOUNTAINS; (Deer)	Medium	100.00
☐ IN THE NORTHERN WILDS — BEAVER TRAPPING	Small	110.00
☐ IN THE SPRINGTIME	Small	40.00
☐ IN THE WOODS	Small	42.50
☐ INAUGURATION OF WASHINGTON; 1876	Small	120.00
☐ INCREASE OF FAMILY, AN; 1863	Medium	42.50
☐ INDEPENDENCE HALL, PHILADELPHIA	Small	120.00
☐ INDEPENDENT GOLD HUNTER GOING TO CALIFORNIA; N. Currier	Small	100.00
☐ INDIAN BALL PLAYERS	Medium	150.00
☐ INDIAN BEAR DANCE, THE	Medium	150.00
☐ INDIAN BUFFALO HUNT	Medium	200.00
☐ INDIAN BUFFALO HUNT — ON THE PRAIRIE BLUFFS	Medium	200.00
☐ INDIAN FALLS	Small	50.00
☐ INDIAN FAMILY; N. Currier	Small	55.00
☐ INDIAN HUNTER; N. Currier; 1845	Small	70.00
☐ INDIAN LAKE — SUNSET; 1860	Large	210.00
☐ INDIAN PASS, THE — ROCKY MOUNTAINS	Medium	210.00
☐ INDIAN SUMMER, SQUAM LAKE, N. H.; 1868	Medium	175.00
☐ INDIAN TOWN	Small	95.00
☐ INDIAN WARRIOR, THE; N. Currier; 1845	Small	55.00
☐ INDIAN ATTACKING THE GRIZZLY BEAR	Medium	225.00
☐ INFANT BROOD, THE	Small	200.00
☐ INGLESIDE WINTER, THE	Small	85.00
☐ INTERIOR OF FORT SUMTER DURING BOMBARDMENT	Small	60.00
☐ INTO MISCHIEF; 1857	Small	25.00
☐ IRON R. M. STEAMSHIP "PERSIA" CUNARD LINE: N. CURRIER	Small	85.00
☐ IRON STEAMSHIP "GREAT BRITAIN"; N. Currier	Small	100.00
☐ IRON STEAMSHIP "GREAT EASTERN"; 1858	Large	400.00
☐ IROQUOIS; 1882	Large	200.00

	Size	Retail
JAMES BUCHANAN; (Democratic Candidate); N. Currier	Small	40.00
JAMES BUCHANAN — 15th PRESIDENT; N. Currier	Small	35.00
JAMES J. CORBETT	Medium	175.00
JAMES K. POLK — 11th PRESIDENT; C. Currier	Small	55.00
JAMES K. POLK — PEOPLE'S CANDIDATE; N. Currier; 1844	Small	55.00
"JAMES K. POLK" (Race Horse); N. Currier; 1850	Medium	150.00
JAMES MADISON — 4th PRESIDENT; N. Currier	Small	65.00
JAMES MONROE — 5th PRESIDENT; N. Currier	Small	65.00
"JAY EYE SEE" — Record 2:14; 1883	Small	55.00
"JAY EYE SEE"; 1883	Large	125.00
"JAY EYE SEE" — THE PHENOMENAL TROTTING GELDING; 1884	Large	125.00
JEFF DAVIS ON HIS OWN PLATFORM	Small	75.00
JENNY LIND — THE SWEDISH NIGHTINGALE'S GREETING TO AMERICA; N. Currier	Medium	70.00
JIB AND MAINSAIL RACE, A; 1882	Large	175.00
JOCKEY'S DREAM, THE; 1880	Small	37.50
JOHN ADAMS — 2nd PRESIDENT; N. Currier	Small	70.00
JOHN BROWN; 1863	Small	60.00
JOHN BROWN — THE MARTYR; 1870	Small	55.00
JOHN BROWN — LEADER OF THE HARPER'S FERRY INSURRECTION	Small	55.00
JOHN C. CALHOUN: N. Currier; 1853	Small	35.00
JOHN C. FREMONT; N. Currier	Small	45.00
JOHN C. HEENAN — THE CHAMPION OF AMERICA; 1860	Small	145.00
JOHN C. HEENAN — CHAMPION OF THE WORLD; 1860	Small	145.00
JOHN HANCOCK'S DEFIANCE; 1876	Small	85.00
JOHN J. DWYER — CHAMPION OF AMERICA	Medium	82.50
JOHN L. SULLIVAN; 1883	Medium	170.00
JOHN MORRISSEY; 1860	Small	100.00
JOHN QUINCY ADAMS — 6th PRESIDENT; N. Currier	Small	50.00
JOHNSON'S HOTEL; C. Currier	Medium	450.00
JOHN TYLER — 10th PRESIDENT; N. Currier	Small	38.00
JOLLY SMOKER, THE; 1880	Large	55.00
JOLLY YOUNG DUCKS; 1866	Small	45.00
"JUNO" — A CELEBRATED SETTER; N. Currier	Small	100.00
"JUNO" — Pointer; N. Currier	Small	100.00
JUST CAUGHT — TROUT AND PICKEREL; 1872	Small	75.00

	Size	Retail
☐ KATZ-KILLS IN WINTER, THE	Small	60.0
☐ KING OF THE ROAD, THE; 1866	Large	145.0
☐ KINGSTON; 1891	Small	47.5
☐ KISS IN THE DARK, A; 1881	Small	55.0
☐ KISS ME QUICK; N. Currier	Small	40.0
☐ KITTY'S BREAKFAST	Large	50.0
☐ "KREMLIN", Record: 2:07¾; 1893	Small	50.0

CURRIER & IVES PRINTS (L)

	Size	Retail
☐ LADDER OF FORTUNE; 1875	Small	35.0
☐ "LADY EMMA", "GEORGE WILKES" AND "GENERAL BUTLER"; 1865	Large	195.0
☐ "LADY MOSCOW"; N. Currier; 1850	Large	150.0
☐ "LADY MOSCOW", "ROCKET" AND "BROWN DICK"; N. Currier	Large	175.0
☐ "LADY SUFFOLK"; N. Currier; 1850	Medium	280.0
☐ "LADY SUFFOLK" — Record 2:26	Large	275.0
☐ "LADY SUFFOLK"; N. Currier; 1852	Large	330.0
☐ "LADY SUFFOLK" AND "LADY MOSCOW"; N. Currier; 1850	Large	245.0
☐ "LADY SUTTON"; N. Currier; 1849	Medium	165.0
☐ "LADY THORN" AND "MOUNTAIN BOY"; 1867	Large	175.0
☐ "LADY WASHINGTON"	Medium	55.0
☐ "LADY WOODRUFF", "MILLER'S DAMSEL", "GENERAL DARCY" AND "STELLA"; 1857	Large	365.00
☐ LAFAYETTE	Medium	70.0
☐ LAFAYETTE AT THE TOMB OF WASHINGTON; N. Currier	Small	45.0
☐ LAKE AND FOREST SCENERY	Medium	115.00
☐ LAKE GEORGE, N. Y.	Small	75.00
☐ LAKE GEORGE, BLACK MOUNTAIN	Small	75.00
☐ LAKE IN THE WOODS, THE	Small	65.00
☐ LAKE MOHONK	Small	75.00
☐ LAKE WINNIPISEOGEE, NEW HAMPSHIRE	Large	225.00
☐ LAKESIDE HOME; 1869	Medium	85.00
☐ LANDING A TROUT; 1879	Small	52.50
☐ LANDING OF COLUMBUS AT SAN SALVADOR; 1876	Small	30.00
☐ LANDING OF COLUMBUS, OCTOBER 11, 1492; N. Currier	Small	40.00
☐ LANDING OF THE AMERICAN FORCES AT VERA CRUZ; N. Currier; 1847	Small	67.50
☐ LANDING OF THE PILGRIMS AT PLYMOUTH; N. Currier	Small	90.00

CURRIER & IVES (L)

LAST HIT IN THE GAME; 1886	Small	30.00
LAST SHOT, THE; 1858	Large	2750.00
LAST WAR-WHOOP, THE; N. Currier; 1856	Large	1750.00
LAYING BACK — STIFF FOR A BRUSH; 1878	Small	40.00
LEADERS, THE; "JAY EYE SEE", 2:10; "MAUD S.", 2:08¾; "ST. JULIEN", 2:11¼; 1888	Large	150.00
LEVEE, NEW ORLEANS, THE 1884	Large	1850.00
LIFE IN THE CAMP — PREPARING FOR SUPPER; 1863	Large	150.00
LIFE IN THE COUNTRY — EVENING	Medium	110.00
LIFE IN THE COUNTRY — MORNING; 1862	Medium	105.00
LIFE IN THE COUNTRY — MORNING	Small	50.00
LIFE IN THE COUNTRY — THE MORNING RIDE; 1859	Large	425.00
LIFE IN THE WOODS — RETURNING TO CAMP; 1860	Large	575.00
LIFE IN THE WOODS — STARTING OUT; 1860	Large	575.00
LIFE OF A FIREMAN — THE FIRE; N. Currier; 1854	Large	500.00
LIFE OF A FIREMAN — THE METROPOLITAN SYSTEM; 1866	Large	525.00
LIFE OF A FIREMAN — THE NEW ERA	Large	525.00
LIFE OF A FIREMAN — THE NIGHT ALARM; N. Currier; 1854	Large	425.00
LIFE OF A FIREMAN — THE RACE; N. Currier; 1854	Large	400.00
LIFE OF A FIREMAN — THE RUINS; N. Currier; 1854	Large	350.00
LIFE OF A HUNTER, THE — CATCHING A TARTAR; 1861	Large	625.00
LIFE OF A HUNTER, THE — A TIGHT FIX; 1861	Large	7500.00
LIFE OF A SPORTSMAN, THE; "Camping In the Woods"	Small	125.00
LIFE OF A SPORTSMAN, THE; "Coming into Camp"	Small	125.00
LIFE OF A SPORTSMAN, THE; "Going Out"; 1872	Small	125.00
LIFE OF A TRAPPER; "A Sudden Halt"; 1866	Large	2800.00
LIFE ON THE PRAIRIE; "The Buffalo Hunt"; 1862	Large	2800.00
LIFE ON THE PRAIRIE; "The Trapper's Defence"; 1862	Large	1700.00
LIGHTNING EXPRESS, THE	Small	390.00
"LIGHTNING EXPRESS" TRAIN LEAVING THE JUNCTION; 1863	Large	2350.00
"LIGHTNING EXPRESS" TRAIN LEAVING THE JUNCTION	Small	460.00

☐ "LIMITED EXPRESS", A; 1884	Small	8⁵
☐ LINCOLN, ABRAHAM; 16th PRESIDENT (Half Length); 1860	Small	7⁵
☐ LINCOLN, ABRAHAM; 16th PRESIDENT; (Portrait)	Small	7⁵
☐ LINCOLN, ABRAHAM; 16th PRESIDENT; 1861	Small	7(
☐ LINCOLN, ABRAHAM	Medium	9⁵
☐ LINCOLN, ABRAHAM — THE NATION'S MARTYR	Small	75
☐ LINCOLN, ABRAHAM — THE NATION'S MARTYR	Large	150
☐ LINCOLN AT HOME; 1867	Small	85
☐ LINCOLN AT HOME	Large	200
☐ LINCOLN FAMILY, THE; 1867	Small	75
☐ LION HUNTER, THE; N. Currier	Small	32
☐ LIONS OF THE DERBY, THE	Small	40
☐ LITTLE FIREMAN, THE; 1857	Large	125.
☐ LITTLE GAME OF BAGATELLE BETWEEN OLD ABE, THE RAIL-SPLITTER, AND LITTLE MACK, THE GUNBOAT GENERAL	Small	125.
☐ LITTLE MORE GRAPE, A; CAPT. BRAGG; N. Currier	Small	47.
☐ LOADING COTTON; 1870	Small	150.
☐ LONG ISLAND SOUND; 1869	Medium	300.
☐ LONG LIVE THE REPUBLIC; N. Currier	Medium	50.
☐ LOOKING DOWN THE YO-SEMITE	Small	65.
☐ LOOKOUT MOUNTAIN, TENNESSEE AND THE CHATTANOOGA RAILROAD; 1866	Large	1000.
☐ LOSS OF THE STEAMBOAT "SWALLOW"; N. Currier	Small	100.(
☐ LOSS OF THE STEAMBOAT "CAMBRIA"; 1883	Small	65.(
☐ LOSS OF THE U.S.M. STEAMSHIP "ARCTIC"; 1854	Small	65.(
☐ LOST IN THE SNOW — DOGS OF ST. BERNARD	Small	90.(
☐ LOW PRESSURE STEAMBOAT "ISAAC NEWTON"; N. Currier; 1855	Large	875.(
☐ LOW WATER IN THE MISSISSIPPI; 1868	Large	580.(
☐ LUCKY ESCAPE, THE; N. Currier	Small	65.0
☐ LUSCIOUS PEACHES	Small	37.5
☐ LUXURY OF TOBACCO, THE; 1876	Small	47.5

	Size	Retail
"MAC" (Race Horse); N. Currier	Large	300.00
MADISON, CAPITOL OF WISCONSIN; C. Currier	Small	150.00
MAGIC LAKE	Medium	32.50
MAGNIFICENT STEAMSHIP SERIES — SHIPS OF VARIOUS LINES	Small	60.00
MAIDEN ROCK, MISSISSIPPI RIVER	Small	95.00
MAIN OF COCKS, A; "The First Battle"	Medium	75.00
"MAJOLICA", Record 2:17, 1885	Large	85.00
MAJ. GEN. GEORGE G. MEADE AT THE BATTLE OF GETTYSBURG; 1863	Small	35.00
MAJ. GEN. JOSEPH HOOKER, COMMANDER-IN-CHIEF "ARMY OF THE POTOMAC"; 1862	Small	40.00
MAJ. GEN. PHILIP SHERIDAN, U. S. ARMY	Small	40.00
MAJ. GEN. U. S. GRANT AT THE SIEGE OF VICKSBURG	Small	40.00
MAJ. GEN. WILLIAM T. SHERMAN, U. S. ARMY	Small	40.00
MAJ. GEN. WINFIELD SCOTT, GENERAL-IN-CHIEF OF THE U. S. ARMY; N. Currier; 1846	Small	40.00
MAJ. GEN. ZACHARY TAYLOR BEFORE MONTEREY; N. Currier; 1848	Small	40.00
MAMA'S DARLING	Large	35.00
"MAMBRINO"	Small	85.00
"MAMBRINO PILOT", "DAISY BURNS" AND "ROSAMOND"	Large	150.00
MAMMOTH IRON STEAMSHIP "GREAT EASTERN"	Small	60.00
MAN OF WORDS — MAN OF DEEDS. WHICH DO YOU THINK THE COUNTRY NEEDS?; 1868	Small	60.00
MAN THAT GAVE BARNUM HIS TURN, THE	Small	67.50
MAN THAT KNOWS A HORSE, THE; (Comic); 1877	Small	65.00
MANAGING A CANDIDATE	Small	47.50
MANSION OF THE OLDEN TIME, A	Small	50.00
MAP OF MT. VERNON; C. Currier	Small	85.00
MAPLE SUGARING — EARLY SPRING IN THE NORTHERN WOODS; 1872	Small	300.00
MARINE BARK "CATALPA"; N. Currier	Small	180.00
MARINE BARK "THE AMAZON"; N. Currier	Small	180.00
MARION'S BRIGADE CROSSING THE PEDEE RIVER, S. C.	Small	85.00
MARRIAGE OF THE FREE SOIL AND LIBERTY PARTIES; (Political Cartoon)	Small	65.00
MARTHA WASHINGTON	Medium	50.00
MARTHA WASHINGTON	Small	35.00
MARTIN VAN BUREN, CHAMPION OF DEMOCRACY	Small	40.00
MARTIN VAN BUREN — 8th PRESIDENT; N. Currier	Medium	45.00
MATCH AGAINST TIME, A; 1878	Small	60.00

	Size	R
☐ MATING IN THE WOODS. "RUFFED GROUSE"; 1871	Small	13
☐ "MATTIE HUNTER"; 1881	Small	5
☐ "MATTIE HUNTER" — RECORD 2:15; 1879	Small	3
☐ "MAUD S." — RECORD 2:08¾; 1881	Small	5
☐ "MAUDE S." AND "ALDINE"	Small	5
☐ "MAUD S." AND "ST. JULIEN"; 1884	Small	5
☐ "MAY QUEEN" (Horse); 1876	Small	5
☐ "MAYFLOWER" SALUTED BY THE U.S. FLEET; 1886	Large	17
☐ McDONOUGH'S VICTORY OF LAKE CHAMPLAIN; 1846	Small	23
☐ MEADOW IN SPRINGTIME — THE TWIN LAMBS; 1867	Large	12
☐ MEADOWSIDE COTTAGE	Medium	7
☐ MEETING OF THE WATERS, THE; 1868	Small	2
☐ MERCHANT'S EXCHANGE, NEW YORK, WALL STREET	Small	30
☐ "MIDNIGHT" — RECORD 2:18½; 1879	Small	5
☐ MIDNIGHT RACE ON THE MISSISSIPPI, A; (Natchez and Eclipse); 1860	Large	87
☐ "MILL BOY: AND "BLONDINE" 1881	Small	8
☐ MILL-STREAM, THE	Medium	8
☐ MILLARD FILLMORE — 13th PRESIDENT; N. Currier; (Very rare); 1856	Small	32
☐ MILLARD FILLMORE — 13th PRESIDENT; N. CURRIER: 1856	Large	175
☐ MINIATURE SHIP "RED, WHITE, AND BLUE"	Small	100
☐ MINK TRAPPING, "PRIME"; 1862	Large	3000
☐ MINNEHAHA — "laughing Water"	Small	37
☐ MINNEHAHA FALLS, MINNESOTA	Medium	100
☐ MINUTE-MEN OF THE REVOLUTION, THE; 1876	Small	150
☐ MISSISSIPPI IN TIME OF PEACE; 1865	Large	275
☐ MISSISSIPPI IN TIME OF WAR; 1865	Large	275
☐ MIXED AT THE FINISH; 1880	Small	35
☐ "MOLLIE McCARTHY", THE RACING QUEEN; 1878	Small	60
☐ MOMENTOUS QUESTION, THE; N. Currier; 1853	Small	65
☐ MONUMENT; (Virginia)	Small	50
☐ MOONLIGHT ON LAKE CATALPA, VIRGINIA	Small	60
☐ MOONLIGHT ON THE LAKE	Small	60
☐ MOONLIGHT ON THE MISSISSIPPI	Small	100
☐ MOOSE AND WOLVES — A NARROW ESCAPE	Small	225
☐ MOOSEHEAD LAKE	Small	70
☐ MORE FREE THAN WELCOME	Small	35
☐ MORE FRIGHTENED THAN HURT; N. Currier	Small	35
☐ MORE PLUCKY THAN PRUDENT; 1885	Small	57

A NIGHT
ON THE
HUDSON

Large
$450.00

A NIGHT ON THE HUDSON.

MORNING IN THE WOODS; 1852	Large	625.00
MORNING IN THE WOODS; 1865	Large	730.00
MORNING RIDE, THE; N. Currier; 1849	Small	50.00
MOSS ROSE, THE; N. Currier; 1847	Small	50.00
MOTHER'S BLESSING, THE	Medium	50.00
MOTHER'S WING; (Birds); 1866	Small	42.50
MT. HOLYOKE FEMALE SEMINARY, SOUTH HADLEY, MASS. N. Currier	Small	150.00
MOUNT WASHINGTON AND THE WHITE MOUNTAINS; 1860	Large	400.00
MOUNTAIN PASS, SIERRA NEVADA; 1867	Large	400.00
MOUNTAIN STREAM, THE	Medium	115.00
MOUNTAINEER'S HOME, THE	Medium	150.00
MR. AUGUST BELMONT'S "POTOMAC" AND "MASHER" 1891	Large	175.00
MR. BONNER'S HORSE "JOE ELLIOTT"; 1873	Large	260.00
MR. PIERRE LORILLARD'S BR. COLT "IROQUOIS"	Small	90.00
MR. WM. H. VANDERBILT'S CELEBRATED ROAD TEAM "LYSANDER" AND "LEANDER"; 1879	Small	95.00
MR. WM. H. VANDERBILT'S CELEBRATED ROAD TEAM "SMALL HOPES" AND "LACY MAC"; 1877	Small	275.00
MRS. FISK AND THE MISSES FOX; N. Currier	Small	55.00
"MUD S." — DE GREAT RECORD BUSTER; 1885	Small	37.50
MULE TRAIN ON A DOWN GRADE, A; 1881	Small	37.50
MULE TRAIN ON AN UP GRADE; 1881	Small	37.50
MUSIC; 1875	Small	35.00
"MUSIC"; (Chestnut Mare); 1875	Large	85.00
MUSTANG TEAM, THE; N. Currier	Small	50.00
MY BOYHOOD HOME	Small	50.00
MY COTTAGE HOME; 1866	Large	220.00

	Size	R
☐ NANCY HANKS; 1892	Small	5
☐ NARRAGANSETT S. S. COMPANY'S STEAMER "PROVIDENCE" OF THE FALL RIVER LINE	Small	7
☐ NARROWS FROM FORT HAMILTON; N. Currier	Small	12
☐ NARROWS FROM STATEN ISLAND, THE; N. Currier	Small	12
☐ NARROWS, NEW YORK BAY FROM STATEN ISLAND	Small	12
☐ NATIONAL DEMOCRATIC BANNER of 1860	Small	4
☐ NATIONAL DEMOCRATIC BANNER OF VICTORY, 1868	Small	50
☐ NATIONAL GAME, THE — THREE "OUTS" AND ONE "RUN" (Politican Cartoon)	Small	55
☐ NATIONAL UNION REPUBLICAN BANNER, 1860; (Lincoln and Hamlin)	Small	62
☐ NATIONAL UNION REPUBLICAN BANNER, 1868; (Grant and Colfax)	Small	42
☐ NATIONAL WASHINGTON MONUMENT, WASH., D. C.	Small	50
☐ NATURAL BRIDGE, VA.	Small	62
☐ NAVAL BOMBARDMENT OF VERA CRUZ; N. Currier	Small	70
☐ NAVAL HEROES OF THE U. S. PLATES 1, 2, 3, 4; 1846; N. Currier	Small	ea. 175
☐ NEAREST WAY IN SUMMER TIME, THE	Medium	100
☐ NEARING THE FINISH LINE; 1888	Large	165
☐ "NETTIE"; (Race Horse); 1874	Small	55
☐ NEW ENGLAND COAST SCENE, OFF BOSTON LIGHT	Small	125
☐ NEW ENGLAND COAST SCENE	Small	150.
☐ NEW ENGLAND HOME, A	Small	55.
☐ NEW ENGLAND HOMESTEAD, A	Small	57.
☐ NEW ENGLAND SCENERY; 1866	Large	500
☐ NEW ENGLAND WINTER SCENE; 1861	Large	1750.
☐ NEW EXCURSION STEAMER "COLUMBIA"; 1877	Large	165.
☐ NEW FOUNTAIN OF DEMOCRACY, THE (Political Cartoon)	Small	85.
☐ NEW JERSEY FOX HUNT; "A Smoking Run"; 1876	Small	75.
☐ NEW JERSEY FOX HUNT; "Taking Breath"; 1876	Small	75.
☐ NEW PALACE STEAMER "PILGRIM" OF THE FALL RIVER LINE	Medium	85.
☐ NEW ST. PATRICK'S CATHEDRAL, THE	Small	55.
☐ NEW STEAMSHIP "UMBRIA" OF THE CUNARD LINE	Small	50.
☐ NEW SUSPENSION BRIDGE, NIAGARA FALLS	Small	110.0
☐ NEW YORK AND BROOKLYN; 1875	Large	475.0
☐ NEW YORK AND BROOKLYN; (Jersey City and Hoboken Waterfront); 1877	Large	475.0
☐ NEW YORK BAY FROM BAY RIDGE, L. I.; 1860	Medium	325.0
☐ NEW YORK BAY FROM BAY RIDGE, L. I.	Small	90.0
☐ NEW YORK BAY FROM TELEGRAPH STATION	Small	115.0

	Size	Retail
NEW YORK CLIPPER SHIP "CHALLENGE"; N. Currier	Small	210.00
NEW YORK CRYSTAL PALACE; N. Currier; 1853	Large	275.00
NEW YORK CRYSTAL PALACE; N. Currier	Small	115.00
NEW YORK FERRY BOAT	Small	85.00
NEW YORK FIREMEN'S MONUMENT, GREENWOOD CEMETERY, L. I.; N. Currier 1855	Medium	60.00
NEW YORK FROM WEEHAWKEN; C. Currier; 1835	Small	175.00
NEW YORK, LOOKING NORTH FROM THE BATTERY; 1860	Small	115.00
NEW YORK PILOT'S MONUMENT; N. Currier; 1855	Medium	72.50
NEW YORK YACHT CLUB REGATTA	Large	860.00
NEWPORT BEACH	Small	125.00
NIAGARA BY MOONLIGHT	Small	65.00
NIAGARA FALLS; N. Currier	Small	65.00
NIAGARA FALLS	Large	150.00
NIAGARA FALLS FROM GOAT ISLAND	Medium	85.00
NIAGARA FALLS FROM GOAT ISLAND	Small	57.50
NIAGARA FALLS FROM TABLE ROCK; N. Currier	Small	57.50
NIAGARA FALLS FROM THE CANADA SIDE	Small	52.50
NIGHT AFTER THE BATTLE — BURYING THE DEAD	Small	30.00
NIGHT BEFORE THE BATTLE — THE PATRIOT'S DREAM	Medium	50.00
NIGHT BY THE CAMPFIRE; 1861	Medium	140.00
NIGHT EXPRESS, THE; "The Start"	Small	550.00
NIGHT ON THE HUDSON, A; "Through at Daylight"; 1864	Large	450.00
NIGHT RACE ON THE MISSISSIPPI; 1875	Small	115.00
NIGHT SCENE AT A JUNCTION; 1884	Small	380.00
NIGHT SCENE AT AN AMERICAN RAILWAY JUNCTION; 1876	Large	2500.00
NIGHTMARE IN THE SLEEPING CAR, A; 1875	Small	62.50
NIP AND TUCK! (Comic); 1878	Small	37.50
NIPPED IN THE ICE	Small	350.00
NOAH'S ARK; N. Currier	Small	50.00
NOONTIDE — A SHADY SPOT	Small	37.50
NORTH AMERICAN INDIANS	Medium	165.00
NORTH RIVER FERRY BOAT	Small	52.50
NORTH SEA WHALE FISHERY; N. Currier	Small	375.00
NOSEGAY, THE; N. Currier; 1848; (Bouquet)	Small	45.00
NOT CAUGHT; (Fox and Rabbit); N. Currier	Medium	60.00
NOT CAUGHT YET; (Fox Trap); N. Currier	Small	50.00
NOTCH HOUSE, WHITE MOUNTAINS, N. H., THE	Small	75.00
NOTICE TO SMOKERS AND CHEWERS; N. Currier	Small	50.00
NOVA SCOTIA SCENERY; 1868	Medium	130.00

	Size	R
☐ "OCCIDENT" 1876	Large	33
☐ "OCCIDENT" — Record 2:16¾	Small	6
☐ OCEAN STEAMER IN A HEAVY GALE, AN	Small	8
☐ OCTOBER LANDSCAPE	Medium	20
☐ OFF A LEE SHORE	Small	14
☐ OFF THE COAST IN A SNOWSTORM — TAKING A PILOT	Small	14
☐ OLD BARN FLOOR, THE	Large	27
☐ OLD BLANFORD CHURCH, PETERSBURG, VA.	Small	6
☐ OLD FARM GATE, THE; 1864	Large	22
☐ OLD FARM HOUSE, THE; N. Currier	Small	10
☐ OLD FARM HOUSE, THE; 1872	Medium	21
☐ OLD HOMESTEAD, THE; N. Currier; 1855	Small	15
☐ OLD HOMESTEAD, THE	Medium	17
☐ OLD HOMESTEAD IN WINTER, THE; 1864	Large	1750
☐ OLD MANSE, THE	Small	85
☐ OLD MANSION HOUSE, GOWANUS ROAD; N. Currier	Small	85
☐ OLD MARE THE BEST HORSE, THE; 1881	Large	195
☐ OLD MILL IN SUMMER, THE	Small	45
☐ OLD MILL-DAM AT SLEEPY HOLLOW	Small	85
☐ OLD OAKEN BUCKET; 1864	Large	285
☐ OLD OAKEN BUCKET; 1872	Small	65
☐ OLD PLANTATION HOME, THE; 1872	Small	90
☐ OLD SAWMILL, L. I.; . Currier	Small	85
☐ OLD SLEDGE	Small	55
☐ OLD STONE HOUSE, THE; N. Currier	Small	80
☐ OLD STONE HOUSE, L. I., THE	Small	70
☐ OLD TENNENT PARSONAGE ON MONMOUTH BATTLEFIELD, THE; C. Currier; 1859	Medium	175
☐ ON A POINT; N. Currier; 1855	Medium	300
☐ ON A STRONG SCENT; 1880	Small	25
☐ ON GUARD; 1876	Small	27
☐ ON THE COAST OF CALIFORNIA	Small	55
☐ ON THE DOWNS, AT EPSOM	Medium	110
☐ ON THE HOME STRETCH; 1882	Small	37
☐ ON THE HUDSON; 1869	Small	75
☐ ON THE JUNIATA; 1869	Medium	85
☐ ON THE LAKE	Small	50
☐ ON THE MISSISSIPPI; 1869	Small	130
☐ ON THE MISSISSIPPI, LOADING COTTON; 1870	Small	145

**THE OLD
OAKEN BUCKET**

Large
$285.00

**OLD
SWISS MILL
PUZZLE
PICTURE**

Small
$45.00

	Size	Retail
ON THE ST. LAWRENCE — INDIAN ENCAMPMENT	Small	110.00
"OREGON"; (Steamship); N. Currier	Small	105.00
ORIGIN OF THE SPECIES; 1874	Small	37.50
ORIGINAL GENERAL TOM THUMB, THE	Small	55.00
OTHELLO; 1879	Medium	55.00
OUR VICTORIOUS FLEETS IN CUBAN WATERS; 1898	Large	115.00
OUT FOR A DAY'S SHOOTING — OFF FOR THE WOODS; 1869	Large	450.00
OUTLET OF THE NIAGARA RIVER, THE	Small	45.00
OUTWARD BOUND; N. Currier; 1845	Small	175.00
OYSTER SUPPER, AN; N. Currier	Small	40.00

	Size	R
☐ PACIFIC COAST STEAMSHIP CO'S "STATE OF CALIFORNIA"; 1878	Small	6
☐ PACIFIC MAIL STEAMSHIP COMPANY'S STEAMER "GREAT REPUBLIC"	Small	8
☐ PACING A FAST HEAT; 1892	Small	5
☐ PACING FOR A GRAND PURSE; 1890	Large	16
☐ PACING HORSE "BILLY BOYCE" OF ST. LOUIS; 1868	Large	18
☐ PACING KING "HAL POINTER", Record 2:04½	Small	6
☐ PACING IN THE LATEST STYLE; 1893	Small	6
☐ PACING KING "ROBERT J.", Record 2:01½; 1894	Large	12
☐ PACING KING "ROBERT J." IN HIS RACE WITH "JOE PATCHEN" 1894	Small	6
☐ PACING WONDER "LITTLE BROWN JUG", Record 2:11¾; 1882	Small	6
☐ PACING WONDER "SLEEPY TOM" THE BLIND HORSE	Small	6
☐ PADDLE WHEEL STEAMSHIP "MASSACHUSETTS", THE	Large	12
☐ PADDY AND THE PIGS	Small	30
☐ PADDY RYAN, "The Trojan Giant"	Medium	85
☐ PAIR OF NUTCRACKERS (Squirrels)	Small	52
☐ PARLEY, A, "Prepared for an Emergency"	Large	2250
☐ PAROLE; 1877	Small	85
☐ PARSON'S COLT, THE; 1880	Large	95
☐ PARTRIDGE SHOOTING; 1852; N. Currier	Medium	1000
☐ PARTRIDGE SHOOTING; 1855; N. Currier	Small	195
☐ PARTRIDGE SHOOTING; 1865; (C & I)	Large	700
☐ PARTRIDGE SHOOTING; 1870	Small	175
☐ PASTURE IN SUMMER, THE — THE DRINKING TROUGH; 1867	Large	300
☐ PASTURE — NOONTIDE	Medium	65
☐ PATH THROUGH THE FIELDS, THE	Small	40
☐ PATH THROUGH THE WOODS, THE	Small	50
☐ PATRIOT OF 1776, A; "Defending His Homestead"; 1876	Small	135
☐ PEACE AND PLENTY; 1871	Medium	105
☐ PEACEFUL RIVER, THE	Small	37
☐ PEACHES AND GRAPES — FIRST PRIZE: 1870	Small	30
☐ PEERLESS GOLDSMITH MAID, THE; 1871	Small	55
☐ PELHAM; 1850; N. Currier	Large	150
☐ PENNSYLVANIA RAILROAD SCENERY	Small	145
☐ PEOPLES LINE, HUDSON RIVER; 1877	Small	75
☐ PEOPLE'S LINE, HUDSON RIVER — THE PALACE STEAMERS OF THE WORLD; 1877	Large	210
☐ PERMANENT FAIR GROUNDS OF THE QUEENS COUNTY AGRICULTURAL SOCIETY, MINEOLA, L. I.; C. Currier; 1867	Large	165

	Size	Retail
RY'S VICTORY ON LAKE ERIE: N. Currier	Small	200.00
TONA" AND "FASHION"; N. Currier	Large	3250.00
ALLAS", Record 2:13¾; 1883	Small	55.00
OSOPHY OF TOBACCO, THE	Small	45.00
NIC PARTY, THE	Medium	180.00
NIC PARTY, THE; 1858	Small	42.50
KEREL; 1872	Small	67.50
OMONT; 1882	Small	55.00
EON SHOOTING — THE PLAYING THE DECOY; 1862	Large	750.00
GRIM"; 1883	Small	57.50
OT BOAT IN A STORM	Small	90.00
NEER CABIN OF THE YO-SE-MITE VALLEY	Small	120.00
NEER'S HOME ON THE WESTERN FRONTIER; 1867	Large	425.00
CID LAKE, ADIRONDACKS	Small	75.00
N OF THE CITY OF NEW YORK: (Bradford Map); 1849; N. Currier	Medium	200.00
YED OUT; 1871	Small	37.50
EASURES OF THE COUNTRY, THE; "Sweet Home"	Medium	90.00
ASURES OF THE COUNTRY, THE; "Winter"	Small	115.00
JCK — ONE OF THE RIGHT SORT; N. Currier	Small	45.00
OCAHONTAS BOY" — Record 2:31	Large	150.00
CAHONTAS SAVING THE LIFE OF CAPTAIN JOHN SMITH; N. Currier	Small	32.50
INTER, THE; 1848; N. Currier	Small	75.00
INTERS; 1846; N. Currier	Small	120.00
INTING A BEVY; 1866	Large	250.00
LITICAL GYMNASIUM, THE; 1860	Medium	100.00
OLITICAL SIAMESE TWINS, THE; 1864	Medium	90.00
OND IN THE WOODS, THE	Medium	75.00
ORT OF NEW YORK, THE; 1872	Large	700.00
ORT OF NEW YORK, THE; 1892	Large	400.00
OST OFFICE, NEW YORK, THE; N. Currier	Small	350.00
OWER OF MUSIC, THE; N. Currier	Small	27.50
RAIRIE FIRES OF THE GREAT WEST; 1871	Small	200.00
RAIRIE HENS	Small	110.00
RAIRIE HUNTER, THE; 1852; N. Currier	Large	1750.00
RAIRIE ON FIRE; N. Currier	Small	165.00
REMIUM FRUIT; 1875	Small	40.00
REPARING FOR CONGRESS; 1863	Small	45.00
REPARING FOR MARKET; 1856; N. Currier	Large	550.00
RESIDENT CLEVELAND AND HIS CABINET; 1885	Small	50.00

Size

☐ PRESIDENT CLEVELAND AND HIS CABINET; 1893 .... Small
☐ PRESIDENT HARRISON AND HIS CABINET; 1889 .... Small
☐ PRESIDENT HAYES AND CABINET; 1877 .... Small
☐ PRESIDENT LINCOLN AND HIS CABINET; 1876 .... Small
☐ PRESIDENT LINCOLN AND SECRETARY SEWARD; 1865; (Oval) .... Small
☐ PRESIDENT LINCOLN AT GENERAL GRANT'S HEADQUARTERS; 1865 Medium
☐ PRESIDENT LINCOLN AT HOME; 1865; (Oval).............................. Small
☐ PRESIDENT LINCOLN AT HOME (Reading from Scriptures) .... Small
☐ PRESIDENTIAL FISHING PARTY OF 1848, the .... Medium
☐ PRESIDENTIAL RECEPTION IN 1789 BY GEN. WASHINGTON AND
    MRS. WASHINGTON; 1876 .... Small
☐ PRESIDENTS OF THE UNITED STATES; 1842; 1845; 1846; 1847;
    1848; 1850; N. Currier .... Small ea.
☐ PRESS GANG, THE; N. Currier .... Small
☐ PRIDE OF THE GARDEN; 1873 .... Small
☐ PRIME TOBACCO .... Small
☐ "PRINCE" AND "LANTERN"; 1847; N. Currier .... Large 2
☐ PRINCE OF THE BLOOD; 1893 .... Small
☐ PRIZE BLACK HAMBURG GRAPES .... Medium 1
☐ PRIZE BOY, THE .... Large
☐ PRIZE FAT CATTLE .... Small
☐ PRIZE GRAPES — A FOUR-POUND BUNCH; 1865 .... Medium 1
☐ PRIZE HERD .... Small
☐ PRIZE SETTER, A .... Small 1
☐ PRIZE TROTTER, A; 1873 .... Small 1
☐ PROGRESS OF INTEMPERANCE, PLATE I; "The Invitation To Drink";
    1841; N. Currier .... Small
☐ PROGRESS OF INTEMPERANCE, PLATE 2; "Sick and Repentant";
    1841; N. Currier .... Small
☐ PROGRESS OF INTEMPERANCE, PLATE 3; "The Relapse"; 1841;
    N. Currier .... Small 7
☐ PROGRESS OF INTEMPERANCE, PLATE 4; "The Ruined Family";
    1841; N. Currier .... Small 7
☐ PROGRESS OF INTEMPERANCE, PLATE 5; "The Expectant Wife";
    1841; N. Currier .... Small. 7
☐ PROGRESS OF INTEMPERANCE, PLATE 6; "The Robber"; 1841;
    N. Currier .... Small 7

"PEYTONA"
AND "FASHION"

Large
$3250.00

THE
PIONEER'S
HOME

Large
$425.00

PROGRESS OF THE CENTURY, THE; 1876		Small	200.00
"PROTEINE", Record 2:18; 1878		Small	50.00
PROVIDENCE AND STONINGTON STEAMSHIP CO.'S STEAMERS, "MASSACHUSETTS" AND "RHODE ISLAND"; 1877		Large	140.00
PROVISIONS DOWN		Small	105.00
"PURITAN" AND "GENESTA" ON THE HOMESTRETCH		Large	325.00
PURSUIT, THE; 1856; N. Currier		Large	1750.00
PURSUIT OF THE MEXICANS BY THE U. S. DRAGOONS; 1847 N. Currier		Small	45.00
PUZZLE FOR A WINTER'S EVENING, A; 1840		Small	65.00
PUZZLED FOX, THE; 1872		Small	50.00

PRAIRIE
FIRES
OF THE
OLD WEST

Small
$200.00

PREPARING
FOR
MARKET

Large
$550.00

	Size	Reta
☐ QUAIL; 1865	Small	100.C
☐ QUAIL OR VIRGINIA PARTRIDGE; 1871	Small	100.C
☐ QUAIL SHOOTING; 1852; N. Currier	Large	1000.C
☐ QUAIL SHOOTING	Small	200.C
☐ QUAILS; 1849; N. Currier	Small	75.C
☐ QUEEN OF THE GARDEN; 1872	Small	35.0
☐ QUEEN OF THE TURF, "MAUD S.", Record 2:10; 1880	Large	415.0
☐ QUEEN OF THE WEST, THE	Small	115.0
☐ QUEEN OF THE WOODS, THE	Medium	40.0

THE ROUTE TO
CALIFORNIA

Small
$400.00

R. B. CONKLING'S BAY GELDING "RARUS", "THE KING OF THE TROTTERS"; 1878	Large	150.00
R. CORNELL WHITE'S NEW PALATIAL EXCURSION STEAMER "COLUMBIA"; 1877	Large	260.00
R. T. Y. C. SCHOONER "CAMBRIA"; 1870	Large	150.00
RABBIT CATCHING — THE TRAP SPRUNG	Small	90.00
RABBIT HUNT, THE — ALL BUT CAUGHT; 1849; N. Currier	Small	110.00
RABBITS IN THE WOODS	Small	65.00
RACE FOR THE AMERICAN DERBY; 1878	Small	200.00
RACE FOR THE BLOOD, A; 1890	Large	175.00
RACE FOR THE QUEEN'S CUP, THE	Small	125.00
RACE FROM THE WORD "GO"; 1890	Small	55.00
RACE ON THE MISSISSIPPI, A; The "Eagle" and "Diana"; 1870	Small	150.00
RACE TO THE WIRE; 1891	Small	57.50
RACING CHAMPIONS ON THEIR METTLE; 1899	Small	55.00
RACING CRACKS; 1886	Small	62.50
RACING KING "SALVATOR", THE; Record 1:35½; 1890	Small	75.00
RACING KING "SALVATOR"; 1891	Large	200.00
RAFTING ON THE ST. LAWRENCE	Small	100.00
RAIL CANDIDATE, THE	Small	70.00
RAIL SHOOTING	Small	285.00
RAIL SHOOTING ON THE DELAWARE; 1852; N. Currier	Large	2000.00
RAILROAD SUSPENSION BRIDGE NEAR NIAGARA FALLS, THE; 1856; N. Currier	Small	110.00
RALLY ROUND THE FLAG BOYS; 1861	Medium	110.00
RAQUET RIVER — ADIRONDACKS	Small	85.00
"RARUS"; Record 2:20¾; 1876	Small	57.50
RATTLING HEAT, A; 1891	Small	62.50

396

CURRIER & IVES PRINTS (R)

	Size	R
RAVENSWOOD, L. I.	Large	30
READY FOR A BATTLE; (Deer)	Small	4
READY FOR THE RACE; 1891	Large	20
READY FOR THE SIGNAL — THE CELEBRATED RUNNING HORSE "HARRY BASSETT"; 1872	Large	22
READY FOR THE START	Small	5
READY FOR THE TROT — BRING UP YOUR HORSES; 1877	Large	21
"RED CLOUD" — Record 2:18; 1874	Small	7
"RED CLOUD" — WINNER OF THE FIRST PRIZE, ETC.; 1876	Large	14
"REDPATH"; 1875; 1885; 1885	Small	ea. 5
REGATTA OF THE NEW YORK YACHT CLUB, "COMING IN"; "THE START"; "ROUNDING THE S.W. SPIT", 1854 N. Currier (Three Prints)	Large	ea. 1000
REGULAR HUMMER; 1879	Small	35
REPUBLICAN BANNER FOR 1860	Small	87
RESCUE, THE (Soldiers)	Small	95
RETURN FROM THE PASTURE	Large	265
RETURN FROM THE WOODS, THE	Medium	255
RE-UNION ON THE SECESH-DEMOCRATIC PLAN; 1862	Small	75
REVENGE; (Dogs); N. Currier	Small	35
RIDE TO SCHOOL, A	Small	65
RIGHT MAN FOR THE RIGHT PLACE, THE	Small	52
RIP VAN WINKLE'S COTTAGE IN THE CATSKILLS	Small	65
RIPE CHERRIES; 1870	Small	30
RIPE STRAWBERRIES	Small	30
RIPTON; 1850; N. Currier	Large	250
RISING FAMILY, A; 1857	Large	2000
RIVAL ROSES; 1873	Small	45
RIVER BOAT PASSING THE PALISADES; 1867	Small	60
RIVERROAD, THE	Medium	425
RIVER-SIDE, THE; N. Currier	Small	45
ROAD — SUMMER, THE; 1853; N. Currier	Large	1150
ROAD TEAM; 1882	Small	60
ROAD TO THE VILLAGE, THE	Medium	95
ROAD — WINTER, THE; 1853; N. Currier	Large	2000
ROADSIDE, THE; N. Currier	Small	50
ROADSIDE COTTAGE	Medium	115
ROADSIDE MILL, THE; 1870	Small	55
"ROBERT McGREGOR" — Record 2:18; 1882	Small	55
ROCKY MOUNTAINS, THE; (Buffalo in foreground)	Small	125
ROCKY MOUNTAINS, THE — EMIGRANTS CROSSING THE PLAINS; 1866	Large	2850

	Size	Retail
ROSE, THE; N. Currier	Small	45.00
ROSE, THE; (1 Rose, 5 Buds)	Small	40.00
ROSE, THE; (2 Roses, 3 Buds)	Small	40.00
ROSES AND ROSEBUDS; 1862	Small	45.00
ROSES OF MAY, THE	Small	35.00
ROUNDING A BEND ON THE MISSISSIPPI — THE PARTING SALUTE; (Ships); 1866	Large	1100.00
ROUNDING THE LIGHT SHIP; 1870	Large	650.00
ROUTE TO CALIFORNIA, THE; 1871	Small	400.00
"ROWDY BOY" — Record 2:13¾; 1879	Small	65.00
"ROY WILKES" — Record 2:12¾; 1890	Small	50.00
ROYAL MAIL STEAMSHIP "AMSTERDAM" OF THE NETHERLANDS LINE	Small	80.00
ROYAL MAIL STEAMSHIP "ARABIA"; 1853; N. Currier	Large	85.00
ROYAL MAIL STEAMSHIP "ASIA"; 1851; N. Currier	Large	250.00
ROYAL MAIL STEAMSHIP "AUSTRALIAN"; 1861	Large	250.00
ROYAL MAIL STEAMSHIP "EUROPA"; N. Currier	Small	175.00
ROYAL MAIL STEAMSHIP "PERSIA"; N. Currier	Large	250.00
ROYAL MAIL STEAMSHIP "SCOTIA"	Large	250.00
ROYAL MAIL STEAMSHIP "SCOTIA"	Small	85.00
ROYAL MAIL STEAMSHIP "VEENDAM"	Small	85.00
RUBBER, THE	Small	85.00
RUBBER, THE; "Put To His Trumps"; N. Currier	Medium	300.00
RUINS OF THE MERCHANT'S EXCHANGE, N. Y.; 1835	Small	200.00
RUINS OF THE PLANTER'S HOTEL, NEW ORLEANS; N. Currier	Small	190.00
RUN OF LUCK, A; 1871	Small	30.00
RUNNING THE "MACHINE"; (Political Cartoon)	Small	27.50
RURAL ARCHITECTURE No. 1; No. 2; 1856; N. Currier	Small	40.00
RURAL LAKE, THE	Small	65.00
RURAL SCENERY	Small	40.00
RUSH FOR THE HEAT: 1884	Large	65.00
RUSH FOR THE POLE; 1887	Large	90.00
RUSTIC BRIDGE, CENTRAL PARK, N. Y.	Small	150.00
RUSTIC STAND OF FLOWERS; 1875	Small	30.00
RUTHERFORD B. HAYES, 19th PRESIDENT	Small	40.00
RYSDYK'S "HAMBLETONIAN" — "The Great Sire of Trotters" 1880	Large	150.00

	Size	R
☐ SAILOR BOY, THE; N. Currier	Small	3
☐ SAILOR, FAR-FAR AT SEA, THE; N. Currier	Small	3
☐ SAILOR'S ADIEU, THE; (Ship Left); N. Currier	Small	7
☐ SAILOR'S ADIEU, THE; (Ship Right); N. Currier	Small	7
☐ SAILOR'S BRIDE, THE; 1849; N. Currier	Small	4
☐ SAILOR'S RETURN, THE; 1847; N. Currier	Small	7
☐ ST. JOHN, N.B., RIVER INDIAN TOWN	Small	9
☐ "ST. JULIEN"; 1879	Small	5
☐ "ST. JULIEN" — "King of the Turf"; 1880	Large	13
☐ ST. LAWRENCE	Small	4
☐ ST. LAWRENCE; 1850; N. Currier	Medium	35
☐ SALE OF THE PET LAMB; N. Currier	Large	15
☐ SALE OF THE PET LAMB	Small	4
☐ SALMON FISHING; 1872	Small	34
☐ "SALVATOR" AND "TENNY"; 1890	Small	5
☐ "SAM PURDY"; (Stallion)	Small	5
☐ "SANCHO"; (Hunting Dog); N. Currier/Setter holding pheasant	Small	12
☐ SANTA CLAUS; 1882	Small	3
☐ SARAH BERNHARDT, Vignette	Small	3
☐ SARATOGA LAKE	Small	5
☐ SARATOGA SPRINGS	Small	75
☐ SCALES OF JUSTICE, THE; N. Currier	Small	30
☐ SCENE OFF NEWPORT, A	Small	175
☐ SCENE ON THE LOWER MISSISSIPPI, A	Small	100
☐ SCENE ON THE SUSQUEHANNA, A	Small	100
☐ SCENERY OF THE CATTSKILLS: "Mountain House";	Small	70
☐ SCENERY OF THE CATTSKILLS; "The Cattskill Falls of The Cattskill Mountains"; N. Currier	Small	75
☐ SCENERY OF THE HUDSON NEAR "ANTHONY'S NOSE"	Large	275.
☐ SCENERY OF THE HUDSON; "The Mountain House"	Small	75
☐ SCENERY OF THE UPPER MISSISSIPPI	Small	75
☐ SCENERY OF THE WISSAHICKON NEAR PHILADELPHIA	Small	75
☐ SCHOONER; 1846; N. Currier	Small	125.
☐ SCHOONER YACHT "CAMBRIA"	Small	80.
☐ SCORING — COMING UP FOR THE WORD; 1869	Large	175.
☐ SCORING FOR THE FIRST HEAT; 1877	Large	145.
☐ SCOTCH CUTTER "MADGE"; 1881	Small	67.
☐ SEASON OF BLOSSOMS, THE	Small	52.
☐ SEASON OF BLOSSOMS, THE; 1865	Large	350.
☐ SEASON OF JOY, THE; 1872	Small	30.

	Size	Retail
SECESSION MOVEMENT, THE; 1861	Small	65.00
SECOND BATTLE OF BULL RUN	Small	45.00
SECOND SMOKE — ALL WRONG; 1870	Small	37.50
SELLING OUT CHEAP; (Political Cartoon)	Small	30.00
"SENSATION" — Record 2:22¼; 1876	Small	45.00
SERGEANT JASPER OF CHARLESTON; 1876	Small	130.00
SETTER AND WOODCOCK	Small	100.00
SETTERS; 1846; N. Currier	Small	125.00
SEVEN STAGES OF MATRIMONY; N. Currier	Small	40.00
SHADE AND TOMB OF WASHINGTON, THE; 1876	Small	45.00
SHAKERS NEAR LEBANON; N. Currier	Small	210.00
SHALL I? — THROW IF YOU DARE	Small	62.50
SHARP BRUSH ON THE LAST QUARTER; 1874	Small	62.50
SHARP PACE, A; 1884	Small	55.00
SHARP RIFLE, A; 1882	Small	30.00
SHARPSHOOTER, A; 1882	Small	32.50
SHEEP PASTURE, THE	Small	35.00
SHERIDAN'S CAVALRY AT THE BATTLE OF FISHER'S HILL	Small	42.50
SHERMAN AND HIS GENERALS; 1865	Medium	45.00
SHIPS "ANTARCTIC" OF NEW YORK, AND "THREE BELLS" OF GLASGOW RESCUING THE PASSENGERS AND CREW FROM THE WRECK OF THE STEAMSHIP "SAN FRANCISCO" N. Currier	Large	2500.00
SHOEING THE HORSE; N. Currier	Small	70.00
SHOEMAKER, THE	Small	30.00
SHOOTING ON THE BAY SHORE; 1883	Small	500.00
SHOOTING ON THE BEACH	Small	325.00
SHOOTING ON THE PRAIRIE	Small	200.00
SHORT STOP AT A WAY STATION, A; 1875	Small	65.00
SICKNESS AND HEALTH; N. Currier	Medium	35.00
SIDE-WHEELER, THE	Small	30.00
SIEGE AND CAPTURE OF VICKSBURG, MISS.	Small	57.50
SIEGE OF CHARLESTON, THE	Small	65.00
SIEGE OF VERA CRUZ; 1847; N. Currier	Small	42.50
SIGHTS AT THE FAIR GROUNDS; 1888	Small	70.00
SIGNAL FIRES ON THE SHEVENAMON MOUNTAINS, IRELAND; 1848; N. Currier	Small	37.50
SILVER CASCADE, NEAR ST. ANTHONY, MINN.	Small	62.50
SILVER CASCADE, WHITE MOUNTAINS	Small	55.00
SILVER CREEK, CALIFORNIA	Small	150.00

	Size	R
☐ SINKING OF THE BRITISH BATTLESHIP "VICTORIA"; 1893	Small	8
☐ SINKING OF THE "CUMBERLAND" BY THE IRON CLAD "MERRIMAC"; 1863	Small	4
☐ SINKING OF THE STEAMSHIP "ELBE"	Small	5
☐ SINKING OF THE STEAMSHIP "OREGON" OF THE CUNARD LINE; 1888	Small	5
☐ SINKING OF THE STEAMSHIP "VILL DU HAVRE"; 1873	Small	6
☐ SKATING CARNIVAL, THE	Small	7
☐ SKATING SCENE — MOONLIGHT; 1868	Small	16
☐ SLEEPY HOLLOW BRIDGE, TARRYTOWN, N. Y.	Small	7
☐ SLEEPY HOLLOW CHURCH NEAR TARRYTOWN, N. Y.	Medium	23
☐ SLEIGH RACE, THE; 1848; N. Currier	Small	27
☐ SLEIGH RACE, THE; 1859	Large	40
☐ SLOOP YACHT "MAYFLOWER"; 1859	Small	68
☐ SLOOP YACHT "POCAHONTAS" OF NEW YORK; 1881	Large	17
☐ SLOOP YACHT "VOLUNTEER" 1887	Small	8
☐ SLOOP YACHTS "MISCHIEF" AND "ATLANTA"; 1882	Large	35
☐ SLUGGED OUT — BETTER LUCK NEXT TIME; 1883	Small	37
☐ SLUICE GATE, THE	Small	55
☐ "SMALL HOPES" AND "LADY MAC"; 1878	Large	150
☐ SMOKER'S PROMENADE; 1876	Small	30
☐ "SMUGGLER"; (Horse); 1874	Small	55
☐ "SMUGGLER" AND "JUDGE FULLERTON"; 1876	Small	85
☐ SNAP APPLE NIGHT — ALL HALLOW EVE	Medium	250
☐ SNIPE SHOOTING	Large	1000
☐ SNIPE SHOOTING	Small	285
☐ SNOW-SHOE DANCE, THE	Medium	185
☐ SNOW STORM, THE	Medium	350
☐ SNOWED UP — RUFFED GROUSE IN WINTER; 1867	Large	1750
☐ SNOWY MORNING, A; 1864	Medium	325
☐ SOFT THING ON SNIPE, A; 1880	Small	42
☐ SOLDIER BOY, THE; "Off Duty"; 1864	Small	35
☐ SOLDIER BOY, THE; "On Duty"; 1864	Small	25
☐ SOLDIER BOYS, THE	Small	30
☐ SOLDIER'S ADIEU, THE; C. Currier	Small	35
☐ SOLDIER'S DREAM OF HOME, THE	Small	30
☐ SOLDIER'S DREAM OF HONOR	Small	30
☐ SOLDIER'S HOME; "The Vision"; 1862	Small	30
☐ SOLDIER'S RETURN; C. Currier	Small	40
☐ SOME PUMPKINS; (Oval)	Small	35
☐ "SONTAG" AND "FLORA TEMPLE"; 1855; N. Currier	Large	350

	Size	Retail
☐ SORREL "DAN"; 1881	Small	65.00
☐ SOURCE OF THE HUDSON, THE	Small	90.00
☐ SOUTH CAROLINA'S "ULTIMATUM"; (Political Cartoon)	Small	42.50
☐ SOUTH SEA WHALE FISHERY; N. Currier	Small	350.00
☐ SOUTHERN RIVER SCENERY; 1870	Small	45.00
☐ SPANIEL, THE; 1848; N. Currier	Small	70.00
☐ SPEARING BLACK BASS — MOONLIGHT	Medium	725.00
☐ SPEEDING ON THE AVENUE; 1870	Large	1000.00
☐ SPEEDING TO THE "BIKE"; 1893	Large	115.00
☐ SPENDTHRIFT; 1880	Small	50.00
☐ SPENDTHRIFT; 1881	Small	40.00
☐ SPERM WHALE, "IN A FLURRY"; N. Currier	Small	250.00
☐ SPICE OF THE TROTTING TURF, THE; 1876	Small	57.50
☐ SPILLOUT ON THE SNOW; 1870	Small	85.00
☐ SPILLOUT ON THE SNOW, A	Large	400.00
☐ SPLENDID NAVAL TRIUMPH ON THE MISSISSIPPI; 1862	Large	265.00
☐ SPLENDID NEW IRON STEAMER "ALBANY"	Small	65.00
☐ SPLITTING THE PARTY; (Political Cartoon); 1872	Small	65.00
☐ SPORTS WHO CAME TO GRIEF, THE; 1881	Small	35.00
☐ SPORTSMAN'S SOLACE; 1879	Medium	60.00
☐ SPRING; 1849; N. Currier	Small	50.00
☐ SPRING; 1870	Medium	75.00
☐ SPRING FLOWERS; 1861	Medium	150.00
☐ SQUALL OFF CAPE HORN, A; N. Currier	Small	175.00
☐ SQUIRREL SHOOTING	Small	80.00
☐ STABLE, THE — No. 1 and No. 2; N. Currier	Medium	ea. 125.00
☐ STABLE SCENES, No. 1 and No. 2; N. Currier	Small	ea. 95.00
☐ STAG AT BAY, THE	Small	50.00
☐ STAG AT BAY, THE	Medium	95.00
☐ STAG HOUNDS; 1846; N. Currier	Small	125.00
☐ STAGES OF MAN'S LIFE	Small	25.00
☐ STAGES OF WOMAN'S LIFE	Small	25.00
☐ STANCH POINTER, A; 1871	Small	100.00
☐ STAR OF THE ROAD, THE; 1849; N. Currier	Small	95.00
☐ STAR SPANGLED BANNER, THE	Small	65.00
☐ STARS OF THE TROTTING TRACK	Large	170.00
☐ STARS OF THE TURF — No. 1 and No. 2; 1885	Large	ea. 125.00
☐ STARTING OUT ON HIS METTLE; 1876	Small	45.00
☐ STATE STREET, BOSTON, MASS.; 1849; N. Currier	Small	190.00
☐ STATEN ISLAND AND THE NARROWS FROM FORT HAMILTON; 1861	Large	325.00

SPEEDING
ON THE
AVENUE

Large
$1000.00

SPEEDING ON THE AVENUE.

	Size	Retail
☐ SUNNY SIDE — THE RESIDENCE OF THE LATE WASHINGTON IRVING, NEAR TARRYTOWN, N. Y.	Large	175.00
☐ SUNNYSIDE — ON THE HUDSON	Small	65.00
☐ SUNRISE ON LAKE SARANAC; 1860	Large	725.00
☐ SUNSET TREE, THE	Medium	85.00
☐ SURE HORSE FOR FIRST MONEY, THE; 1886	Small	65.00
☐ SURPRISE, THE; 1858	Large	1250.00
☐ SURPRISE PARTY, A; 1883	Small	27.50
☐ SURRENDER OF CORNWALLIS; N. Currier; 1846	Small	115.00
☐ SURRENDER OF GEN. BURGOYNE AT SARATOGA, N. Y.; 1852; N. Currier	Large	2200.00
☐ SURRENDER OF GENL. JOE JOHNSTON NEAR GREENBORO, N. C.; 1865	Small	47.50
☐ SURRENDER OF GENL. LEE AT APPOMATTOX C. H., VA; 1865	Small	65.00
☐ SURRENDER OF GENL. LEE AT APPOMATTOX C. H., VA.; 1868	Small	65.00
☐ SURRENDER OF LORD CORNWALLIS; 1876	Small	100.00
☐ SURROUNDING THE HERD	Medium	175.00
☐ SWEET SPRING TIME	Medium	40.00
☐ "SWEETSER"; 1877	Small	85.00
☐ SWELL SPORT ON A BUFFALO HUNT, A; 1882	Small	55.00
☐ SWELL SPORT STAMPEDED, A; 1882	Small	50.00
☐ SWIFT PACER "ARROW", Record 2:13¼; 1888	Small	50.00
☐ SWING OF THE FIRST HEAT, THE; 1877	Small	50.00
☐ SYLVAN LAKE; 1868	Small	42.50

	Size	Retail
☐ "TACONY"; 1853; N. Currier	Large	315.00
☐ "TACONY" AND "MAC"; 1853; N. Currier	Large	330.00
☐ TAKE A PINCH; N. Currier	Small	35.00
☐ TAKING A SMASH	Small	50.00
☐ TAKING A SMILE; 1854; N. Currier	Small	45.00
☐ TAKING THE BACK TRACK — A DANGEROUS NEIGHBORHOOD; 1866	Large	2500.00
☐ TALLULAH FALLS, GEORGIA	Small	65.00
☐ TASTE FOR THE FINE ARTS, A	Small	50.00
☐ TEAM FAST ON THE POLE, A; 1883	Small	45.00
☐ TEAM FAST ON THE SNOW, A; 1883	Small	50.00
☐ TEAM ON THE SNOW, A; 1883	Medium	85.00
☐ TEAM THAT TAKES NO DUST, A; 1875	Small	45.00
☐ TEMPTED	Small	100.00
☐ TEMPTING FRUIT; 1870	Small	40.00
☐ TEMPTING LUNCH; 1870	Small	35.00
☐ TEN BROECK; 1877	Small	75.00
☐ "TENNY"; 1891	Small	42.50
☐ TERRA COTTA; 1888	Small	45.00
☐ TERRIBLE COLLISION; 1880	Small	60.00
☐ TERRIBLE COLLISION BETWEEN THE STEAMBOATS "DEAN RICHMOND" AND "C. VANDERBILT"	Small	85.00
☐ TERRIBLE COLLISION BETWEEN THE STEAMBOATS "STONINGTON" AND "NARRAGANSETT"; 1880	Small	85.00
☐ TERRIFIC COMBAT BETWEEN THE "MONITOR" 2 GUNS, AND "MERRIMAC" 10 GUNS; 1862	Small	135.00
☐ TERRIFIC ENGAGEMENT BETWEEN "MONITOR" 2 GUNS, AND "MERRIMAC" 10 GUNS; 1862	Large	350.00
☐ THAT'S SO	Small	52.50
☐ THATCHED COTTAGE, THE	Small	40.00
☐ THATCHED ROOF, THE	Small	40.00
☐ THIRD HEAT IN TWO SIXTEEN, A; 1874	Large	125.00
☐ "THISTLE"; (Yacht); 1887	Large	95.00
☐ THOMAS JEFFERSON — 3rd PRESIDENT; N. Currier	Small	47.50
☐ "THOMAS JEFFERSON" — THE BLACK WHIRLWIND OF THE EAST; 1875	Large	125.00
☐ THREE FAVORITES, THE; N. Currier	Small	32.50
☐ THROUGH EXPRESS, THE	Small	435.00
☐ THROUGH THE BAYOU BY TORCHLIGHT	Small	85.00
☐ THROUGH TO THE PACIFIC; 1870	Small	265.00
☐ THROW IF YOU DARE	Small	75.00

	Size	Retail
☐ TIME IS MONEY; 1873	Small	35.00
☐ TO AVOID A SMASH, WE SELL FOR CASH; 1875	Small	30.00
☐ TO THE MEMORY OF WM. H. HARRISON	Small	50.00
☐ TOBOGGANING IN THE ALPS	Medium	180.00
☐ TOBOGGANING ON DARKTOWN HILL, "GETTING A HIST"; 1890	Small	30.00
☐ TOBOGGANING ON DARKTOWN HILL, "AN UNTIMELY MOVE; 1890	Small	32.50
☐ TOCSIN OF LIBERTY, THE; 1876	Small	85.00
☐ TOLL-GATE, JAMAICA PLANT ROAD; N. Currier	Small	100.00
☐ TOM OCHILTREE; 1877	Small	60.00
☐ TOM PADDOCK	Small	85.00
☐ TOM SAYERS; (Boxing Champion); 1860	Small	85.00
☐ TOMB AND SHADE OF WASHINGTON, THE; 1842	Small	40.00
☐ TOMB OF GENL. W. H. HARRISON, THE; 1842; N. Currier	Small	85.00
☐ TOMB OF LINCOLN, SPRINGFIELD, ILLINOIS	Small	55.00
☐ TOMB OF WASHINGTON, MOUNT VERNON, VA.	Medium	75.00
☐ TONSORIAL ART IN THE DARKTOWN STYLE; 1890	Small	30.00
☐ "TORONTO CHIEF", "GENL. BUTLER" AND "DEXTER" 1866	Large	175.00
☐ TRAPPER'S CAMPFIRE, THE; 1866	Large	475.00
☐ TRAPPER'S LAST SHOT, THE	Medium	245.00
☐ TRAPPERS ON THE PRAIRIE — PEACE OR WAR?; 1866	Large	2500.00
☐ TREE OF EVIL, THE; N. Currier	Small	35.00
☐ TREE OF GOOD, THE; N. Currier	Small	52.50
☐ TREE OF INTEMPERANCE; 1849; N. Currier	Small	60.00
☐ TREE OF LIFE, THE; C. Currier	Small	47.50
☐ TREE OF LIFE, THE CHRISTIAN; N. Currier	Small	65.00
☐ TREE OF TEMPERANCE; 1849; N. Currier	Small	65.00
☐ TRENTON FALLS, NEW YORK	Small	60.00
☐ TRENTON HIGH FALLS, NEW JERSEY	Small	60.00
☐ TRIAL OF PATIENCE, THE	Medium	95.00
☐ TRIBUTE OF AUTUMN, THE; 1870	Small	45.00
☐ TRINKET; 1881	Small	50.00
☐ "TRINKET", Record 2:14; 1879	Small	55.00
☐ "TRINKET", Record 2:14; 1884	Large	110.00
☐ TROLLING FOR BLUE FISH; 1866	Large	1350.00
☐ TROPICAL AND SUMMER FRUITS; 1867	Small	40.00
☐ TROPICAL AND SUMMER FRUITS; 1867	Medium	90.00
☐ TROT WITH MODERN IMPROVEMENTS, A; 1881	Small	55.00
☐ "TROTTERS"	Large	285.00
☐ TROTTERS ON THE SNOW, Vignette	Small	100.00
☐ TROTTERS ON THE GRAND CIRCUIT — WARMING UP; 1877	Large	200.00
☐ TROTTING CRACKS AT HOME; 1868	Large	900.00

	Size	Retail
☐ TROTTING CRACKS AT THE FORGE; 1869	Large	900.00
☐ TROTTING CRACKS ON THE SNOW; 1858	Large	1050.00
☐ TROTTING FOR A GREAT STAKE; 1890	Large	165.00
☐ TROTTING GELDING "BILLY D." WITH "RUNNING MATE"	Large	135.00
☐ TROTTING GELDING "FRANK"; WITH "RUNNING MATE"; 1884	Large	135.00
☐ TROTTING GELDING "HARRY WILKES", Record 2:13½; 1885	Small	55.00
☐ TROTTING GELDING "PRINCE WILKES", Record 2:14¾; 1882	Small	47.50
☐ TROTTING GELDING "ST. JULIEN", Record 2:11¼	Small	47.50
☐ TROTTING GELDING "STEVE MAXWELL"	Small	47.50
☐ TROTTING HORSE "DARBY", Record 2:16½; 1879	Small	50.00
☐ TROTTING HORSE "JUDGE FULLERTON"; 1874	Medium	80.00
☐ TROTTING MARE "AMERICAN GIRL"	Large	165.00
☐ TROTTING MARE "AMERICAN GIRL"; 1871	Small	70.00
☐ TROTTING MARE "BELLE HAMLIN", Record 2:12¾; 1889	Small	50.00
☐ TROTTING MARE "GOLDSMITH MAID" 1870	Large	175.00
☐ TROTTING MARE "MARTHA WILKES", Record 2:08	Small	55.00
☐ TROTTING MARE "NANCY HANKS", Record 2:04; 1892	Small	65.00
☐ TROTTING MARE "SUNOL"; 1889	Small	65.00
☐ TROTTING ON THE ROAD	Small	45.00
☐ TROTTING QUEEN "MAUD S.", Record 2:08¾; 1881	Small	55.00
☐ TROTTING QUEEN "NANCY HANKS", Record 2:04	Large	135.00
☐ TROTTING STALLION "ALCRYON"; 1889	Small	50.00
☐ TROTTING STALLION "COMMODORE VANDERBILT", 1866	Large	160.00
☐ TROTTING STALLION "DAN RICE"; 1866	Large	160.00
☐ TROTTING STALLION "DIRECTUM", Record 2:05¼	Large	130.00
☐ TROTTING STALLION "GEORGE M. PATCHEN, JR." OF CALIFORNIA	Large	160.00
☐ TROTTING STALLION "GRAY EAGLE" OF KENTUCKY	Large	120.00
☐ TROTTING STALLION "HAMBLETONIAN MAMBRINO"	Small	65.00
☐ TROTTING STALLION "HANNIS"; 1877	Small	50.00
☐ TROTTING STALLION "MAMBRINO CHAMPION"; 1867	Large	160.00
☐ TROTTING STALLION "MONROE CHIEF", Record 2:18½; 1881	Small	50.00
☐ TROTTING STALLION "NELSON", Record 2:14¼	Small	55.00
☐ TROTTING STALLION "PALO ALTO"; 1890	Small	50.00
☐ TROTTING STALLION "PATRON", Record 2:14¼	Small	50.00
☐ TROTTING STALLION "PHALLAS"; 1883	Large	130.00
☐ TROTTING STALLION "SANTA CLAUS", Record 2:17½	Small	55.00
☐ TROTTING STALLION "STAMBOUL", Record 2:12¼	Small	55.00
☐ TROTTING STALLION "STEAMBOAT"; 1890	Small	47.50
☐ TROTTING STALLION "TOM MOORE"; 1870	Large	175.00
☐ TROUT BROOK, THE; 1862	Medium	195.00
☐ TROUT FISHING	Large	900.00

"TROTTING CRACKS" ON THE SNOW   Small $100.00

		Size	Retail
☐	TROUT POOL, THE	Small	225.00
☐	TROUT STREAM, THE; 1852	Large	750.00
☐	TROUT VERSUS GOUT	Small	67.50
☐	TROY FIRE COMPANY; N. Currier	Small	40.00
☐	TRUE PEACE COMMISSIONER, THE	Small	45.00
☐	TRUE YANKEE SAILOR, THE; N. Currier	Small	47.50
☐	TRUST ME TILL I SELL MY DOG; 1873	Small	55.00
☐	TRY OUT CLAMS; 1875	Small	30.00
☐	TRYING IT ON; 1874	Small	47.50
☐	TURN OF THE TUNE, THE; 1875	Small	47.50
☐	TWILIGHT HOUR, THE	Small	35.00
☐	TWIN-SCREW S. S. "KENSINGTON" OF THE RED STAR LINE	Small	50.00
☐	TWIN-SCREW STEAMER "DEUTSCHLAND" OF THE HAMBURG AMERICAN LINE	Small	45.00
☐	TWIN-SCREW STEAMER "LUCANIA" OF THE CUNARD LINE	Small	75.00
☐	TWO MINUTE CLIP, A; 1893	Medium	55.00
☐	TWO TO GO; 1882	Small	32.50
☐	TWO TWENTY ON THE ROAD; 1875	Small	55.00

	Size	Retail
UNBOLTED	Small	42.50
UNCLE SAM MAKING NEW ARRANGEMENTS; (Political Cartoon)	Small	85.00
UNCLE TOM AND LITTLE EVA; N. Currier	Small	32.50
UNDER CLIFF — ON THE HUDSON	Small	47.50
UNION IRON CLAD MONITOR "MONTAUK" DESTROYING THE REBEL STEAMSHIP "NASHVILLE"	Small	85.00
UNION PLACE HOTEL, UNION SQUARE, N. Y.; N. Currier	Small	300.00
UNION VOLUNTEER, THE — HOME FROM THE WAR; 1863	Large	57.50
UNION VOLUNTEER, THE — OFF FOR THE WAR; 1863	Large	35.00
U. S. ARMY LEAVING THE GULF SQUADRON; 1847	Small	125.00
U. S. BRIG OF WAR "SOMERS"; N. Currier	Small	185.00
U. S. BRIG "PORPOISE" IN A SQUALL; N. Currier	Small	115.00
UNITED STATES CAPITOL, WASHINGTON, D. C.	Small	95.00
UNITED STATES CAPITOL ON CAPITOL HILL, WASHINGTON, D. C. EAST FRONT	Small	95.00
U. S. CRUISER "NEW YORK"	Large	145.00
U. S. DRAGOONS; 1846; N. Currier	Small	42.50
U. S. FRIGATE "CONSTITUTION"; N. Currier	Small	175.00
U. S. FRIGATE "CUMBERLAND"; 1848; N. Currier	Small	200.00
U. S. FRIGATE "INDEPENDENCE"; 1841; N. Currier	Small	165.00
U. S. FRIGATE "ST. LAWRENCE"; N. Currier	Small	150.00
U. S. FRIGATE "SAVANNAH"; 1843; N. Currier	Small	125.00
U. S. FRIGATE "UNITED STATES" CAPTURING H. M. FRIGATE "MACEDONIAN"; N. Currier	Small	150.00
U. S. MAIL STEAMSHIP "ADRIATIC"; N. Currier	Small	100.00
U. S. MAIL STEAMSHIP "ARCTIC"; 1850; N. Currier	Medium	180.00
U. S. M. STEAMSHIP "ARCTIC" OF COLLINS LINE	Large	185.00
U. S. M. STEAMSHIP "ATLANTIC" OF COLLINS LINE; 1852; N. Currier	Medium	125.00
U. S. MAIL STEAMSHIP "BALTIC"; 1850	Large	225.00
U. S. MAIL STEAMSHIP "CALIFORNIA"	Small	70.00
U. S. MAIL STEAMSHIP "PACIFIC"; N. Currier	Large	215.00
U. S. MILITARY ACADEMY, WEST POINT; 1862	Medium	225.00
U. S. POST OFFICE, NEW YORK	Small	95.00
U. S. SHIP "NORTH CAROLINA" 1843; N. Currier	Small	245.00
U. S. SHIP "NORTH CAROLINA"; 1844; N. Currier	Small	245.00
U. S. SHIP OF THE LINE "DELAWARE"; N. Currier	Small	235.00
U. S. SHIP OF THE LINE IN A GALE; N. Currier	Small	110.00
U. S. SHIP OF THE LINE "OHIO"; N. Currier	Small	245.00
U. S. SHIP OF THE LINE "PENNSYLVANIA"; N. Currier	Small	245.00
U. S. SLOOP OF WAR "ALBANY"; N. Currier	Small	135.00

UNITED STATES CAPITOL, WASHINGTON, D. C.   Small $55.00

	Size	Retail
☐ U. S. SLOOP OF WAR IN A GALE; N. Currier	Small	125.00
☐ U. S. SLOOP OF WAR "KEARSARGE"; 1864	Small	150.00
☐ U. S. SLOOP OF WAR "VINCENNES"; 1845; N. Currier	Small	155.00
☐ U. S. STEAM FRIGATE "MISSISSIPPI"; 1848; N. Currier	Small	130.00
☐ U. S. STEAM FRIGATE "MISSISSIPPI" IN A TYPHOON	Large	300.00
☐ U. S. STEAM FRIGATE "MISSOURI"; N. Currier	Small	125.00
☐ U. S. STEAM FRIGATE "NIAGARA" 1857	Large	225.00
☐ U. S. STEAM FRIGATE "NIAGARA"	Small	125.00
☐ U. S. STEAM FRIGATE "PRINCETON"; 1844; N. Currier	Small	150.00
☐ U. S. STEAM FRIGATE "WABASH"	Small	125.00
☐ UPPER CANADA COLLEGE; N. Currier	Medium	385.00
☐ UP IN A BALLOON; 1876	Small	85.00
☐ UP THE HUDSON	Small	110.00
☐ UPPER AND LOWER BAY OF NEW YORK FROM THE BATTERY LOOKING SOUTHWEST	Small	200.00

	Size	Retail
VALLEY FALLS, VIRGINIA	Small	67.50
VALLEY OF THE SHENANDOAH, THE; 1864	Large	215.00
VALLEY OF THE SUSQUEHANNA	Large	220.00
VAN AMBURG & CO.'S TRIUMPHAL CAR PASSING THE ASTOR HOUSE; 1846; N. Currier	Small	135.00
VASE OF FLOWERS, THE; 1847; N. Currier	Small	50.00
VASE OF FRUIT; 1864	Medium	95.00
VELOCIPEDE, THE; 1869	Small	175.00
VICTORIOUS ATTACK ON FORT FISHER, N. C.; 1865	Large	215.00
VICTORIOUS BOMBARDMENT OF PORT ROYAL, S. C.	Small	75.00
VICTORY OF ROANOKE, THE	Small	50.00
VIEW DOWN THE RAVINE AT TRENTON FALLS, N. Y.	Medium	95.00
VIEW FROM FORT PUTNAM, N. Y.	Small	55.00
VIEW FROM PEEKSKILL, HUDSON RIVER, N. Y.; 1862	Medium	150.00
VIEW FROM WEST POINT; C. Currier	Small	90.00
VIEW IN DUTCHESS COUNTY, N. Y.	Large	350.00
VIEW NEAR HIGHBRIDGE, N. Y.	Medium	650.00
VIEW OF BALTIMORE; 1848; N. Currier	Small	165.00
VIEW OF BOSTON; 1848; N. Currier	Small	175.00
VIEW OF BUNKER HILL AND MONUMENT; N. Currier	Small	100.00
VIEW OF ESOPUS CREEK	Small	85.00
VIEW OF HARPERS FERRY, VA.	Large	300.00
VIEW OF NEW YORK; 1860	Small	150.00
VIEW OF NEW YORK FROM WEEHAWKEN; 1848; N. Currier	Small	200.00
VIEW OF NEW YORK, JERSEY CITY, HOBOKEN AND BROOKLYN	Large	400.00
VIEW OF NEW YORK BAY FROM STATEN ISLAND	Small	135.00
VIEW OF PHILADELPHIA; 1875	Small	100.00
VIEW OF SAN FRANCISCO, CALIFORNIA; N. Currier	Large	1800.00
VIEW OF THE DISTRIBUTING RESERVOIR ON MURRAY'S HILL, CITY OF NEW YORK; 1842; N. Currier	Small	300.00
VIEW OF THE FEDERAL HALL OF THE CITY OF NEW YORK; C. Currier	Medium	265.00
VIEW OF THE GREAT CONFLAGRATION OF DEC. 16th AND 17th, 1835	Medium	275.00
VIEW OF THE GREAT CONFLAGRATION AT NEW YORK, JULY 19th, 1845; N. Currier, 1845	Small	210.00
VIEW OF THE GREAT RECEIVING RESERVOIR, YORKVILLE, CITY OF NEW YORK; 1841; N. Currier	Small	175.00
VIEW OF THE HUDSON	Large	225.00
VIEW OF THE HUDSON RIVER FROM RUGGLES HOUSE; N. Currier	Small	85.00

	Size	Retail
☐ VIEW OF THE PARK FOUNTAIN AND CITY HALL, N. Y.; 1846; N. Currier	Small	150.00
☐ VIEW OF THE TERRIFIC EXPLOSION; 1845; N. Currier	Small	285.00
☐ VIEW OF WATERBURY, CONN; N. Currier	Large	300.00
☐ VIEW OF WEST ROCK, NEAR NEW HAVEN, CONN.	Large	325.00
☐ VIEW ON ESOPUS CREEK	Small	90.00
☐ VIEW ON FULTON AVENUE, BROOKLYN; N. Currier	Small	75.00
☐ VIEW ON LAKE GEORGE, N. Y.; 1866	Large	225.00
☐ VIEW ON LAKE GEORGE, N. Y.	Medium	175.00
☐ VIEW ON LONG ISLAND, N. Y.; 1857	Large	375.00
☐ VIEW ON MONTGOMERY CREEK NEAR THE HUDSON	Small	85.00
☐ VIEW ON THE DELAWARE, NEAR EASTON, PENNA.	Small	100.00
☐ VIEW ON THE HARLEM RIVER, N. Y. — THE HIGHBRIDGE IN THE DISTANCE	Large	315.00
☐ VIEW ON THE HOUSATONIC; 1867	Large	295.00
☐ VIEW ON THE HUDSON	Large	250.00
☐ VIEW ON THE HUDSON — CROW'S NEST	Small	85.00
☐ VIEW ON THE HUDSON FROM RUGGLES HOUSE, NEWBURGH	Small	65.00
☐ VIEW ON THE POTOMAC NEAR HARPERS FERRY; 1866	Large	225.00
☐ VIEW ON THE RONDOUT	Medium	110.00
☐ VIEW ON THE RONDOUT	Small	50.00
☐ VIEW ON THE ST. LAWRENCE — INDIAN ENCAMPMENT	Small	80.00
☐ "VIGILANT"	Small	95.00
☐ "VIGILANT" AND "VALKYRIE" IN A THRASH TO WINDWARD; 1893	Large	265.00
☐ VILLA ON THE HUDSON; 1869	Medium	95.00
☐ VILLA ON THE HUDSON	Small	55.00
☐ VILLAGE BLACKSMITH, THE; N. Currier	Medium	135.00
☐ VILLAGE BLACKSMITH, THE; 1864	Large	275.00
☐ VILLAGE STREET, THE; 1855; N. Currier	Medium	115.00
☐ VIRGINIA HOME IN THE OLDEN TIME, A; 1872	Small	80.00
☐ VIRTUE, LOVE AND TEMPERANCE, LOVE, PURITY AND FIDELITY; 1851; N. Currier	Small	42.50
☐ "VOLTAIRE", Record 2:20¼; 1879	Small	57.50
☐ VOLUNTEER"; 1880	Small	52.50
☐ "VOLUNTEER" CROSSING THE FINISH LINE; 1887	Large	200.00
☐ VOLUNTEERING MANNER IN WHICH SOME OF THE SOUTHERN VOLUNTEERS ENLIST, THE	Small	47.50

	Size	Retail
WAITING FOR A BITE; N. Currier	Small	65.00
WAITING FOR A DRINK; N. Currier	Small	42.50
WAKING UP THE OLD MARE; 1881	Large	175.00
WAKING UP THE WRONG PASSENGER; 1875	Small	55.00
WARMING UP; 1884	Small	35.00
WASHINGTON; (Bust Portrait); N. Currier	Large	115.00
WASHINGTON; (Full length Portrait); N. Currier	Small	50.00
WASHINGTON; (Three-quarter length)	Medium	50.00
WASHINGTON; (Standing by horse); N. Currier	Small	50.00
WASHINGTON; (Resting on rock); N. Currier	Small	50.00
WASHINGTON — CINCINNATUS OF THE WEST	Small	50.00
WASHINGTON — FIRST IN WAR, FIRST IN PEACE; C. Currier	Small	50.00
WASHINGTON FROM THE PRESIDENT'S HOUSE; 1848; N. Currier	Small	42.50
"WASHINGTON"; (Race Horse); 1853; N. Currier	Large	215.00
WASHINGTON AND HIS CABINET; 1876	Small	85.00
WASHINGTON AND LINCOLN; 1865	Medium	95.00
WASHINGTON APPOINTED COMMANDER-IN-CHIEF; 1876	Small	50.00
WASHINGTON AS A MASON; 1868	Small	35.00
WASHINGTON AT HOME; 1867	Large	175.00
WASHINGTON AT MOUNT VERNON; 1852; N. Currier	Small	125.00
WASHINGTON AT PRAYER; C. Currier	Small	85.00
WASHINGTON AT PRINCETON; 1846; N. Currier	Small	300.00
WASHINGTON AT VALLEY FORGE; N. Currier	Small	85.00
WASHINGTON COLUMNS, THE — YOSEMITE VALLEY	Small	50.00
WASHINGTON CROSSING THE DELAWARE; N. Currier	Small	100.00
WASHINGTON FAMILY, THE	Small	52.50
WASHINGTON IN THE FIELD; N. Currier	Small	40.00
WASHINGTON, McCLELLAN AND SCOTT	Medium	425.00
WASHINGTON'S DREAM	Large	165.00
WASHINGTON, SHERMAN AND GRANT	Small	175.00
WASHINGTON TAKING LEAVE OF THE OFFICERS OF HIS ARMY AT FRAUNCE'S TAVERN, N. Y.; N. Currier	Small	90.00
WASHINGTON'S ENTRY INTO NEW YORK; 1857	Medium	550.00
WASHINGTON'S FAREWELL TO THE OFFICERS OF HIS ARMY; 1876	Small	125.00
WASHINGTON'S HEADQUARTERS, AT NEWBURGH ON THE HUDSON	Small	85.00
WASHINGTON'S RECEPTION ON THE BRIDGE AT TRENTON IN 1789	Small	65.00
WASHINGTON'S RECEPTION BY THE LADIES; 1845; N. Currier	Small	65.00
WATER FOWL SHOOTING; C. Currier	Small	150.00
WATER JUMP, THE; 1884	Large	200.00
WATER JUMP AT JEROME PARK, THE	Small	165.00

	Size	Reta
☐ WATER LILY, THE; N. Currier	Medium	30.
☐ WATER RAIL SHOOTING; 1855; N. Currier	Small	295.
☐ WATKIN'S GLEN, NEW YORK	Small	85.
☐ WAVERLY HOUSE; N. Currier	Medium	425.
☐ WAY THEY COME FROM CALIFORNIA, THE; 1849; N. Currier	Medium	240.
☐ WAY THEY GET MARRIED IN CALIFORNIA, THE; N. Currier	Medium	185.
☐ WAY THEY GO TO CALIFORNIA; 1849; N. Currier	Medium	225.
☐ WAY THEY RAISE A CALIFORNIA OUTFIT; 1849; N. Currier	Medium	185.
☐ WAY THEY WAIT FOR THE "STEAMER" AT PANAMA; 1849; N. Currier	Medium	180.
☐ WAY TO GROW POOR, THE; 1875	Small	42.5
☐ WAYSIDE INN, THE; 1864	Large	310.
☐ WE PARTED ON THE HILLSIDE; 1880	Small	25.
☐ WEDGEWOOD; 1881	Small	55.
☐ WELCOME; 1873	Small	30.
☐ WELL-BRED SETTER, A; 1871	Small	65.
☐ WELL BROKEN RETRIEVER, A; 1870	Small	70.0
☐ WELL BUNCHED AT THE LAST HURDLE; 1887	Large	175.0
☐ WELL, I'M BLOWED; 1883	Small	25.0
☐ WELL TOGETHER; 1886	Small	70.0
☐ WELL TOGETHER AT THE FIRST TURN; 1873	Large	175.0
☐ WEST POINT FOUNDRY — COLD SPRING, HUDSON RIVER, N. Y.	Medium	150.0
☐ WESTERN BEAUTH, THE	Small	15.5
☐ WESTERN FARMER'S HOME, THE; 1871	Small	65.0
☐ WESTERN RIVER SCENERY; 1866	Medium	145.0
☐ WHALE FISHERY — ATTACKING A RIGHT WHALE	Small	300.0
☐ WHALE FISHERY — ATTACKING A SPERM WHALE AND "CUTTING IN"	Large	2400.0
☐ WHALE FISHERY — IN A FLURRY; 1852; N. Currier	Small	300.0
☐ WHALE FISHERY — CUTTING IN	Small	300.0
☐ WHALE FISHERY — LAYING ON; 1852; N. Currier	Small	300.0
☐ WHAT'S SAUCE FOR THE GOOSE IS SAUCE FOR THE GANDER; 1851; N. Currier	Medium	175.0
☐ WHEAT FIELD, THE; N. Currier	Small	37.50
☐ WHEELMAN IN RED HOT FINISH; 1894	Small	165.0
☐ WHEN THE FLOWING TIDE COMES IN; 1879	Small	30.0
☐ WHICH DONKEY SHALL I TAKE?; 1881	Small	30.0
☐ WHITE FAWN, THE; 1868	Small	45.0
☐ WHITE SQUADRON, U. S. NAVY; 1893	Small	90.0
☐ WHO COMES HERE!; N. Currier	Small	32.50

	Size	Retail
WHO GOES THERE!; N. Currier	Small	30.00
WHY DON'T YER COME ALONG?; 1883	Small	32.50
WIDE PATH, THE; N. Currier	Small	30.00
"WIDOW McCHREE" AND "HAMBLETONIAN"; 1867	Small	62.50
WILD CAT BANKER, A; 1853; N. Currier	Small	57.50
WILD CAT TRAIN, A — NO STOPOVERS	Small	75.00
WILD DUCK SHOOTING; C. Currier	Small	125.00
WILD DUCK SHOOTING; N. Currier	Medium	215.00
WILD DUCK SHOOTING; 1852; N. Currier	Large	1200.00
WILD DUCK SHOOTING — A GOOD DAY'S SPORT; 1854; N. Currier	Large	1200.00
WILD DUCK SHOOTING — ON THE WING; 1870	Small	150.00
WILD FLOWERS	Small	25.00
WILD HORSES AT PLAY ON THE AMERICAN PRAIRIES	Medium	150.00
"WILD IRISHMAN" (Race Horse); (Rare); N. Currier	Large	750.00
WILD TURKEY SHOOTING; 1871	Small	155.00
WILD WEST IN DARKTOWN, THE — ATTACK ON THE DEADHEAD COACH; 1893	Small	27.50
WILD WEST IN DARKTOWN, THE — THE BUFFALO CHASE; 1893	Small	30.00
WILLIAM HENRY HARRISON; N. Currier	Small	40.00
WILLIAM P. DEWEES, M.D.; 1834; N. Currier; (Earliest Currier print)	Small	50.00
WILLIAM PENN'S TREATY WITH THE INDIANS; N. Currier	Small	52.50
WINFIELD SCOTT — PEOPLE'S CHOICE FOR 13th PRESIDENT; 1847; N. Currier	Small	65.00
WINFIELD SCOTT — WHIG CANDIDATE; 1852; N. Currier	Small	65.00
WINNING "HANDS DOWN", WITH A GOOD SECOND; 1887	Large	265.00
WINNING IN STYLE; 1893	Medium	85.00
WINTER; N. Currier	Small	62.50
WINTER EVENING; 1854; N. Currier	Medium	325.00
WINTER IN THE COUNTRY — A COLD MORNING; 1864	Large	1850.00
WINTER IN THE COUNTRY — GETTING ICE; 1864	Large	1850.00
WINTER IN THE COUNTRY — THE OLD GRIST MILL; 1864	Large	1850.00
WINTER MOONLIGHT; 1866	Large	545.00
WINTER MORNING; 1861	Medium	375.00
WINTER MORNING — FEEDING THE CHICKENS; 1863	Large	1850.00
WINTER MORNING IN THE COUNTRY; 1873	Small	215.00
WINTER PASTIME; 1855; N. Currier	Small	300.00
WINTER SCENE	Small	50.00
WINTER SPORTS — PICKEREL FISHING; 1872	Small	325.00
WITH MALICE TOWARD NONE; 1865	Small	30.00
WIZARD'S GLEN, THE; 1868	Medium	40.00

WILD DUCK SHOOTING.

WILD DUCK
SHOOTING

Small
$125.00

☐ WOMAN' HOLY WAR; (On Liquor); 1874	Small	90.
☐ WOMEN OF '76; 1848; N. Currier	Small	85.
☐ WON BY A DASH	Medium	55.
☐ WON BY A NECK; 1869	Large	365.0
☐ WONDERFUL MARE "MAUD S.", Record 2:10¾ 1890	Small	85.
☐ WONDERFUL MARE "MAUD S." — PROPERTY OF WM. H. VANDERBILT, ESQ.; 1878	Small	85.0
☐ WOOD DUCKS	Small	90.0
☐ WOODCOCK; 1871	Small	100.0
☐ WOODCOCK SHOOTING; N. Currier	Small	190.0
☐ WOODCOCK SHOOTING; 1852; N. Currier	Large	875.0
☐ WOODCOCK SHOOTING; 1855; N. Currier	Small	200.0
☐ "WOODING UP" ON THE MISSISSIPPI; 1863	Large	950.0
☐ WOODLAND GATE, THE; N. Currier	Medium	125.0
☐ WOODLANDS IN SUMMER	Small	65.00
☐ WOODLANDS IN WINTER	Small	65.0
☐ WOODS IN AUTUMN, THE	Medium	125.0
☐ WORKING MAN'S BANNER; 1872	Small	65.0
☐ WOUNDED BITTERN, THE; N. Currier	Small	30.0
☐ WREATH OF FLOWERS, A	Small	42.5
☐ WRECK OF THE "ATLANTIC"; 1873	Small	75.0
☐ WRECK OF THE SHIP "JOHN MINTURN"; 1846; N. Currier	Small	190.00
☐ WRECK OF THE STEAMSHIP "CAMBRIA"; 1883	Small	80.00
☐ WRECK OF THE STEAMSHIP "SCHILLER"; 1875	Small	65.00
☐ WRECK OF THE U. S. M. STEAMSHIP "ARCTIC"; 1854; N. Currier	Large	365.00
☐ WRECKED BY A COW CATCHER; 1885	Small	40.00
☐ WRONG WAY — RIGHT WAY	Small	45.00